Stephen Crane (November 1, 1871 – June 5, 1900) was an American poet, novelist, and short story writer. Prolific throughout his short life, he wrote notable works in the Realist tradition as well as early examples of American Naturalism and Impressionism. He is recognized by modern critics as one of the most innovative writers of his generation. The ninth surviving child of Methodist parents, Crane began writing at the age of four and had published several articles by the age of 16. Having little interest in university studies though he was active in a fraternity, he left Syracuse University in 1891 to work as a reporter and writer. Crane's first novel was the 1893 Bowery tale Maggie: A Girl of the Streets, generally considered by critics to be the first work of American literary Naturalism. He won international acclaim in 1895 for his Civil War novel The Red Badge of Courage, which he wrote without having any battle experience. (Source: Wikipedia)

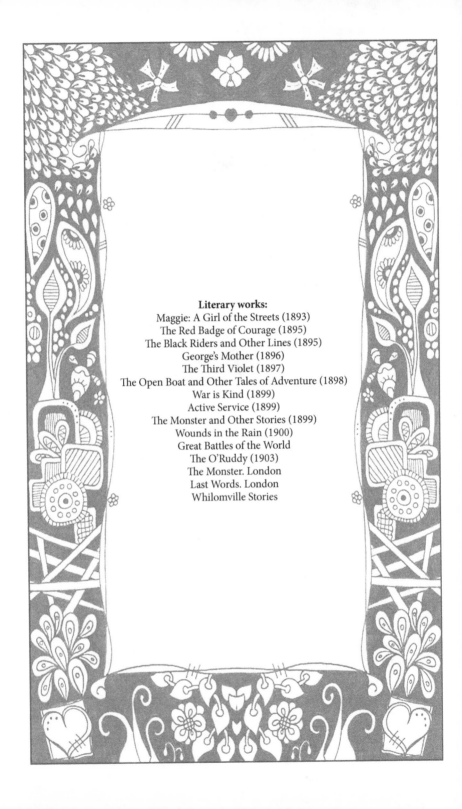

Literary works:
Maggie: A Girl of the Streets (1893)
The Red Badge of Courage (1895)
The Black Riders and Other Lines (1895)
George's Mother (1896)
The Third Violet (1897)
The Open Boat and Other Tales of Adventure (1898)
War is Kind (1899)
Active Service (1899)
The Monster and Other Stories (1899)
Wounds in the Rain (1900)
Great Battles of the World
The O'Ruddy (1903)
The Monster. London
Last Words. London
Whilomville Stories

THRONE CLASSICS

THE BLACK RIDERS
AND OTHER LINES
&
THE O'RUDDY
Stephen Crane

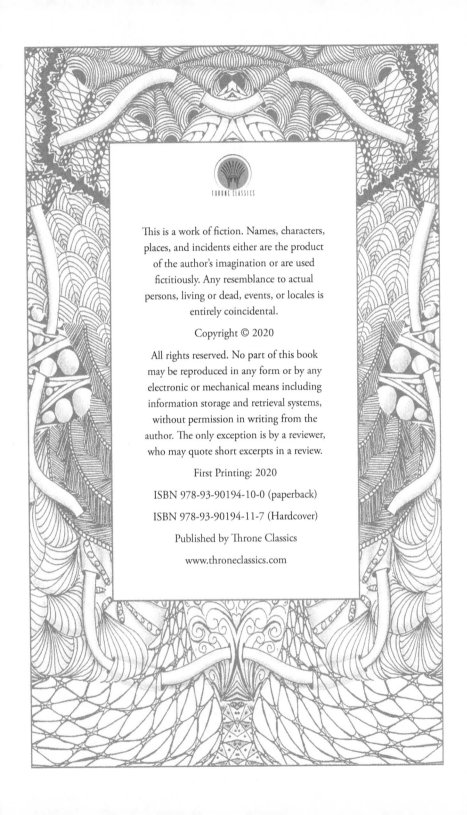

THRONE CLASSICS

First Printing: 2020

ISBN 978-93-90194-10-0 (paperback)

ISBN 978-93-90194-11-7 (Hardcover)

Published by Throne Classics

www.throneclassics.com

Contents

THE BLACK RIDERS
AND OTHER LINES
&
THE O'RUDDY

THE BLACK RIDERS AND OTHER LINES

I

Black Riders came from the sea.

There was clang and clang of spear and shield,

And clash and clash of hoof and heel,

Wild shouts and the wave of hair

In the rush upon the wind:

Thus the ride of Sin.

II

Three little birds in a row

Sat musing.

A man passed near that place.

Then did the little birds nudge each other.

They said, "He thinks he can sing."

They threw back their heads to laugh,

With quaint countenances

They regarded him.

They were very curious,

Those three little birds in a row.

III

In the desert

I saw a creature, naked, bestial,

Who, squatting upon the ground,

Held his heart in his hands,

And ate of it.

I said, "Is it good, friend?"

"It is bitter--bitter," he answered;

"But I like it

Because it is bitter,

And because it is my heart."

IV

Yes, I have a thousand tongues,

And nine and ninety-nine lie.

Though I strive to use the one,

It will make no melody at my will,

But is dead in my mouth.

V

Once there came a man

Who said,

"Range me all men of the world in rows."

And instantly

There was terrific clamor among the people

Against being ranged in rows.

There was a loud quarrel, world-wide.

It endured for ages;

And blood was shed

By those who would not stand in rows,

And by those who pined to stand in rows,

Eventually, the man went to death, weeping.

And those who staid in bloody scuffle

Knew not the great simplicity.

VI

God fashioned the ship of the world carefully

With the infinite skill of an All-Master

Made He the hull and the sails,

Held He the rudder

Ready for adjustment.

Erect stood He, scanning his work proudly.

Then--at fateful time--a Wrong called,

And God turned, heeding.

Lo, the ship, at this opportunity, slipped slyly,

Making cunning noiseless travel down the ways.

So that, forever rudderless, it went upon the seas

Going ridiculous voyages,

Making quaint progress,

Turning as with serious purpose

Before stupid winds.

And there were many in the sky

Who laughed at this thing.

VII

Mystic Shadow, bending near me,

Who art thou?

Whence come ye?

And--tell me--is it fair

Or is the truth bitter as eaten fire?

Tell me!

Fear not that I should quaver,

For I dare--I dare.

Then, tell me!

VIII

I looked here;

I looked there;

Nowhere could I see my love.

And--this time--

She was in my heart.

Truly, then, I have no complaint,

For though she be fair and fairer,

She is none so fair as she

In my heart.

IX

I stood upon a high place,

And saw, below, many devils

Running, leaping,

And carousing in sin.

One looked up, grinning,

And said, "Comrade! Brother!"

X

Should the wide world roll away,

Leaving black terror,

Limitless night,

Nor God, nor man, nor place to stand

Would be to me essential,

If thou and thy white arms were there,

And the fall to doom a long way.

XI

In a lonely place,

I encountered a sage

Who sat, all still,

Regarding a newspaper.

He accosted me:

"Sir, what is this?"

Then I saw that I was greater,

Aye, greater than this sage.

I answered him at once,

"Old, old man, it is the wisdom of the age."

The sage looked upon me with admiration.

XII

"and the sins of the fathers shall be

visited upon the heads of the children,

even unto the third and fourth

generation of them that hate me."

Well, then, I hate thee, Unrighteous Picture;

Wicked Image, I hate thee;

So, strike with thy vengeance

The heads of those little men

Who come blindly.

It will be a brave thing.

XIII

If there is a witness to my little life,

To my tiny throes and struggles,

He sees a fool;

And it is not fine for gods to menace fools.

XIV

There was crimson clash of war.

Lands turned black and bare;

Women wept;

Babes ran, wondering.

There came one who understood not these things.

He said, "Why is this?"

Whereupon a million strove to answer him.

There was such intricate clamor of tongues,

That still the reason was not.

XV

"Tell brave deeds of war."

Then they recounted tales,--

"There were stern stands

"And bitter runs for glory."

Ah, I think there were braver deeds.

XVI

Chanty, thou art a lie,

A toy of women,

A pleasure of certain men.

In the presence of justice,

Lo, the walls of the temple

Are visible

Through thy form of sudden shadows.

XVII

There were many who went in huddled procession,

They knew not whither;

But, at any rate, success or calamity

Would attend all in equality.

There was one who sought a new road.

He went into direful thickets,

And ultimately he died thus, alone;

But they said he had courage.

XVIII

In Heaven,

Some little blades of grass

Stood before God.

"What did you do?"

Then all save one of the little blades

Began eagerly to relate

The merits of their lives.

This one stayed a small way behind,

Ashamed.

Presently, God said,

"And what did you do?"

The little blade answered, "Oh, my Lord,

"Memory is bitter to me,

"For, if I did good deeds,

"I know not of them."

Then God, in all His splendor,

Arose from His throne.

"Oh, best little blade of grass!" He said.

XIX

A god in wrath

Was beating a man;

He cuffed him loudly

With thunderous blows

That rang and rolled over the earth.

All people came running.

The man screamed and struggled,

And bit madly at the feet of the god.

The people cried,

"Ah, what a wicked man!"

And--

"Ah, what a redoubtable god!"

XX

A learned man came to me once.

He said, "I know the way,--come."

And I was overjoyed at this.

Together we hastened.

Soon, too soon, were we

Where my eyes were useless,

And I knew not the ways of my feet

I clung to the hand of my friend;

But at last he cried, "I am lost."

XXI

There was, before me,

Mile upon mile

Of snow, ice, burning sand.

And yet I could look beyond all this,

To a place of infinite beauty;

And I could see the loveliness of her

Who walked in the shade of the trees.

When I gazed,

All was lost

But this place of beauty and her.

When I gazed,

And in my gazing, desired,

Then came again

Mile upon mile,

Of snow, ice, burning sand.

XXII

Once I saw Mountains angry,

And ranged in battle-front.

Against them stood a little man;

Aye, he was no bigger than my finger.

I laughed, and spoke to one near me,

"Will he prevail?"

"Surely," replied this other;

"His grandfathers beat them many times."

Then did I see much virtue in grandfathers,--

At least, for the little man

Who stood against the Mountains.

XXIII

Places among the stars,

Soft gardens near the sun,

Keep your distant beauty;

Shed no beams upon my weak heart.

Since she is here

In a place of blackness,

Not your golden days

Nor your silver nights

Can call me to you.

Since she is here

In a place of blackness,

Here I stay and wait.

XXIV

I saw a man pursuing the horizon;

Round and round they sped.

I was disturbed at this;

I accosted the man.

"It is futile," I said,

"You can never"--

"You lie," he cried,

And ran on.

XXV

Behold, the grave of a wicked man,

And near it, a stern spirit.

There came a drooping maid with violets,

But the spirit grasped her arm.

"No flowers for him," he said.

The maid wept:

"Ah, I loved him."

But the spirit, grim and frowning:

"No flowers for him."

Now, this is it--

If the spirit was just,

Why did the maid weep?

XXVI

There was set before me a mighty hill,

And long days I climbed

Through regions of snow.

When I had before me the summit-view,

It seemed that my labor

Had been to see gardens

Lying at impossible distances.

XXVII

A youth in apparel that glittered

Went to walk in a grim forest.

There he met an assassin

Attired all in garb of old days;

He, scowling through the thickets,

And dagger poised quivering,

Rushed upon the youth.

"Sir," said this latter,

"I am enchanted, believe me,

"To die, thus,

"In this medieval fashion,

"According to the best legends;

"Ah, what joy!"

Then took he the wound, smiling,

And died, content.

XXVIII

"Truth," said a traveller,

"Is a rock, a mighty fortress;

"Often have I been to it,

"Even to its highest tower,

"From whence the world looks black."

"Truth," said a traveller,

"Is a breath, a wind,

"A shadow, a phantom;

"Long have I pursued it,

"But never have I touched

"The hem of its garment."

And I believed the second traveller;

For truth was to me

A breath, a wind,

A shadow, a phantom,

And never had I touched

The hem of its garment.

XXIX

Behold, from the land of the farther suns

I returned.

And I was in a reptile-swarming place,

Peopled, otherwise, with grimaces,

Shrouded above in black impenetrableness.

I shrank, loathing,

Sick with it.

And I said to him,

"What is this?"

He made answer slowly,

"Spirit, this is a world;

"This was your home."

XXX

Supposing that I should have the courage

To let a red sword of virtue

Plunge into my heart,

Letting to the weeds of the ground

My sinful blood,

What can you offer me?

A gardened castle?

A flowery kingdom?

What? A hope?

Then hence with your red sword of virtue.

XXXI

Many workmen

Built a huge ball of masonry

Upon a mountain-top.

Then they went to the valley below,

And turned to behold their work.

"It is grand," they said;

They loved the thing.

Of a sudden, it moved:

It came upon them swiftly;

It crushed them all to blood.

But some had opportunity to squeal.

XXXII

Two or three angels

Came near to the earth.

They saw a fat church.

Little black streams of people

Came and went in continually.

And the angels were puzzled

To know why the people went thus,

And why they stayed so long within.

XXXIII

There was one I met upon the road

Who looked at me with kind eyes.

He said, "Show me of your wares."

And this I did,

Holding forth one.

He said, "It is a sin."

Then held I forth another;

He said, "It is a sin."

Then held I forth another;

He said, "It is a sin."

And so to the end;

Always he said, "It is a sin."

And, finally, I cried out,

"But I have none other."

Then did he look at me

With kinder eyes.

"Poor soul!" he said.

XXXIV

I stood upon a highway,

And, behold, there came

Many strange pedlers.

To me each one made gestures.

Holding forth little images, saying,

"This is my pattern of God.

"Now this is the God I prefer."

But I said, "Hence!

"Leave me with mine own,

"And take you yours away;

"I can't buy of your patterns of God,

"The little Gods you may rightly prefer."

XXXV

A man saw a ball of gold in the sky;

He climbed for it,

And eventually he achieved it--

It was clay.

Now this is the strange part:

When the man went to the earth

And looked again,

Lo, there was the ball of gold.

Now this is the strange part:

It was a ball of gold.

Aye, by the Heavens, it was a ball of gold.

XXXVI

I met a seer.

He held in his hands

The book of wisdom.

"Sir," I addressed him,

"Let me read."

"Child--" he began.

"Sir," I said,

"Think not that I am a child,

"For already I know much

"Of that which you hold.

"Aye, much."

He smiled.

Then he opened the book

And held it before me.--

Strange that I should have grown so suddenly blind.

XXXVII

On the horizon the peaks assembled;

And as I looked,

The march of the mountains began.

As they marched, they sang,

"Aye! We come! We come!"

XXXVIII

The ocean said to me once,

"Look!

"Yonder on the shore

"Is a woman, weeping.

"I have watched her.

"Go you and tell her this,--

"Her lover I have laid

"In cool green hall.

"There is wealth of golden sand

"And pillars, coral-red;

"Two white fish stand guard at his bier.

"Tell her this

"And more,--

"That the king of the seas

"Weeps too, old, helpless man.

"The bustling fates

"Heap his hands with corpses

"Until he stands like a child,

"With surplus of toys."

XXXIX

The livid lightnings flashed in the clouds;

The leaden thunders crashed.

A worshipper raised his arm.

"Hearken! Hearken! The voice of God!"

"Not so," said a man.

"The voice of God whispers in the heart

"So softly

"That the soul pauses,

"Making no noise,

"And strives for these melodies,

"Distant, sighing, like faintest breath,

"And all the being is still to hear."

XL

And you love me?

I love you.

You are, then, cold coward.

Aye; but, beloved,

When I strive to come to you,

Man's opinions, a thousand thickets,

My interwoven existence,

My life,

Caught in the stubble of the world

Like a tender veil,--

This stays me.

No strange move can I make

Without noise of tearing.

I dare not.

If love loves,

There is no world

Nor word.

All is lost

Save thought of love

And place to dream.

You love me?

I love you.

You are, then, cold coward.

Aye; but beloved--

XLI

Love walked alone.

The rocks cut her tender feet,

And the brambles tore her fair limbs.

There came a companion to her,

But, alas, he was no help,

For his name was Heart's Pain.

XLII

I walked in a desert.

And I cried,

"Ah, God, take me from this place!"

A voice said, "It is no desert."

I cried, "Well, but--

"The sand, the heat, the vacant horizon."

A voice said, "It is no desert."

XLIII

There came whisperings in the winds

"Good bye! Good bye!"

Little voices called in the darkness:

"Good bye! Good bye!"

Then I stretched forth my arms.

"No--no--"

There came whisperings in the wind:

"Good bye! Good bye!"

Little voices called in the darkness:

"Good bye! Good bye!"

XLIV

I was in the darkness;

I could not see my words

Nor the wishes of my heart.

Then suddenly there was a great light--

"Let me into the darkness again."

XLV

Tradition, thou art for suckling children,

Thou art the enlivening milk for babes;

But no meat for men is in thee.

Then--

But, alas, we all are babes.

XLVI

Many red devils ran from my heart

And out upon the page,

They were so tiny

The pen could mash them.

And many struggled in the ink.

It was strange

To write in this red muck

Of things from my heart.

XLVII

"Think as I think," said a man,

"Or you are abominably wicked;

"You are a toad."

And after I had thought of it,

I said, "I will, then, be a toad."

XLVIII

Once there was a man,--

Oh, so wise!

In all drink

He detected the bitter,

And in all touch

He found the sting.

At last he cried thus:

"There is nothing,--

"No life,

"No joy,

"No pain,--

"There is nothing save opinion,

"And opinion be damned."

XLIX

I stood musing in a black world,

Not knowing where to direct my feet.

And I saw the quick stream of men

Pouring ceaselessly,

Filled with eager faces,

A torrent of desire.

I called to them,

"Where do you go? What do you see?"

A thousand voices called to me.

A thousand fingers pointed.

"Look! Look! There!"

I know not of it.

But, lo! in the far sky shone a radiance
Ineffable, divine,--
A vision painted upon a pall;
And sometimes it was,
And sometimes it was not.
I hesitated.
Then from the stream
Came roaring voices,
Impatient:
"Look! Look! There!"

So again I saw,
And leaped, unhesitant,
And struggled and fumed
With outspread clutching fingers.
The hard hills tore my flesh;
The ways bit my feet.
At last I looked again.
No radiance in the far sky,
Ineffable, divine;
No vision painted upon a pall;
And always my eyes ached for the light.

Then I cried in despair,

"I see nothing! Oh, where do I go?"

The torrent turned again its faces:

"Look! Look! There!"

And at the blindness of my spirit

They screamed,

"Fool! Fool! Fool!"

L

You say you are holy,

And that

Because I have not seen you sin.

Aye, but there are those

Who see you sin, my friend.

LI

A man went before a strange god,--

The god of many men, sadly wise.

And the deity thundered loudly,

Fat with rage, and puffing,

"Kneel, mortal, and cringe

"And grovel and do homage

"To my particularly sublime majesty."

The man fled.

Then the man went to another god,--

The god of his inner thoughts.

And this one looked at him

With soft eyes

Lit with infinite comprehension,

And said, "My poor child!"

LII

Why do you strive for greatness, fool?

Go pluck a bough and wear it.

It is as sufficing.

My lord, there are certain barbarians

Who tilt their noses

As if the stars were flowers,

And thy servant is lost among their shoe-buckles.

Fain would I have mine eyes even with their eyes.

Fool, go pluck a bough and wear it.

LIII

I

Blustering god,

Stamping across the sky

With loud swagger,

I fear you not.

No, though from your highest heaven

You plunge your spear at my heart,

I fear you not.

No, not if the blow

Is as the lightning blasting a tree,

I fear you not, puffing braggart.

II

If thou can see into my heart

That I fear thee not,

Thou wilt see why I fear thee not,

And why it is right.

So threaten not, thou, with thy bloody spears,

Else thy sublime ears shall hear curses.

III

Withal, there is one whom I fear;

I fear to see grief upon that face.

Perchance, Friend, he is not your god;

If so, spit upon him.

By it you will do no profanity.

But I--

Ah, sooner would I die

Than see tears in those eyes of my soul.

LIV

"It was wrong to do this," said the angel.

"You should live like a flower,

"Holding malice like a puppy,

"Waging war like a lambkin."

"Not so," quoth the man

Who had no fear of spirits;

"It is only wrong for angels

"Who can live like the flowers,

"Holding malice like the puppies,

"Waging war like the lambkins."

LV

A man toiled on a burning road,

Never resting.

Once he saw a fat, stupid ass

Grinning at him from a green place.

The man cried out in rage,

"Ah! Do not deride me, fool!

"I know you--

"All day stuffing your belly,

"Burying your heart

"In grass and tender sprouts:

"It will not suffice you."

But the ass only grinned at him from the green place.

LVI

A man feared that he might find an assassin;

Another that he might find a victim.

One was more wise than the other.

LVII

With eye and with gesture

You say you are holy.

I say you lie;

For I did see you

Draw away your coats

From the sin upon the hands

Of a little child.

Liar!

LVIII

The sage lectured brilliantly.

Before him, two images:

"Now this one is a devil,

"And this one is me."

He turned away.

Then a cunning pupil

Changed the positions.

Turned the sage again:

"Now this one is a devil,

"And this one is me."

The pupils sat, all grinning,

And rejoiced in the game.

But the sage was a sage.

LIX

Walking in the sky,

A man in strange black garb

Encountered a radiant form.

Then his steps were eager;

Bowed he devoutly.

"My Lord," said he.

But the spirit knew him not.

LX

Upon the road of my life,

Passed me many fair creatures,

43

Clothed all in white, and radiant.

To one, finally, I made speech:

"Who art thou?"

But she, like the others,

Kept cowled her face,

And answered in haste, anxiously,

"I am Good Deed, forsooth;

"You have often seen me."

"Not uncowled," I made reply.

And with rash and strong hand,

Though she resisted,

I drew away the veil

And gazed at the features of Vanity

She, shamefaced, went on;

And after I had mused a time,

I said of myself,

     "Fool!"

LXI

I

There was a man and a woman

Who sinned.

Then did the man heap the punishment

All upon the head of her,

And went away gayly.

II

There was a man and a woman

Who sinned.

And the man stood with her.

As upon her head, so upon his,

Fell blow and blow,

And all people screaming, "Fool!"

He was a brave heart.

III

He was a brave heart.

Would you speak with him, friend?

Well, he is dead,

And there went your opportunity.

Let it be your grief

That he is dead

And your opportunity gone;

For, in that, you were a coward.

LXII

There was a man who lived a life of fire.

Even upon the fabric of time,

Where purple becomes orange

And orange purple,

This life glowed,

A dire red stain, indelible;

Yet when he was dead,

He saw that he had not lived.

LXIII

There was a great cathedral.

To solemn songs,

A white procession

Moved toward the altar.

The chief man there

Was erect, and bore himself proudly.

Yet some could see him cringe,

As in a place of danger,

Throwing frightened glances into the air,

A-start at threatening faces of the past.

LXIV

Friend, your white beard sweeps the ground,

Why do you stand, expectant?

Do you hope to see it

In one of your withered days?

With your old eyes

Do you hope to see

The triumphal march of Justice?

Do not wait, friend

Take your white beard

And your old eyes

To more tender lands.

LXV

Once, I knew a fine song,

--It is true, believe me,--

It was all of birds,

And I held them in a basket;

When I opened the wicket,

Heavens! They all flew away.

I cried, "Come back, little thoughts!"

But they only laughed.

They flew on

Until they were as sand

Thrown between me and the sky.

LXVI

If I should cast off this tattered coat,

And go free into the mighty sky;

If I should find nothing there

But a vast blue,

Echoless, ignorant,--

What then?

LXVII

God lay dead in Heaven;

Angels sang the hymn of the end;

Purple winds went moaning,

Their wings drip-dripping

With blood

That fell upon the earth.

It, groaning thing,

Turned black and sank.

Then from the far caverns

Of dead sins

Came monsters, livid with desire.

They fought,

Wrangled over the world,

A morsel.

But of all sadness this was sad,--

A woman's arms tried to shield

48

The head of a sleeping man

From the jaws of the final beast.

LXVIII

A spirit sped

Through spaces of night;

And as he sped, he called,

"God! God!"

He went through valleys

Of black death-slime,

Ever calling,

"God! God!"

Their echoes

From crevice and cavern

Mocked him:

"God! God! God!"

Fleetly into the plains of space

He went, ever calling,

"God! God!"

Eventually, then, he screamed,

Mad in denial,

"Ah, there is no God!"

A swift hand,

A sword from the sky,

Smote him,

And he was dead.

THE O'RUDDY

CHAPTER I

My chieftain ancestors had lived at Glandore for many centuries and were very well known. Hardly a ship could pass the Old Head of Kinsale without some boats putting off to exchange the time of day with her, and our family name was on men's tongues in half the seaports of Europe, I dare say. My ancestors lived in castles which were like churches stuck on end, and they drank the best of everything amid the joyous cries of a devoted peasantry. But the good time passed away soon enough, and when I had reached the age of eighteen we had nobody on the land but a few fisher-folk and small farmers, people who were almost law-abiding, and my father came to die more from disappointment than from any other cause. Before the end he sent for me to come to his bedside.

"Tom," he said, "I brought you into existence, and God help you safe out of it; for you are not the kind of man ever to turn your hand to work, and there is only enough money to last a gentleman five more years.

"The 'Martha Bixby,' she was, out of Bristol for the West Indies, and if it hadn't been for her we would never have got along this far with plenty to eat and drink. However, I leave you, besides the money, the two swords,—the grand one that King Louis, God bless him, gave me, and the plain one that will really be of use to you if you get into a disturbance. Then here is the most important matter of all. Here are some papers which young Lord Strepp gave me to hold for him when we were comrades in France. I don't know what they are, having had very little time for reading during my life, but do you return them to him. He is now the great Earl of Westport, and he lives in London in a grand house, I hear. In the last campaign in France I had to lend him a pair of breeches or he would have gone bare. These papers are important to him, and he may reward you, but do not you depend on it, for you may get the back of his hand. I have not seen him for years. I am glad I had you taught to read. They read considerably in England, I hear. There is one more cask of the best brandy remaining, and I recommend you to leave for England as soon as it is finished. And now, one more thing, my lad, never be civil to a king's officer. Wherever you see a red coat, depend there is a rogue between the front and the back of it. I have said everything. Push the bottle near me."

Three weeks after my father's burial I resolved to set out, with no more words, to deliver the papers to the Earl of Westport. I was resolved to be prompt in obeying my father's command, for I was extremely anxious to see the world, and my feet would hardly wait for me. I put my estate into the hands of old Mickey Clancy, and told him not to trouble the tenants too much over the rent, or they probably would split his skull for him. And I bid Father Donovan look out for old Mickey Clancy, that he stole from me only what was reasonable.

I went to the Cove of Cork and took ship there for Bristol, and arrived safely after a passage amid great storms which blew us so near Glandore that I feared the enterprise of my own peasantry. Bristol, I confess, frightened me greatly. I had not imagined such a huge and teeming place. All the ships in the world seemed to lie there, and the quays were thick with sailor-men. The streets rang with noise. I suddenly found that I was a young gentleman from the country.

I followed my luggage to the best inn, and it was very splendid, fit to be a bishop's palace. It was filled with handsomely dressed people who all seemed to be yelling, "Landlord! landlord!" And there was a little fat man in a white apron who flew about as if he were being stung by bees, and he was crying, "Coming, sir! Yes, madam! At once, your ludship!" They heeded me no more than if I had been an empty glass. I stood on one leg, waiting until the little fat man should either wear himself out or attend all the people. But it was to no purpose. He did not wear out, nor did his business finish, so finally I was obliged to plant myself in his way, but my speech was decent enough as I asked him for a chamber. Would you believe it, he stopped abruptly and stared at me with sudden suspicion. My speech had been so civil that he had thought perhaps I was a rogue. I only give you this incident to show that if later I came to bellow like a bull with the best of them, it was only through the necessity of proving to strangers that I was a gentleman. I soon learned to enter an inn as a drunken soldier goes through the breach into a surrendering city.

Having made myself as presentable as possible, I came down from my chamber to seek some supper. The supper-room was ablaze with light and well filled with persons of quality, to judge from the noise that they were making. My seat was next to a garrulous man in plum-colour, who seemed to know the affairs of the entire world. As I dropped into my chair he was saying—

"—the heir to the title, of course. Young Lord Strepp. That is he—the slim youth with light hair. Oh, of course, all in shipping. The Earl must own twenty sail that trade from Bristol. He is posting down from London, by the way, to-night."

You can well imagine how these words excited me. I half arose from my chair with the idea of going at once to the young man who had been indicated as Lord Strepp, and informing him of my errand, but I had a sudden feeling of timidity, a feeling that it was necessary to be proper with these people of high degree. I kept my seat, resolving to accost him directly after supper. I studied him with interest. He was a young man of about twenty years, with fair unpowdered hair and a face ruddy from a life in the open air. He looked generous and kindly, but just at the moment he was damning a waiter in language that would have set fire to a stone bridge. Opposite him was a clear-eyed soldierly man of about forty, whom I had heard called "Colonel," and at the Colonel's right was a proud, dark-skinned man who kept looking in all directions to make sure that people regarded him, seated thus with a lord.

They had drunk eight bottles of port, and in those days eight bottles could just put three gentlemen in pleasant humour. As the ninth bottle came on the table the Colonel cried—

"Come, Strepp, tell us that story of how your father lost his papers. Gad, that's a good story."

"No, no," said the young lord. "It isn't a good story, and besides my father never tells it at all. I misdoubt it's truth."

The Colonel pounded the table. "'Tis true. 'Tis too good a story to be false. You know the story, Forister?" said he, turning to the dark-skinned man. The latter shook his head.

"Well, when the Earl was a young man serving with the French he rather recklessly carried with him some valuable papers relating to some estates in the North, and once the noble Earl—or Lord Strepp as he was then—found it necessary, after fording a stream, to hang his breeches on a bush to dry, and then a certain blackguard of a wild Irishman in the corps came along and stole—"

But I had arisen and called loudly but with dignity up the long table, "That, sir, is a lie." The room came still with a bang, if I may be allowed that expression. Every one gaped at me, and the Colonel's face slowly went the colour of a tiled roof.

"My father never stole his lordship's breeches, for the good reason that at the time his lordship had no breeches. 'Twas the other way. My father—"

Here the two long rows of faces lining the room crackled for a moment, and then every man burst into a thunderous laugh. But I had flung to the winds my timidity of a new country, and I was not to be put down by these clowns.

"'Tis a lie against an honourable man and my father," I shouted. "And if my father hadn't provided his lordship with breeches, he would have gone bare, and there's the truth. And," said I, staring at the Colonel, "I give the lie again. We are never obliged to give it twice in my country."

The Colonel had been grinning a little, no doubt thinking, along with everybody else in the room, that I was drunk or crazy; but this last twist took the smile off his face clean enough, and he came to his feet with a bound. I awaited him. But young Lord Strepp and Forister grabbed him and began to argue. At the same time there came down upon me such a deluge of waiters and pot-boys, and, may be, hostlers, that I couldn't have done anything if I had been an elephant. They were frightened out of their wits and painfully respectful, but all the same and all the time they were bundling me toward the door. "Sir! Sir! Sir! I beg you, sir! Think of the 'ouse, sir! Sir! Sir! Sir!" And I found myself out in the hall.

Here I addressed them calmly. "Loose me and takes yourselves off quickly, lest I grow angry and break some dozen of these wooden heads." They took me at my word and vanished like ghosts. Then the landlord came bleating, but I merely told him that I wanted to go to my chamber, and if anybody inquired for me I wished him conducted up at once.

In my chamber I had not long to wait. Presently there were steps in the corridor and a knock at my door. At my bidding the door opened and Lord Strepp entered. I arose and we bowed. He was embarrassed and rather dubious.

"Aw," he began, "I come, sir, from Colonel Royale, who begs to be informed who he has had the honour of offending, sir?"

"'Tis not a question for your father's son, my lord," I answered bluntly at last.

"You are, then, the son of The O'Ruddy?"

"No," said I. "I am The O'Ruddy. My father died a month gone and more."

"Oh!" said he. And I now saw why he was embarrassed. He had feared from the beginning that I was altogether too much in the right. "Oh!" said he again. I made up my mind that he was a good lad. "That is dif—" he began awkwardly. "I mean, Mr. O'Ruddy—oh, damn it all, you know what I mean, Mr. O'Ruddy!"

I bowed. "Perfectly, my lord!" I did not understand him, of course.

"I shall have the honour to inform Colonel Royale that Mr. O'Ruddy is entitled to every consideration," he said more collectedly. "If Mr. O'Ruddy will have the goodness to await me here?"

"Yes, my lord." He was going in order to tell the Colonel that I was a gentleman. And of course he returned quickly with the news. But he did not look as if the message was one which he could deliver with a glib tongue. "Sir," he began, and then halted. I could but courteously wait. "Sir, Colonel Royale bids me say that he is shocked to find that he has carelessly and publicly inflicted an insult upon an unknown gentleman through the memory of the gentleman's dead father. Colonel Royale bids me to say, sir, that he is overwhelmed with regret, and that far from taking an initial step himself it is his duty to express to you his feeling that his movements should coincide with any arrangements you may choose to make."

I was obliged to be silent for a considerable period in order to gather head and tail of this marvellous sentence. At last I caught it. "At daybreak I shall walk abroad," I replied, "and I have no doubt that Colonel Royale will be good enough to accompany me. I know nothing of Bristol. Any cleared space will serve."

My Lord Strepp bowed until he almost knocked his forehead on the floor. "You are most amiable, Mr. O'Ruddy. You of course will give me the name of some friend to whom I can refer minor matters?"

I found that I could lie in England as readily as ever I did in Ireland. "My friend will be on the ground with me, my lord; and as he also is a very amiable man it will not take two minutes to make everything clear and fair." Me, with not a friend in the world but Father O'Donovan and Mickey Clancy at Glandore!

Lord Strepp bowed again, the same as before. "Until the morning then, Mr. O'Ruddy," he said, and left me.

I sat me down on my bed to think. In truth I was much puzzled and amazed. These gentlemen were actually reasonable and were behaving like men of heart. Neither my books nor my father's stories—great lies, many of them, God rest him!—had taught me that the duelling gentry could think at all, and I was quite certain that they never tried. "You were looking at me, sir?" "Was I, 'faith? Well, if I care to look at you I shall look at you." And then away they would go at it, prodding at each other's bellies until somebody's

58

flesh swallowed a foot of steel. "Sir, I do not like the colour of your coat!" Clash! "Sir, red hair always offends me." Cling! "Sir, your fondness for rabbit-pie is not polite." Clang!

However, the minds of young Lord Strepp and Colonel Royale seemed to be capable of a process which may be termed human reflection. It was plain that the Colonel did not like the situation at all, and perhaps considered himself the victim of a peculiarly exasperating combination of circumstances. That an Irishman should turn up in Bristol and give him the lie over a French pair of breeches must have seemed astonishing to him, notably when he learned that the Irishman was quite correct, having in fact a clear title to speak authoritatively upon the matter of the breeches. And when Lord Strepp learned that I was The O'Ruddy he saw clearly that the Colonel was in the wrong, and that I had a perfect right to resent the insult to my father's memory. And so the Colonel probably said: "Look you, Strepp. I have no desire to kill this young gentleman, because I insulted his father's name. It is out of all decency. And do you go to him this second time and see what may be done in the matter of avoidance. But, mark you, if he expresses any wishes, you of course offer immediate accommodation. I will not wrong him twice." And so up came my Lord Strepp and hemmed and hawed in that way which puzzled me. A pair of thoughtful, honourable fellows, these, and I admired them greatly.

There was now no reason why I should keep my chamber, since if I now met even the Colonel himself there would be no brawling; only bows. I was not, indeed, fond of these latter,—replying to Lord Strepp had almost broken my back; but, any how, more bows were better than more loud words and another downpour of waiters and pot-boys.

But I had reckoned without the dark-skinned man, Forister. When I arrived in the lower corridor and was passing through it on my way to take the air, I found a large group of excited people talking of the quarrel and the duel that was to be fought at daybreak. I thought it was a great hubbub over a very small thing, but it seems that the mainspring of the excitement was the tongue of this black Forister. "Why, the Irish run naked through their native forests," he was crying. "Their sole weapon is the great knotted club, with which, however, they do not hesitate, when in great numbers, to attack lions and tigers. But how can this barbarian face the sword of an officer of His Majesty's army?"

Some in the group espied my approach, and there was a nudging of elbows. There was a general display of agitation, and I marvelled at the way in which many made it to appear that they had not formed part of the group at all. Only Forister was cool and insolent. He stared full at me and grinned, showing very white teeth. "Swords are very different from clubs, great knotted clubs," he said with admirable deliberation.

"Even so," rejoined I gravely. "Swords are for gentlemen, while clubs are to clout the heads of rogues—thus." I boxed his ear with my open hand, so that he fell against the wall. "I will now picture also the use of boots by kicking you into the inn yard which is adjacent." So saying I hurled him to the great front door which stood open, and then, taking a sort of hop and skip, I kicked for glory and the Saints.

I do not know that I ever kicked a man with more success. He shot out as if he had been heaved by a catapult. There was a dreadful uproar behind me, and I expected every moment to be stormed by the waiter-and-pot-boy regiment. However I could hear some of the gentlemen bystanding cry:

"Well done! Well kicked! A record! A miracle!"

But my first hours on English soil contained still other festivities. Bright light streamed out from the great door, and I could plainly note what I shall call the arc or arcs described by Forister. He struck the railing once, but spun off it, and to my great astonishment went headlong and slap-crash into some sort of an upper servant who had been approaching the door with both arms loaded with cloaks, cushions, and rugs.

I suppose the poor man thought that black doom had fallen upon him from the sky. He gave a great howl as he, Forister, the cloaks, cushions, and rugs spread out grandly in one sublime confusion.

Some ladies screamed, and a bold commanding voice said: "In the devil's name what have we here?" Behind the unhappy servant had been coming two ladies and a very tall gentleman in a black cloak that reached to his heels. "What have we here?" again cried this tall man, who looked like an old eagle. He stepped up to me haughtily. I knew that I was face to face with the Earl of Westport.

But was I a man for ever in the wrong that I should always be giving down and walking away with my tail between my legs? Not I; I stood bravely to the Earl:

"If your lordship pleases, 'tis The O'Ruddy kicking a blackguard into the yard," I made answer coolly.

I could see that he had been about to shout for the landlord and more waiters and pot-boys, but at my naming myself he gave a quick stare.

"The O'Ruddy?" he repeated. "Rubbish!"

He was startled, bewildered; but I could not tell if he were glad or grieved.

"'Tis all the name I own," I said placidly. "My father left it me clear, it being something that he could not mortgage. 'Twas on his death-bed he told me of lending you the breeches, and that is why I kicked the man into the yard; and if your lordship had arrived sooner I could have avoided this duel at daybreak, and, any how, I wonder at his breeches fitting you. He was a small man."

Suddenly the Earl raised his hand. "Enough," he said sternly. "You are your father's son. Come to my chamber in the morning, O'Ruddy."

There had been little chance to see what was inside the cloaks of the ladies, but at the words of the Earl there peeped from one hood a pair of bright liquid eyes—God save us all! In a flash I was no longer a free man; I was a dazed slave; the Saints be good to us!

The contents of the other hood could not have been so interesting, for from it came the raucous voice of a bargeman with a cold:

"Why did he kick him? Whom did he kick? Had he cheated at play?

Where has he gone?"

The upper servant appeared, much battered and holding his encrimsoned nose.

"My lord—" he began.

But the Earl roared at him,—

"Hold your tongue, rascal, and in future look where you are going and don't get in a gentleman's way."

The landlord, in a perfect anguish, was hovering with his squadrons on the flanks. They could not think of pouncing upon me if I was noticed at all by the great Earl; but, somewhat as a precaution perhaps, they remained in form for attack. I had no wish that the pair of bright eyes should see me buried under a heap of these wretches, so I bowed low to the ladies and to the Earl and passed out of doors. As I left, the Earl moved his hand to signify that he was now willing to endure the attendance of the landlord and his people, and in a moment the inn rang with hurried cries and rushing feet.

As I passed near the taproom window the light fell full upon a railing; just beneath and over this railing hung two men. At first I thought they were ill, but upon passing near I learned that they were simply limp and helpless with laughter, the sound of which they contrived to keep muffled. To my surprise I recognized the persons of young Lord Strepp and Colonel Royale.

CHAPTER II

The night was growing, and as I was to fight at daybreak I needed a good rest; but I could not forget that in my pride I had told Lord Strepp that I was provided with a friend to attend me at the duel. It was on my mind. I must achieve a friend, or Colonel Royale might quite properly refuse to fight me on the usual grounds that if he killed me there would be present no adherent of my cause to declare that the fight was fair. And any how I had lied so thoroughly to Lord Strepp. I must have a friend.

But how was I to carve a friend out of this black Bristol at such short notice? My sense told me that friends could not be found in the road like pebbles, but some curious feeling kept me abroad, scanning by the light of the lanterns or the torches each face that passed me. A low dull roar came from the direction of the quay, and this was the noise of the sailor-men, being drunk. I knew that there would be none found there to suit my purpose, but my spirit led me to wander so that I could not have told why I went this way or that way.

Of a sudden I heard from a grassy bank beside me the sound of low and strenuous sobbing. I stopped dead short to listen, moved by instinctive recognition. Aye, I was right. It was Irish keening. Some son of Erin was spelling out his sorrow to the darkness with that profound and garrulous eloquence which is in the character of my people.

"Wirra, wirra! Sorrow the day I would be leaving Ireland against my own will and intention, and may the rocks go out to meet the lugger that brought me here! It's beginning to rain, too! Sure it never rains like this in Ireland! And me without a brass penny to buy a bed! If the Saints save me from England, 'tis al—"

"Come out of that, now!" said I.

The monologue ceased; there was a quick silence. Then the voice, much altered, said: "Who calls? 'Tis may be an Irish voice!"

"It is," said I. "I've swallowed as much peat smoke as any man of my years. Come out of that now, and let me have a look at you."

He came trustfully enough, knowing me to be Irish, and I examined him as well as I was able in the darkness. He was what I expected, a bedraggled vagabond with tear-stains on his dirty cheeks and a vast shock of hair which I well knew would look, in daylight, like a burning haycock. And as I examined him he just as carefully examined me. I could see his shrewd blue eyes twinkling.

"You are a red man," said I. "I know the strain; 'tis better than some. Your family must have been very inhospitable people." And then, thinking that I had spent enough time, I was about to give the fellow some coin and send him away. But here a mad project came into my empty head. I had ever been the victim of my powerful impulses, which surge up within me and sway me until I can only gasp at my own conduct. The sight of this red-headed scoundrel had thrust an idea into my head, and I was a lost man.

"Mark you!" said I to him. "You know what I am?"

"'Tis hard to see in the dark," he answered; "but I mistrust you are a gentleman, sir. McDermott of the Three Trees had a voice and a way with him like you, and Father Burk too, and he was a gentleman born if he could only remain sober."

"Well, you've hit it, in the dark or whatever," said I. "I am a gentleman. Indeed I am an O'Ruddy. Have you ever been hearing of my family?"

"Not of your honour's branch of it, sure," he made answer confidently. "But I have often been hearing of the O'Ruddys of Glandore, who are well known to be such great robbers and blackguards that their match is not to be found in all the south of Ireland. Nor in the west, neither, for that matter."

"Aye," said I, "I have heard that that branch of the family was much admired by the peasantry for their qualities. But let us have done with it and speak of other matters. I want a service of you."

"Yes, your honour," said he, dropping his voice. "May be 'twill not be

64

the first time I've been behind a ditch; but the light to-night is very bad unless I am knowing him well, and I would never be forgetting how Tim Malone let fly in the dark of a night like this, thinking it was a bailiff, until she screamed out with the pain in her leg, the poor creature, and her beyond seventy and a good Catholic."

"Come out of it now!" said I impatiently. "You will be behind no ditch." And as we walked back to the inn I explained to my new man the part I wished him to play. He was amazed at it, and I had to explain fifty times; but when it once was established in his red head Paddy was wild with enthusiasm, and I had to forbid him telling me how well he would do it.

I had them give him some straw in the stable, and then retired to my chamber for needed rest. Before dawn I had them send Paddy to me, and by the light of a new fire I looked at him. Ye Saints! What hair! It must have been more than a foot in length, and the flaming strands radiated in all directions from an isolated and central spire which shot out straight toward the sky. I knew what to do with his tatters, but that crimson thatch dumfounded me. However there was no going back now, so I set to work upon him. Luckily my wardrobe represented three generations of O'Ruddy clothes, and there was a great plenty. I put my impostor in a suit of blue velvet with a flowered waistcoat and stockings of pink. I gave him a cocked hat and a fine cloak. I worked with success up to the sword-belt, and there I was checked. I had two swords, but only one belt. However, I slung the sword which King Louis had given my father on a long string from Paddy's neck and sternly bid him keep his cloak tight about him. We were ready.

"Now, Paddy," said I, "do you bow in this manner." I bowed as a gentleman should. But I will not say how I strove with him. I could do little in that brief space. If he remained motionless and kept his tongue still he was somewhat near his part, but the moment he moved he was astonishing. I depended on keeping him under my eye, and I told him to watch me like a cat. "Don't go thinking how grand you are, that way," I cried to him angrily. "If you make a blunder of it, the gentlemen will cudgel you, mark you that. Do you as I direct you. And the string, curse you. Mind your cloak!" The villain had bethought him of his flowered waistcoat, and with a comic air flung back his coat to display it. "Take your fingers out of your mouth. Stop scratching your shin with your foot. Leave your hair alone. 'Tis as good and as bad as you can make it. Come along now, and hold your tongue like a graven image if you would not be having me stop the duel to lather you."

We marched in good order out of the inn. We saw our two gentlemen awaiting us, wrapped in their cloaks, for the dawn was cold. They bowed politely, and as I returned their salute I said in a low, quick aside to Paddy:

"Now, for the love of God, bow for your life!"

My intense manner must have frightened the poor thing, for he ducked as swiftly as if he had been at a fair in Ireland and somebody had hove a cobble at his head.

"Come up!" I whispered, choking with rage. "Come up! You'll be breaking your nose on the road."

He straightened himself, looking somewhat bewildered, and said:

"What was it? Was I too slow? Did I do it well?"

"Oh, fine," said I. "Fine. You do it as well as that once more, and you will probably break your own neck, and 'tis not me will be buying masses for your soul, you thief. Now don't drop as if a gamekeeper had shot at you. There is no hurry in life. Be quiet and easy."

"I mistrusted I was going too fast," said he; "but for the life of me I couldn't pull up. If I had been the Dublin mail, and the road thick as fleas with highwaymen, I should have gone through them grand."

My Lord Strepp and Colonel Royale had not betrayed the slightest surprise at the appearance of my extraordinary companion. Their smooth, regular faces remained absolutely imperturbable. This I took to be very considerate of them, but I gave them just a little more than their due, as I afterward perceived when I came to understand the English character somewhat. The great reason was that Paddy and I were foreigners. It is not to be thought that gentlemen of their position would have walked out for a duel with an Englishman in the party of so fantastic an appearance. They would

66

have placed him at once as a person impossible and altogether out of their class. They would have told a lackey to kick this preposterous creation into the horse-pond. But since Paddy was a foreigner he was possessed of some curious license, and his grotesque ways could be explained fully in the simple phrase, "'Tis a foreigner."

So, then, we preceded my Lord Strepp and Colonel Royale through a number of narrow streets and out into some clear country. I chose a fine open bit of green turf as a goodly place for us to meet, and I warped Paddy through the gate and moved to the middle of the field. I drew my sword and saluted, and then turned away. I had told Paddy everything which a heaven-sent sense of instruction could suggest, and if he failed I could do no more than kill him.

After I had kicked him sharply he went aside with Lord Strepp, and they indulged in what sounded like a very animated discussion. Finally I was surprised to see Lord Strepp approaching me. He said:

"It is very irregular, but I seem unable to understand your friend. He has proposed to me that the man whose head is broken first—I do not perfectly understand what he could mean by that; it does not enter our anticipations that a man could possibly have his head broken—he has proposed that the man whose head may be broken first should provide 'lashings'—I feel sure that is the word—lashings of meat and drink at some good inn for the others. Lashings is a word which I do not know. We do not know how to understand you gentlemen when you speak of lashings. I am instructed to meet any terms which you may suggest, but I find that I cannot make myself clear to your friend who speaks of nothing but lashings."

"Sir," said I, as I threw coat and waistcoat on the grass, "my friend refers to a custom of his own country. You will, I feel sure, pardon his misconception of the circumstances. Pray accept my regrets, and, if you please, I am ready."

He immediately signified that his mind was now clear, and that the incident of Paddy's lashings he regarded as closed. As for that flame-headed imp of crime, if I could have got my hands upon him he would have taken a short road to his fathers. Him and his lashings! As I stood there with a black glare at him, the impudent scoundrel repeatedly winked at me with the readable information that if I only would be patient and bide a moment he would compass something very clever. As I faced Colonel Royale I was so wild with thinking of what I would do to Paddy, that, for all I knew, I might have been crossing swords with my mother.

And now as to this duel. I will not conceal that I was a very fine fencer in both the French and Italian manners. My father was in his day one of the finest blades in Paris, and had fought with some of the most skillful and impertinent gentlemen in all France. He had done his best to give me his eye and his wrist, and sometimes he would say that I was qualified to meet all but the best in the world. He commonly made fun of the gentlemen of England, saying that a dragoon was their ideal of a man with a sword; and he would add that the rapier was a weapon which did not lend itself readily to the wood-chopper's art. He was all for the French and Italian schools.

I had always thought that my father's judgment was very good, but I could not help reflecting that if it turned out to be bad I would have a grievance as well as a sword-thrust in the body. Colonel Royale came at me in a somewhat leisurely manner, and, as I said, my mind was so full of rage at Paddy that I met the first of my opponent's thrusts through sheer force of habit. But my head was clear a moment later, and I knew that I was fighting my first duel in England and for my father's honour. It was no time to think of Paddy.

Another moment later I knew that I was the Colonel's master. I could reach him where I chose. But he did not know it. He went on prodding away with a serious countenance, evidently under the impression that he had me hard put to it. He was as grave as an owl-faced parson. And now here I did a sorry thing. I became the victim of another of my mad impulses. I was seized with an ungovernable desire to laugh. It was hideous. But laugh I did, and, of necessity, square in the Colonel's face. And to this day I regret it.

Then the real duel began. At my laugh the Colonel instantly lost his grave air, and his countenance flushed with high, angry surprise. He beset me in a perfect fury, caring no more for his guard than if he had been made of iron. Never have I seen such quick and tremendous change in a man. I had

68

laughed at him under peculiar conditions: very well, then; he was a demon. Thrice my point pricked him to keep him off, and thrice my heart was in my mouth that he would come on regardless. The blood oozed out on his white ruffled shirt; he was panting heavily, and his eyes rolled. He was a terrible sight to face. At last I again touched him, and this time sharply and in the sword arm, and upon the instant my Lord Strepp knocked our blades apart.

"Enough," he cried sternly. "Back, Colonel! Back!"

The Colonel flung himself sobbing into his friend's arms, choking out, "O God, Strepp! I couldn't reach him. I couldn't reach him, Strepp! Oh, my God!"

At the same time I disappeared, so to speak, in the embrace of my red-headed villain, who let out an Irish howl of victory that should have been heard at Glandore. "Be quiet, rascal," I cried, flinging him off. But he went on with his howling until I was obliged forcibly to lead him to a corner of the field, where he exclaimed:

"Oh, your honour, when I seen the other gentleman, all blazing with rage, rush at you that way, and me with not so much as a tuppence for all my service to you excepting these fine clothes and the sword, although I am thinking I shall have little to do with swords if this is the way they do it, I said, 'Sorrow the day England saw me!'"

If I had a fool for a second, Colonel Royale had a fine, wise young man. Lord Strepp was dealing firmly and coolly with his maddened principal.

"I can fight with my left hand," the Colonel was screaming. "I tell you, Strepp, I am resolved! Don't bar my way! I will kill him! I will kill him!"

"You are not in condition to fight," said the undisturbed young man. "You are wounded in four places already. You are in my hands. You will fight no more to-day."

"But, Strepp!" wailed the Colonel. "Oh, my God, Strepp!"

"You fight no more to-day," said the young lord.

Then happened unexpected interruptions. Paddy told me afterward that during the duel a maid had looked over a wall and yelled, and dropped a great brown bowl at sight of our occupation. She must have been the instrument that aroused the entire county, for suddenly men came running from everywhere. And the little boys! There must have been little boys from all over England.

"What is it? What is it?"

"Two gentlemen have been fighting!"

"Oh, aye, look at him with the blood on him!"

"Well, and there is young my Lord Strepp. He'd be deep in the matter, I warrant you!"

"Look yon, Bill! Mark the gentleman with the red hair. He's not from these parts, truly. Where, think you, he comes from?"

"'Tis a great marvel to see such hair, and I doubt not he comes from Africa."

They did not come very near, for in those days there was little the people feared but a gentleman, and small wonder. However, when the little boys judged that the delay in a resumption of the fight was too prolonged, they did not hesitate to express certain unconventional opinions and commands.

"Hurry up, now!"

"Go on!"

"You're both afeared!"

"Begin! Begin!"

"Are the gentlemen in earnest?"

"Sirs, do you mean ever to fight again? Begin, begin."

But their enthusiasm waxed high after they had thoroughly comprehended Paddy and his hair.

"You're alight, sir; you're alight!"

"Water! Water!"

"Farmer Pelton will have the officers at you and you go near his hay. Water!"

Paddy understood that they were paying tribute to his importance, and he again went suddenly out of my control. He began to strut and caper and pose with the air of knowing that he was the finest gentleman in England.

"Paddy, you baboon," said I, "be quiet and don't be making yourself a laughing-stock for the whole of them."

But I could give small heed to him, for I was greatly occupied in watching Lord Strepp and the Colonel. The Colonel was listening now to his friend for the simple reason that the loss of blood had made him too weak to fight again. Of a sudden he slumped gently down through Lord Strepp's arms to the ground, and, as the young man knelt, he cast his eyes about him until they rested upon me in what I took to be mute appeal. I ran forward, and we quickly tore his fine ruffles to pieces and succeeded in quite stanching his wounds, none of which were serious. "'Tis only a little blood-letting," said my Lord Strepp with something of a smile. "'Twill cool him, perchance."

"None of them are deep," I cried hastily. "I—"

But Lord Strepp stopped me with a swift gesture. "Yes," he said, "I knew. I could see. But—" He looked at me with troubled eyes. "It is an extraordinary situation. You have spared him, and—he will not wish to be spared, I feel sure. Most remarkable case."

"Well, I won't kill him," said I bluntly, having tired of this rubbish. "Damme if I will!"

Lord Strepp laughed outright. "It is ridiculous," he said. "Do you return, O'Ruddy, and leave me the care of this business. And," added he, with embarrassed manner, "this mixture is full strange; but—I feel sure—any how, I salute you, sir." And in his bow he paid a sensible tribute to my conduct.

Afterward there was nought to do but gather in Paddy and return to the inn. I found my countryman swaggering to and fro before the crowd. Some ignoramus, or some wit, had dubbed him the King of Ireland, and he was playing to the part.

"Paddy, you red-headed scandal," said I, "come along now!"

When he heard me, he came well enough; but I could not help but feel from his manner that he had made a great concession.

"And so they would be taking me for the King of Ireland, and, sure, 'tis an advantage to be thought a king whatever, and if your honour would be easy 'tis you and me that would sleep in the finest beds in Bristol the night, and nothing to do but take the drink as it was handed and—I'll say no more."

A rabble followed us on our way to the inn, but I turned on them so fiercely from time to time that ultimately they ran off. We made direct for my chamber, where I ordered food and drink immediately to be served. Once alone there with Paddy I allowed my joy to take hold on me. "Eh, Paddy, my boy," said I, walking before him, "I have done grand. I am, indeed, one of the finest gentlemen in the world."

"Aye, that's true," he answered, "but there was a man at your back throughout who—"

To his extreme astonishment I buffeted him heavily upon the cheek. "And we'll have no more of that talk," said I.

CHAPTER III

Aye!" said Paddy, holding his jowl; "'tis what one gets for serving a gentleman. 'Tis the service of a good truthful blackguard I'd be looking for, and that's true for me."

"Be quiet and mind what I tell you," I cried to him. "I'm uplifted with my success in England, and I won't be hearing anything from you while I am saying that I am one of the grandest gentlemen in all the world. I came over here with papers—papers!" said I; and then I bethought me that I would take the papers and wave them in my hand. I don't know why people wish to wave important documents in their hands, but the impulse came to me. Above all things I wished to take these papers and wave them defiantly, exultantly, in the air. They were my inheritance and my land of promise; they were everything. I must wave them even to the chamber, empty save for Paddy.

When I reached for them in the proper place in my luggage they were gone. I wheeled like a tiger upon Paddy.

"Villain," I roared, grasping him at the throat, "you have them!"

He sank in full surrender to his knees.

"I have, your honour," he wailed; "but, sure, I never thought your honour would care, since one of them is badly worn at the heel, and the other is no better than no boot at all."

I was cooled by the incontestable verity of this man. I sat heavily down in a chair by the fire.

"Aye," said I stupidly, "the boots! I did not mean the boots, although when you took them passes my sense of time. I mean some papers."

"Some papers!" cried he excitedly. "Your honour never thought it would be me that would steal papers? Nothing less than good cows would do my people, and a bit of turf now and then, but papers—"

"Peace!" said I sombrely, and began to search my luggage thoroughly for my missing inheritance. But it was all to no purpose. The papers were not there. I could not have lost them. They had been stolen. I saw my always-flimsy inheritance melt away. I had been, I thought, on the edge of success, but I now had nothing but my name, a successful duel, and a few pieces of gold. I was buried in defeat.

Of a sudden a name shot through my mind. The name of this black Forister was upon me violently and yet with perfect sureness. It was he who had stolen the papers. I knew it. I felt it in every bone. He had taken the papers.

I have since been told that it is very common for people to be moved by these feelings of omen, which are invariably correct in their particulars; but at the time I thought it odd that I should be so certain that Forister had my papers. However, I had no time to waste in thinking. I grasped my pistols. "A black man—black as the devil," cried I to Paddy. "Help me catch a little black man."

"Sure!" said Paddy, and we sallied forth.

In a moment I was below and crying to the landlord in as fine a fury as any noble:

"This villain Forister! And where be he?"

The landlord looked at me with bulging eyes. "Master Forister," he stammered. "Aye—aye—he's been agone these many hours since your lordship kicked him. He took horse, he did, for Bath, he did."

"Horses!" I roared. "Horses for two gentlemen!" And the stableyard, very respectful since my duel, began to ring with cries. The landlord pleaded something about his bill, and in my impatience I hurled to him all of my gold save one piece. The horses came soon enough, and I leaped into the saddle and was away to Bath after Forister. As I galloped out of the inn yard I heard a tumult behind me, and, looking back, I saw three hostlers lifting hard at Paddy to raise him into the saddle. He gave a despairing cry when he perceived me leaving him at such speed, but my heart was hardened to my work. I must catch Forister.

It was a dark and angry morning. The rain swept across my face, and the wind flourished my cloak. The road, glistening steel and brown, was no better than an Irish bog for hard riding. Once I passed a chaise with a flogging post-boy and steaming nags. Once I overtook a farmer jogging somewhere on a fat mare. Otherwise I saw no travellers.

I was near my journey's end when I came to a portion of the road which dipped down a steep hill. At the foot of this hill was an oak-tree, and under this tree was a man masked and mounted, and in his hand was a levelled pistol.

"Stand!" he said. "Stand!"

I knew his meaning, but when a man has lost a documentary fortune and given an innkeeper all but his last guinea, he is sure to be filled with fury at the appearance of a third and completing misfortune. With a loud shout I drew my pistol and rode like a demon at the highwayman. He fired, but his bullet struck nothing but the flying tails of my cloak. As my horse crashed into him I struck at his pate with my pistol. An instant later we both came a mighty downfall, and when I could get my eyes free of stars I arose and drew my sword. The highwayman sat before me on the ground, ruefully handling his skull. Our two horses were scampering away into the mist.

I placed my point at the highwayman's throat.

"So, my fine fellow," cried I grandly, "you rob well. You are the principal knight of the road of all England, I would dare say, by the way in which an empty pistol overcomes you."

He was still ruefully handling his skull.

"Aye," he muttered sadly, more to himself than to me, "a true knight of the road with seven ballads written of me in Bristol and three in Bath. Ill betide me for not minding my mother's word and staying at home this day. 'Tis all the unhappy luck of Jem Bottles. I should have remained an honest sheep-stealer and never engaged in this dangerous and nefarious game of lifting purses."

The man's genuine sorrow touched me. "Cheer up, Jem Bottles," said I. "All may yet be well. 'Tis not one little bang on the crown that so disturbs you?"

"'Tis not one—no," he answered gloomily; "'tis two. The traveller riding to the east before you dealt me a similar blow—may hell catch the little black devil."

"Black!" cried I. "Forister, for my life!"

"He took no moment to tell me his name," responded the sullen and wounded highwayman. "He beat me out of the saddle and rode away as brisk as a bird. I know not what my mother will say. She be for ever telling me of the danger in this trade, and here come two gentlemen in one day and unhorse me without the profit of a sixpence to my store. When I became a highwayman I thought me I had profited me from the low estate of a sheep-stealer, but now I see that happiness in this life does not altogether depend upon—"

"Enough," I shouted in my impatience. "Tell me of the black man! The black man, worm!" I pricked his throat with my sword very carefully.

"He was black, and he rode like a demon, and he handled his weapons finely," said Jem Bottles. "And since I have told you all I know, please, good sir, move the point from my throat. This will be ill news for my mother."

I took thought with myself. I must on to Bath; but the two horses had long since scampered out of sight, and my pursuit of the papers would make small way afoot.

"Come, Jem Bottles," I cried, "help me to a horse in a comrade's way and for the sake of your mother. In another case I will leave you here a bloody corse. Come; there's a good fellow!"

He seemed moved to help me. "Now, if there comes a well-mounted traveller," he said, brightening, "I will gain his horse for you if I die for it."

"And if there comes no well-mounted traveller?"

"I know not, sir. But—perhaps he will come."

"'Tis a cheap rogue who has but one horse," I observed contemptuously. "You are only a footpad, a simple-minded marquis of the bludgeon."

Now, as I had hoped, this deeply cut his pride.

"Did I not speak of the ballads, sir?" he demanded with considerable spirit. "Horses? Aye, and have I not three good nags hid behind my mother's cottage, which is less than a mile from this spot?"

"Monsieur Jem Bottles," said I, not forgetting the French manners which my father had taught me, "unless you instantly show me the way to these horses I shall cut off your hands, your feet, and your head; and, ripping out your bowels, shall sprinkle them on the road for the first post-horses to mash and trample. Do you understand my intention, Monsieur Jem Bottles?"

"Sir," he begged, "think of my mother!"

"I think of the horses," I answered grimly. "'Tis for you to think of your mother. How could I think of your mother when I wouldn't know her from the Head of Kinsale, if it didn't happen that I know the Head of Kinsale too well to mistake it for anybody's mother?"

"You speak like a man from foreign parts, sir," he rejoined in a meek voice; "but I am able to see that your meaning is serious."

"'Tis so serious," said I, rapping him gently on the head with the butt of my pistol, "that if you don't instantly display a greedy activity you will display a perfect inability to move."

"The speeching is obscure," said he, "but the rap on the head is clear to me. Still, it was not kind of you to hit me on the same spot twice."

He now arose from his mournful seat on the ground, and, still rubbing his pate, he asked me to follow him. We moved from the highway into a very narrow lane, and for some time proceeded in silence.

"'Tis a regular dog's life," spoke Jem Bottles after a period of reflection.

By this time I had grown a strong sympathy for my scoundrel.

"Come, cheer yourself, Jem Bottles," said I. "I have known a lesser ruffian who was hanged until he was dry, whereas you march along the lane with nought to your discouragement but three cracks in your crown."

"'Tis not the cracks in the crown," he answered moodily. "'Tis what my mother will say."

"I had no thought that highwaymen had mothers," said I. I had resolved now to take care of his pride, for I saw that he was bound to be considered a great highwayman, and I did not wish to disturb his feelings until I gained possession of one of the horses. But now he grew as indignant as he dared.

"Mother? Mother, sir? Do you think me an illegitimate child? I say to you flat in your face, even if you kill me the next instant, that I have a mother. Perchance I am not of the lofty gentry who go about beating honest highwaymen to the earth, but I repulse with scorn any man's suggestion that I am illegitimate. In a quarter of an hour you shall see my mother for yourself."

"Peace, Jem Bottles," said I soothingly. "I took no thought of such a thing. I would be thinking only of the ballads, and how honourable it is that a gallant and dashing life should be celebrated in song. I, for certain, have never done anything to make a pothouse ring with my name, and I liken you to the knights of olden days who tilted in all simple fair bravery without being able to wager a brass farthing as to who was right and who was wrong. Admirable Jem Bottles," I cried enthusiastically, "tell me, if you will, of your glories; tell me with your own tongue, so that when I hear the ballads waxing furious with praise of you, I shall recall the time I marched with your historic person."

"My beginning was without pretence," said the highwayman. "Little Susan, daughter of Farmer Hants, was crossing the fields with a basket of eggs. I, a masked figure, sprang out at her from a thicket. I seized the basket. She screamed. There was a frightful tumult. But in the end I bore away this basket of eight eggs, creeping stealthily through the wood. The next day Farmer Hants met me. He had a long whip. There was a frightful tumult. But he little knew that he was laying with his whip the foundation of a career so illustrious. For a time I stole his sheep, but soon grew weary of this business. Once, after they had chased me almost to Bristol, I was so weary that I resolved to forego the thing entirely. Then I became a highwayman, whom you see before you. One of the ballads begins thus:

"What ho! the merry Jem!

Not a pint he gives for them.

All his—"

"Stop," said I, "we'll have it at Dame Bottles's fireside. Hearing songs in the night air always makes me hoarse the next morning."

"As you will," he answered without heat. "We're a'most there."

Soon a lighted window of the highwayman's humble home shone out in the darkness, and a moment later Jem Bottles was knocking at the door. It was immediately opened, and he stalked in with his blood-marks still upon his face. There was a great outcry in a feminine voice, and a large woman rushed forward and flung her arms about the highwayman.

"Oh, Jemmie, my son, my son!" she screamed, "whatever have they done to ye this time?"

"Silence, mother dear," said Bottles. "'Tis nought but a wind-broken bough fallen on my head. Have you no manners? Do you not see the gentleman waiting to enter and warm himself?"

The woman turned upon me, alarmed, but fiery and defiant. After a moment's scrutiny she demanded:

"Oh, ho, and the gentleman had nought to do of course with my Jem's broken head?"

"'Tis a priest but newly arrived from his native island of Asia," said Bottles piously; "and it ill beseems you, mother dear, to be haggling when you might be getting the holy man and I some supper."

"True, Jemmie, my own," responded Dame Bottles. "But there are so many rogues abroad that you must forgive your old mother if she grow often affrighted that her good Jemmie has been misled." She turned to me. "Pardon, my good gentleman," she said almost in tears. "Ye little know what it is to be the mother of a high-spirited boy."

"I can truthfully say that I do not, Dame Bottles," said I, with one of my father's French bows. She was immensely pleased. Any woman may fall a victim to a limber, manly, and courteous bow.

Presently we sat down to a supper of plum-stew and bread. Bottles had washed the blood from his face and now resembled an honest man.

"You may think it strange, sir," said Dame Bottles with some housewifely embarrassment, "that a highwayman of such distinction that he has had written of him in Bristol six ballads—"

"Seven," said the highwayman.

"Seven in Bristol and in Bath two."

"Three," said the highwayman.

"And three in Bath," continued the old woman. "You may think it strange, sir, that a highwayman of such distinction that he has had written of him in Bristol seven ballads, and in Bath three, is yet obliged to sit down to a supper of plum-stew and bread."

"Where is the rest of that cheese I took on last Michaelmas?" demanded Bottles suddenly.

"Jemmie," answered his mother with reproach, "you know you gave the last of it to the crippled shepherd over on the big hill."

"So I did, mother dear," assented the highwayman, "and I regret now that I let no less than three cheeses pass me on the highway because I thought we had plenty at home."

"If you let anything pass on the road because you do not lack it at the moment, you will ultimately die of starvation, Jemmie dear," quoth the mother. "How often have I told you?"

"Aye," he answered somewhat irritably, "you also often have told me to take snuff-boxes."

"And was I at fault," she retorted, "because the cheating avarice of the merchants led them to make sinful, paltry snuff-boxes that were mere pictures of the good old gold and silver? Was it my mischief? Or was it the mischief of the plotting swineherds who now find it to their interest to deal in base and imitative metals?"

"Peace, my mother," said the highwayman. "The gentleman here has not the same interest in snuff-boxes which moves us to loud speech."

"True," said Dame Bottles, "and I readily wish that my Jemmie had no reason to care if snuff-boxes were made from cabbage-leaves."

I had been turning a scheme in my mind, and here I thought I saw my opportunity to introduce it. "Dame Bottles," said I, "your words fit well with the plan which has brought me here to your house. Know you, then, that I am a nobleman—"

"Alack, poor Jemmie!" cried the woman, raising her hands.

"No," said I, "I am not a nobleman rampant. I am a nobleman in trouble, and I need the services of your son, for which I will reward him with such richness that he will not care if they make snuff-boxes out of water or wind. I am in pursuit of a man—"

"The little black man," cried the alert Bottles.

"And I want your son to ride with me to catch this thief. He need never pass through the shadow of the creeping, clanking tree. He will be on an honest hunt to recover a great property. Give him to me. Give him fourteen guineas from his store, and bid us mount his horses and away. Save your son!"

The old woman burst into tears. "Sir," she answered, "I know little of you, but, as near as I can see in the light of this one candle, you are a hangel. Take my boy! Treat him as you would your own stepson, and if snuff-boxes ever get better I will let you both hear of it."

Less than an hour later Jem Bottles and I were off for Bath, riding two very good horses.

CHAPTER IV

Now my whole mind was really bent on finding my black Forister, but yet, as Jem Bottles and I rode toward Bath, I thought of a cloaked figure and a pair of shining eyes, and it seemed to me that I recalled the curve of sweet, proud lips. I knew that I should be thinking of my papers, my future; but a quick perversity made me dwell for a long trotting time in a dream of feminine excellence, in a dream of feminine beauty which was both ascetic and deeply sensuous. I know hardly how to say that two eyes, a vision of lips, a conception of a figure, should properly move me as I bounced along the road with Jem Bottles. But it is certain that it came upon me. The eyes of the daughter of the great Earl of Westport had put in chains the redoubtable O'Ruddy. It was true. It was clear. I admitted it to myself. The admission caused a number of reflections to occur in my mind, and the chief of these was that I was a misfortunate wretch.

Jem Bottles recalled me to the immediate business.

"'Tis the lights of Bath, sir," he said, "and if it please you, sir, I shall await you under yonder tree, since the wretched balladists have rendered me so well known in the town that I dare not venture in it for fear of a popular welcome from the people who have no snuff-boxes whatever."

"I will go and listen to the ballads," I replied, "and in the mean time do you await me here under that tree."

So saying I galloped into Bath, my soul sharp to find Forister and to take him by the neck and strangle out of him those papers which were my sole reasons for living. But the landlord of the best inn met me with an unmistakable frankness.

"Mr. Forister?" said he. "Yes, your lordship, but Mr. Forister is gone back to Bristol."

I was so pleased with his calling me "your lordship" that I hesitated a moment. But I was recalled to sense by the thought that although Jem Bottles and I had fifteen guineas between us, he had fourteen and I had the one. Thanking the landlord I galloped out of Bath.

Bottles was awaiting me under the tree. "To Bristol," I cried. "Our chase lies toward Bristol. He has doubled back."

"'Twas while we were at supper," said Bottles, as he cantered up to my shoulder. "I might have had two trials at him if I had not had the honour of meeting your worship. I warrant you, sir, he would not have escaped me twice."

"Think of his crack in your skull, and be content," I replied. "And in the mean time ride for Bristol."

Within five miles of Bristol we came upon a wayside inn in which there was progressing a great commotion. Lights flashed from window to window, and we could hear women howling. To my great surprise Bottles at once became hugely excited.

"Damme, sir," he shouted, "my sweetheart is a chambermaid here, and if she be hurted I will know it."

He spurred valiantly forward, and, after futilely calling to him to check his career, I followed. He leaped from his horse at the door of the inn and bounced into the place, pistol in hand. I was too confused to understand much, but it seemed to my ears that his entrance was hailed with a roar of relief and joy. A stable-boy, fearfully anxious, grasped my bridle, crying, "Go in, sir, in God's name. They will be killing each other." Thinking that, whatever betide, it was proper to be at the back of my friend Bottles, I too sprang from my horse and popped into the inn.

A more unexpected sight never met my experienced gaze. A fat landlady, mark you, was sobbing in the arms of my villainous friend, and a pretty maid was clinging to his arm and screaming. At the same time there were about him a dozen people of both sexes who were yelling,—

"Oh, pray, Master Bottles! Good Master Bottles, do stop them. One is a great Afric chief, red as a fire, and the other is Satan, Satan himself! Oh, pray, good Master Bottles, stop them!"

My fine highwayman was puffed out like a poisoned frog. I had no thought that he could be so grand.

"What is this disturbance?" he demanded in a bass voice.

"O good Master Bottles," clamoured the people. "Satan wishes to kill the Red Giant, who has Satan barred in the best room in the inn. And they make frightful destruction of chairs and tables. Bid them cease, O good Master Bottles!"

From overhead we could hear the sound of blows upon wood mingled with threatening talk.

"Stand aside," said the highwayman in a great gruff voice which made me marvel at him. He unhesitatingly dumped the swooning form of the landlady into another pair of arms, shook off the pretty maid, and moved sublimely upon the foot of the stairs amid exclamations of joy, wonder, admiration, even reverence.

But the voice of an unseen person hailed suddenly from the head of the stairs.

"And if ye have not said enough masses for your heathen soul," remarked the voice, "you would be better mustering the neighbours this instant to go to church for you and bid them do the best they can in a short time. You will never be coming downstairs if you once come up."

Bottles hesitated; the company shuddered out: "'Tis the Red Giant."

"And I would be having one more word with you," continued the unseen person. "I have him here, and here I keep him. 'Tis not me that wants the little black rogue, what with his hammering on the door and his calling me out of my name. 'Tis no work that I like, and I would lever go in and put my heel in his face. But I was told to catch a little black man, and I have him, and him I will keep. 'Tis not me that wished to come here and catch little black men for anybody; but here I am in this foreign country, catching little black men, and I will have no interference."

84

But here I gave a great call of recognition.

"Paddy!"

I saw the whole thing. This wild-headed Paddy, whom I had told to catch me a little black man, had followed after me toward Bath and somehow managed to barricade in a room the very first man he saw who was small and black. At first I wished to laugh; an instant later I was furious.

"Paddy," I thundered; "come down out of that now! What would you be doing? Come down out of that now!"

The reply was sulky, but unmistakably from Paddy. Most of it was mumbled.

"Sure I've gone and caught as little and as black a man as is in the whole world, and was keeping the scoundrel here safe, and along he comes and tells me to come down out of that now with no more gratitude than if he had given me a gold goose. And yet I fought a duel for him and managed everything so finely that he came away well enough to box me on the ear, which was mere hilarity and means nothing between friends."

Jem Bottles was still halted on the stair. He and all the others had listened to Paddy's speeches in a blank amazement which had much superstition in it.

"Shall I go up, sir?" he asked, not eagerly.

"No," said I. "Leave me to deal with it. I fear a great mistake. Give me ten minutes, and I promise to empty the inn of all uproar."

A murmur of admiration arose, and as the sound leaped about my ears I moved casually and indifferently up against Paddy. It was a grand scene.

"Paddy," I whispered as soon as I had reached a place on the stairs safe from the ears of the people below. "Paddy, you have made a great blunder. You have the wrong man."

"'Tis unlikely," replied Paddy with scorn. "You wait until you see him, and if he is not little and black, then—"

"Yes, yes," said I hastily, "but it was not any little black man at all which

I wanted. It was a particular little black man."

"But," said the ruffian brightly, "it would be possible this one will serve your end. He's little and he's black."

At this moment the voice of the captive came intoning through the door of a chamber.

"When I am free I will first cut out your liver and have it grilled, and feed it to you as you are dying."

Paddy had stepped forward and placed his lips within about six inches of one of the panels.

"Come now, be easy!" he said. "You know well that if you should do as you say, I would beat your head that it would have the looks of a pudding fallen from a high window, and that's the truth."

"Open the door, rascal," called the captive, "and we shall see."

"I will be opening no doors," retorted Paddy indignantly. "Remain quiet, you little black devil, or, by the mass, I'll—"

"I'll slice your heart into pieces of paper," thundered Paddy's prisoner, kicking and pounding.

By this time I was ready to interfere. "Paddy," said I, catching him by the shoulder, "you have the wrong man. Leave it to me; mind you, leave it to me."

"He's that small and black you'd think—" he began dejectedly, but I cut him short.

Jem Bottles, unable to endure the suspense, had come up from below. He was still bristling and blustering, as if all the maids were remarking him.

"And why does this fine gentleman kick and pound on the door?" he demanded in a gruff voice loud enough to be heard in all appreciative parts of the inn. "I'll have him out and slit his nose."

The thunder on the door ceased, and the captive observed:

"Ha! another scoundrel! If my ears do not play me false, there are now three waiting for me to kick them to the hangman."

Restraining Paddy and Bottles, who each wished to reply in heroic verse to this sally, I stepped to the door.

"Sir," said I civilly, "I fear a great blunder has been done. I—"

"Why," said the captive with a sneer, "'tis the Irishman! 'Tis the king of the Irelands. Open the door, pig."

My elation knew no bounds.

"Paddy," cried I, "you have the right little black man." But there was no time for celebration. I must first answer my enemy. "You will remember that I kicked you once," said I, "and if you have a memory as long as my finger be careful I do not kick you again, else even people as far away as the French will think you are a meteor. But I would not be bandying words at long range. Paddy, unbar the door."

"If I can," muttered Paddy, fumbling with a lot of machinery so ingenious that it would require a great lack of knowledge to thoroughly understand it. In the mean time we could hear Forister move away from the door, and by the sound of a leisurely scrape of a chair on the floor I judge he had taken his seat somewhere near the centre of the room. Bottles was handling his pistol and regarding me.

"Yes," said I, "if he fires, do you pepper him fairly. Otherwise await my orders. Paddy, you slug, unbar the door."

"If I am able," said Paddy, still muttering and fumbling with his contrivances. He had no sooner mouthed the words than the door flew open as if by magic, and we discovered a room bright with the light of a fire and candles. Forister was seated negligently at a table in the centre of the room. His legs were crossed, but his naked sword lay on the table at his hand. He had the first word, because I was amazed, almost stunned, by the precipitous opening of the door.

"Ho! ho!" he observed frigidly, "'tis indeed the king of the Irelands, accompanied by the red-headed duke who has entertained me for some time, and a third party with a thief's face who handles a loaded pistol with such abandon as leads me to suppose that he once may have been a highwayman. A very pretty band."

"Use your tongue for a garter, Forister," said I. "I want my papers."

CHAPTER V

Your 'papers'?" said Forister. "Damn you and your papers. What would I know of your papers?"

"I mean," said I fiercely, "the papers that you stole out of my chamber in the inn at Bristol."

The man actually sank back in his chair and laughed me up to the roof.

"'Papers'!" he shouted. "Here's the king of the Irelands thinking that I have made off with his papers!"

"You choose a good time for laughing," said I, with more sobriety. "In a short time you will be laughing with the back of your head."

He sat up and looked at me with quick decision.

"Now, what is all this rubbish about papers?" he said sharply. "What have I to do with your filthy papers? I had one intention regarding you,—of that I am certain. I was resolved to kill you on the first occasion when we could cross swords, but—'papers'—faugh! What do you mean?"

The hoarse voice of Jem Bottles broke in from somewhere behind me. "We might easily throw him to the earth and tie him, sir, and then make search of him."

"And you would know how to go about the business, I warrant me," laughed Forister. "You muzzle-faced rogue, you!"

To my astonishment the redoubtable highwayman gave back before the easy disdain of this superior scoundrel.

"My ways may not always have been straight and narrow, master," he rejoined, almost in a whine, "but you have no call to name me muzzle-faced."

Forister turned from him contemptuously and fixed his regard with much enthusiasm upon Paddy.

"Very red," said he. "Very red, indeed. And thick as fagots, too. A very delectable head of hair, fit to be spun into a thousand blankets for the naked savages in heathen parts. The wild forests in Ireland must indeed be dark when it requires a lantern of this measure to light the lonely traveller on his way."

But Paddy was an honest man even if he did not know it, and he at once walked to Forister and held against his ear a fist the size of a pig's hind-leg.

"I cannot throw the talk back to you," he said. "You are too fast for me, but I tell you to your face that you had better change your tongue for a lock of an old witch's hair unless you intend to be battered this moment."

"Peace," said Forister calmly. "I am a man of natural wit, and I would entertain myself. Now, there is your excellent chieftain the king of the Irelands. Him I regard as a very good specimen, whose ancestors were not very long ago swinging by their tails from the lofty palms of Ireland and playing with cocoanuts to and fro." He smiled and leaned back, well satisfied with himself.

All this time I had been silent, because I had been deep in reflection upon Forister. Now I said:

"Forister, you are a great rogue. I know you. One thing is certain. You have not my papers and never did you have them."

He looked upon me with some admiration and cried:

"Aye, the cannibal shows a glimmer of reason. No, I have not your foolish papers, and I only wish I had them in order to hurl the bundle at your damned stupid head."

"For a kicked man you have a gay spirit," I replied. "But at any rate I have no time for you now. I am off to Bristol after my papers, and I only wish for the sake of ease that I had to go no farther than this chamber. Come, Paddy! Come, Jem!"

My two henchmen were manifestly disappointed; they turned reluctantly at my word.

"Have I the leave of one crack at him, your honour?" whispered Paddy earnestly. "He said my head was a lantern."

"No," said I, "leave him to his meditations."

As we passed down the corridor we heard him laugh loudly, and he called out to me,—

"When I come to Bristol I will kill you."

I had more than a mind to go back and stuff this threat into his throat, but I better knew my business, which was to recover the papers.

"Come," said I, and we passed down stairs.

The people of the inn made way for Paddy as if he had been a falling tree, and at the same time they worshipped Jem Bottles for having performed everything. I had some wonder as to which would be able to out-strut the other. I think Jem Bottles won the match, for he had the advantage of being known as one of the most dangerous men in southwestern England, whereas Paddy had only his vanity to help him.

"'Tis all arranged," said Bottles pompously. "Your devil will come forth as quiet as a rabbit."

We ordered our horses, and a small crowd of obsequious stable-boys rushed to fetch them. I marvelled when I saw them lead out Paddy's horse. I had thought from what I perceived over my shoulder when I left Bristol that he would never be able to make half a league in the saddle. Amid the flicker of lanterns, Bottles and I mounted and then I heard Paddy calling to him all the stable-boys:

"Now, when I give the word, you heave for your lives. Stand, you beast! Cannot four of you hold him by the legs? I will be giving the word in a moment. Are you all ready? Well, now, ready again—heave!"

There was a short scuffle in the darkness, and presently Paddy appeared above the heads of the others in the mêlée.

"There, now," said he to them, "that was well done. One would easily be telling that I was an ex-trooper of the king." He rode out to us complacently.

"'Tis a good horse, if only he steered with a tiller instead of these straps," he remarked, "and he goes well before the wind."

"To Bristol," said I. "Paddy, you must follow as best you may. I have no time to be watching you, although you are interesting."

An unhappy cry came from behind Bottles, and I spurred on, but again I could not wait for my faithful countryman. My papers were still the stake for which I played. However I hoped that Paddy would now give over his ideas about catching little black men.

As we neared Bristol Jem Bottles once more became backward. He referred to the seven ballads, and feared that the unexpected presence of such a well-known character would create an excitement which would not be easy to cool. So we made a rendezvous under another tree, and I rode on alone. Thus I was separated from both my good companions. However, before parting, I took occasion to borrow five guineas from Jem's store.

I was as weary as a dog, although I had never been told that gentlemen riding amid such adventures were ever aweary. At the inn in Bristol a sleepy boy took my horse, and a sleepy landlord aroused himself as he recognized me.

"My poor inn is at your disposal, sir," he cried as he bowed. "The Earl has inquired for you to-day, or yesterday, as well as my young Lord Strepp and Colonel Royale."

"Aye?" said I carelessly. "Did they so? Show me to a chamber. I am much enwearied. I would seek a good bed and a sound sleep, for I have ridden far and done much since last I had repose."

"Yes, sir," said the landlord deferentially.

After a long hard sleep I was aroused by a constant pounding on my door. At my cry a servant entered. He was very abject. "His lordship's valet has been waiting to give you a message from his lordship, sir." I bid him let the valet enter. The man whose heroic nose had borne the brunt of Forister's swift departure from the inn when I kicked him came into my chamber with distinguished grace and dignity and informed me that his noble master cared to see me in his chamber when it would suit my convenience.

Of course the old Earl was after his papers. And what was I to tell him,—that I was all befooled and befuddled?—that after my father had kept these papers for so many years in faithful trust I had lost them on the very brink of deliverance of them to their rightful owner? What was I to speak?

I did not wish to see the Earl of Westport, but some sudden and curious courage forced me into my clothes and out to the corridor. The Earl's valet was waiting there. "I pray you, sir, follow me," he said. I followed him to an expensive part of the inn, where he knocked upon a door. It was opened by a bending serving-man. The room was a kind of parlour, and in it, to my surprise, were Lord Strepp and Colonel Royale. They gazed at me with a surprise equivalent to mine own.

Young Lord Strepp was the first one thoroughly to collect himself. Then he advanced upon me with outstretched hand.

"Mr. O'Ruddy," he cried, "believe me, we are glad to see you. We thought you had gone for all time."

Colonel Royale was only a moment behind his friend, but as he extended his hand his face flushed painfully.

"Sir," he said somewhat formally, "not long ago I lost my temper, I fear. I know I have to thank you for great consideration and generosity. I—I—you—"

Whereupon we both began to stammer and grimace. All the time I was chocking out:

"Pray—pray—, don't speak of it—a—nothing—in truth, you kindly exaggerate—I—"

It was young Lord Strepp who brought us out of our embarrassment. "Here, you two good fellows," he cried heartily, "a glass of wine with you."

We looked gratefully at him, and in the business of filling our glasses we lost our awkwardness. "To you," said Lord Strepp; and as we drained our wine I knew that I had two more friends in England.

During the drinking the Earl's valet had been hovering near my coat-tails. Afterward he took occasion to make gentle suggestion to me:

"His lordship awaits your presence in his chamber, sir, when it pleases you."

The other gentlemen immediately deferred to my obligation, and I followed the valet into a large darkened chamber. It was some moments before my eyes could discover that the Earl was abed. Indeed, a rasping voice from beneath the canopies called to me before I knew that anybody was in the chamber but myself and the valet.

"Come hither, O'Ruddy," called the Earl. "Tompkins, get out! Is it your duty to stand there mummified? Get out!"

The servant hastily withdrew, and I walked slowly to the great man's bedside. Two shining shrewd eyes looked at me from a mass of pillows, and I had a knowledge of an aged face, half smiling and yet satirical, even malignant.

"And so this is the young fortune-hunter from Ireland," he said in a hoarse sick-man's voice. "The young fortune-hunter! Ha! With his worthless papers! Ha!"

"Worthless?" cried I, starting.

"Worthless!" cried the Earl vehemently. He tried to lift himself in his bed, in order to make more emphasis. "Worthless! Nothing but straw—straw—straw!" Then he cackled out a laugh.

And this was my inheritance! I could have sobbed my grief and anger, but I took firm hold on myself and resolved upon another way of dealing with the nobleman.

"My lord," said I coolly, "My father is dead. When he was dying he gave certain papers into my hands,—papers which he had guarded for many years,—and bade me, as his son, to deliver them into the hands of an old friend and comrade; and I come to this old friend and comrade of my father, and he lies back in his bed and cackles at me like a hen. 'Tis a small foot I would have set upon England if I had known more of you, you old skate!"

But still he laughed and cried: "Straw! Straw! Nothing but straw!"

"Well, sir," said I with icy dignity, "I may be a fool of an Irishman with no title save an older one than yours; but I would be deeply sorry if there came a day when I should throw a trust back in the teeth of a dead comrade's son."

"No," said the bright-eyed old man, comforting himself amid his pillows. "Look you, O'Ruddy! You are a rascal! You came over in an attempt to ruin me! I know it!"

I was awed by this accusation. It seemed to me to be too grand, too gorgeous for my personal consumption. I knew not what to do with this colossus. It towered above me in splendour and gilt. I had never expected to be challenged with attempting to ruin earls. My father had often ruined sea-captains, but he never in his life ruined so much as a baronet. It seemed altogether too fine for my family, but I could only blurt weakly, "Yessir." I was much like a lackey.

"Aye," said the old man, suddenly feeble from the excitement, "I see you admit it, you black Irish rogue." He sank back and applied a napkin to his mouth. It seemed to come away stained with blood. "You scoundrel!"

I had a strange cowardly inclination to fling myself upon this ancient survival and squeeze his throat until it closed like a pursel. And my inclination was so strong that I stood like a stone.

The valet opened the door. "If it please your Lordship—Lady Mary," he announced, and stood aside to let a lady pass. The Earl seemed immediately to forget my presence. He began at once to make himself uncomfortable in his bed. Then he cried fretfully: "Come, Mary, what caused you to be so long? Make me easy! Ruffle my pillows! Come, daughter."

"Yes, father," answered a soothing and sweet voice. A gracious figure passed before me and bended over the bed of the Earl. I was near blinded. It was not a natural blindness. It was an artificial blindness which came from my emotion. Was she tall? I don't know. Was she short? I don't know. But I am certain that she was exactly of the right size. She was, in all ways, perfection. She was of such glory, she was so splendid, that my heart ceased to beat. I remained standing like a stone, but my sword scabbard, reminiscent of some movement, flapped gently against my leg. I thought it was a horrible sound. I sought to stay it, but it continued to tinkle, and I remember that, standing there in the room with the old Earl and my love-'til-death, I thought most of my scabbard and its inability to lay quiet at my thigh.

She smoothed his bed and coaxed him and comforted him. Never had I seen such tenderness. It was like a vision of a classic hereafter. In a second I would have exchanged my youth for the position of this doddering old nobleman who spat blood into a napkin.

Suddenly the Earl wheeled his eyes and saw me.

"Ha, Mary!" he cried feebly, "I wish to point out a rogue. There he stands! The O'Ruddy! An Irishman and a fine robber! Mark him well, and keep stern watch of your jewels."

The beautiful young lady turned upon me an affrighted glance. And I stood like a stone.

"Aye," said the old wretch, "keep stern watch of your jewels. He is a very demon for skill. He could take a ring from your finger while you were thinking he was fluttering his hands in the air."

I bowed gallantly to the young lady. "Your rings are safe, my lady. I would ill requite the kindness shown by your father to the son of an old friend if I deprived your white fingers of a single ornament."

"Clever as ever, clever as ever," chuckled the wicked old man.

The young lady flushed and looked first at me and then at her father. I thought her eye, as it rested upon me, was not without some sympathetic feeling. I adored her. All the same I wished to kill her father. It is very curious

96

when one wishes to kill the father of the woman one adores. But I suppose the situation was made more possible for me by the fact that it would have been extremely inexpedient to have killed the Earl in his sick bed. I even grinned at him.

"If you remember my father, your lordship," said I amiably, "despite your trying hard to forget him, you will remember that he had a certain native wit which on occasion led him to be able to frustrate his enemies. It must have been a family trait, for I seem to have it. You are an evil old man! You yourself stole my papers!"

CHAPTER VI

At first I thought that my speech had given the aged Earl a stroke. He writhed on his bed, and something appeared at his lips which was like froth. His lovely daughter sprang to him with a cry of fear and woe. But he was not dying; he was only mad with rage.

"How dare you? How dare you?" he gasped. "You whelp of Satan!"

"'Tis me that would not be fearing to dare anything," I rejoined calmly. "I would not so. I came here with a mind for fair words, but you have met me with insult and something worse. We cannot talk the thing. We must act it. The papers are yours, but you took them from me unfairly. You may destroy them. Otherwise I will have them back and discover what turned you into a great rogue near the end of your days."

"Hearken!" screamed the Earl. "Hearken! He threatens." The door into the parlour flew open, and Lord Strepp and Colonel Royale appeared on the threshold, their faces blank with wonder.

"Father," cried the young lord, stepping hastily forward, "whatever is wrong?"

"That!" screamed the Earl, pointing a palsied finger at me. "That! He comes here and threatens me,—a peer of England."

The Lady Mary spoke swiftly to her brother and the Colonel.

"'Tis a sick man's fancy," she said. "There have been no threats. Father has had a bad day. He is not himself. He talks wildly. He—"

"Mary!" yelled the Earl as well as he was able. "Do you betray me? Do you betray your own father? Oh, a woman Judas and my daughter!"

Lord Strepp and Colonel Royale looked as if their minds were coming apart. They stared at Lady Mary, at the Earl, at me. For my part I remained silent and stiff in a corner, keeping my eye upon the swords of the other gentlemen. I had no doubt but that presently I would be engaged in a desperate attempt to preserve my life. Lady Mary was weeping. She had never once glanced in my direction. But I was thrilling with happiness. She had flung me her feeble intercession even as a lady may fling a bun to a bear in a pit, but I had the remembrance to prize, to treasure, and if both gentlemen had set upon me and the sick Earl had advanced with the warming-pan I believe my new strength would have been able to beat them off.

In the meantime the Earl was screeching meaningless rubbish in which my name, with epithets, occurred constantly. Lady Mary, still weeping, was trying to calm him.

Young Lord Strepp at last seemed to make up his mind. He approached me and remarked:

"An inexplicable situation, Mr. O'Ruddy."

"More to me than to you," I repeated suavely.

"How?" he asked, with less consideration in his manner. "I know nought of this mummery."

"At least I know no more," I replied, still suave.

"How, Mr. O'Ruddy?" he asked, frowning. "I enter and find you wrangling with my father in his sick chamber. Is there to be no word for this?"

"I dare say you will get forty from your father; a hundred, it may be," said I, always pleasant. "But from me you will get none."

He reflected for a moment. "I dare say you understand I will brook no high-handed silence in a matter of this kind. I am accustomed to ask for the reasons for certain kinds of conduct, and of course I am somewhat prepared to see that the reasons are forthcoming."

"Well, in this case, my lord," said I with a smile, "you can accustom yourself to not getting a reason for a certain kind of conduct, because I do not intend to explain myself."

But at this moment our agreeable conversation was interrupted by the old Earl who began to bay at his son. "Arthur, Arthur, fling the rascal out; fling the rascal out! He is an impostor, a thief!" He began to fume and sputter, and threw his arms wildly; he was in some kind of convulsion; his pillows tossed, and suddenly a packet fell from under them to the floor. As all eyes wheeled toward it, I stooped swiftly and picked it up.

"My papers!" said I.

On their part there was a breathless moment of indecision. Then the swords of Lord Strepp and the Colonel came wildly from their scabbards. Mine was whipped out no less speedily, but I took it and flung it on the floor at their feet, the hilt toward them. "No," said I, my hands empty save for the papers, "'tis only that I would be making a present to the fair Lady Mary, which I pray her to receive." With my best Irish bow I extended to the young lady the papers, my inheritance, which had caused her father so much foaming at the mouth.

She looked at me scornfully, she looked at her father, she looked at me pathetically, she looked at her father, she looked at me piteously; she took the papers.

I walked to the lowering and abashed points of the other men's swords, and picked my blade from the floor. I paid no heed to the glittering points which flashed near my eyes. I strode to the door; I turned and bowed; as I did so, I believe I saw something in Lady Mary's eyes which I wished to see there. I closed the door behind me.

But immediately there was a great clamour in the room I had left, and the door was thrown violently open again. Colonel Royale appeared in a high passion:

"No, no, O'Ruddy," he shouted, "you are a gallant gentleman. I would stake my life that you are in the right. Say the word, and I will back you to the end against ten thousand fiends."

And after him came tempestuously young Lord Strepp, white on the lips with pure rage. But he spoke with a sudden steadiness.

"Colonel Royale, it appears," he said, "thinks he has to protect my friend

100

The O'Ruddy from some wrong of my family or of mine?"

The Colonel drew in his breath for a dangerous reply, but I quickly broke in:

"Come, come, gentlemen," said I sharply. "Are swords to flash between friends when there are so many damned scoundrels in the world to parry and pink? 'Tis wrong; 'tis very wrong. Now, mark you, let us be men of peace at least until to-morrow morning, when, by the way, I have to fight your friend Forister."

"Forister!" they cried together. Their jaws fell; their eyes bulged; they forgot everything; there was a silence.

"Well," said I, wishing to reassure them, "it may not be to-morrow morning. He only told me that he would kill me as soon as he came to Bristol, and I expect him to-night or in the morning. I would of course be expecting him to show here as quickly as possible after his grand speech; but he would not be entirely unwelcome, I am thinking, for I have a mind to see if the sword of an honest man, but no fighter, would be able to put this rogue to shame, and him with all his high talk about killing people who have never done a thing in life to him but kick him some number of feet out into the inn yard, and this need never to have happened if he had known enough to have kept his sense of humour to himself, which often happens in this world."

Reflectively, Colonel Royale murmured:

"One of the finest swordsmen in England."

For this I cared nothing.

Reflectively, Lord Strepp murmured: "My father's partner in the shipping trade."

This last made me open my eyes. "Your father's partner in the shipping trade, Lord Strepp? That little black rascal?"

The young nobleman looked sheepish.

"Aye, I doubt not he may well be called a little black rascal, O'Ruddy," he

101

answered; "but in fact he is my father's partner in certain large—fairly large, you know—shipping interests. Of course that is a matter of no consequence to me personally—but—I believe my father likes him, and my mother and my sister are quite fond of him, I think. I, myself, have never been able to quite—quite understand him in certain ways. He seems a trifle odd at moments. But he certainly is a friend of the family."

"Then," said I, "you will not be able to have the felicity of seeing him kill me, Lord Strepp."

"On the contrary," he rejoined considerately, "I would regard it as usual if he asked me to accompany him to the scene of the fight."

His remark, incidentally, that his sister was fond of Forister, filled me with a sudden insolent madness.

"I would hesitate to disturb any shipping trade," I said with dignity. "It is far from me to wish that the commerce of Great Britain should be hampered by sword-thrust of mine. If it would please young Lord Strepp, I could hand my apologies to Forister all tied up in blue-silk ribbon."

But the youthful nobleman only looked at me long with a sad and reproachful gaze.

"O'Ruddy," he said mournfully, "I have seen you do two fine things. You have never seen me do anything. But, know you now, once and for all, that you may not quarrel with me."

This was too much for an Irish heart. I was moved to throw myself on this lad's neck. I wished to swear to him that I was a brother in blood, I wished to cut a vein to give him everlasting strength—but perhaps his sister Mary had something to do with this feeling.

Colonel Royale had been fidgeting. Now he said suddenly:

"Strepp, I wronged you. Your pardon, Mr. O'Ruddy; but, damme, Strepp, if I didn't think you had gone wrong for the moment."

Lord Strepp took the offered hand. "You are a stupid old firebrain," he said affectionately to the Colonel.

"Well," said the Colonel jubilantly, "now everything is clear. If Mr. O'Ruddy will have me, I will go with him to meet this Forister; and you, Strepp, will accompany Forister; and we all will meet in a friendly way— ahem!"

"The situation is intimately involved," said Lord Strepp dejectedly. "It will be a ridiculous business—watching each blade lunge toward the breast of a friend. I don't know that it is proper. Royale, let us set ourselves to part these duellists. It is indecent."

"Did you note the manner in which he kicked him out of the inn?" asked the Colonel. "Do you think a few soothing words would calm the mind of one of the finest swordsmen in England?"

I began to do some profound thinking.

"Look you, Colonel," said I. "Do you mean that this wretched little liar and coward is a fine swordsman?"

"I haven't heard what you call him," said the Colonel, "but his sword-play is regular firelight on the wall. However," he added hopefully, "we may find some way to keep him from killing you. I have seen some of the greatest swordsmen lose by chance to a novice. It is something like cards. And yet you are not an ignorant player. That, I, Clarence Royale, know full well. Let us try to beat him."

I remembered Forister's parting sentence. Could it be true that a man I had kicked with such enthusiasm and success was now about to take revenge by killing me? I was really disturbed. I was a very brave youth, but I had the most advanced ideas about being killed. On occasion of great danger I could easily and tranquilly develop a philosophy of avoidance and retirement. I had no antiquated notions about going out and getting myself killed through sheer bull-headed scorn of the other fellow's hurting me. My father had taught me this discretion. As a soldier he claimed that he had run away from nine battles, and he would have run away from more, he said, only that all the others had turned out to be victories for his side. He was admittedly a brave man, but, more than this, he had a great deal of sense. I was the child of my father. It did not seem to me profitable to be killed for the sake of a sentiment which seemed weak and dispensable. This little villain! Should I allow him to gratify a furious revenge because I was afraid to take to my heels? I resolved to have the courage of my emotions. I would run away.

But of all this I said nothing. It passed through my mind like light and left me still smiling gayly at Colonel Royale's observations upon the situation.

"Wounds in the body from Forister," quoth he academically, "are almost certain to be fatal, for his wrist has a magnificent twist which reminds one of a top. I do not know where he learned this wrist movement, but almost invariably it leads him to kill his man. Last year I saw him—I digress. I must look to it that O'Ruddy has quiet, rest, and peace of mind until the morning."

Yes; I would have great peace of mind until the morning! I saw that clearly.

"Well," said I, "at any rate we will know more to-morrow. A good day to you, Lord Strepp, and I hope your principal has no more harm come to him than I care to have come to me, which is precious little, and in which case the two of us will be little hurted."

"Good-bye, O'Ruddy," said the young man.

In the corridor the Colonel slapped my shoulder in a sudden exuberant outburst.

"O'Ruddy," he cried, "the chance of your life! Probably the best-known swordsman in all England! 'Pon my word, if you should even graze him, it would almost make you a peer. If you truly pinked him, you could marry a duchess. My eye, what an opportunity for a young and ambitious man."

"And what right has he to be such a fine swordsman?" I demanded fretfully. "Damn him! 'Tis no right of a little tadpole like him to be a great cut-throat. One could never have told from the look of him, and yet it simply teaches one to be always cautious with men."

The Colonel was bubbling over with good nature, his mind full of the prospective event.

"I saw Ponsonby kill Stewart in their great fight several years agone," he cried, rubbing his hands, "but Ponsonby was no such swordsman as Forister, and I misdoubt me that Stewart was much better than you yourself."

Here was a cheerful butcher. I eyed him coldly.

"And out of this," said I slowly, "comes a vast deal of entertainment for you, and a hole between two ribs for me. I think I need a drink."

"By all means, my boy," he answered, heartily. "Come to my chamber. A quart of port under your waistcoat will cure a certain bilious desire in you to see the worst of things, which I have detected lately in your manner. With grand sport before us, how could you be otherwise than jolly? Ha, Ha!"

So saying, he affectionately took my arm and led me along the corridor.

CHAPTER VII

When I reached my own chamber I sank heavily into a chair. My brain was in a tumult. I had fallen in love and arranged to be killed in one short day's work. I stared at my image in a mirror. Could I be The O'Ruddy? Perhaps my name was Paddy or Jem Bottles? Could I pick myself out in a crowd? Could I establish my identification? I little knew.

At first I thought of my calm friend who apparently drank blood for his breakfast. Colonel Royale to me was somewhat of a stranger, but his charming willingness to grind the bones of his friends in his teeth was now quite clear. I fight the best swordsman in England as an amusement, a show? I began to see reasons for returning to Ireland. It was doubtful if old Mickey Clancy would be able to take full care of my estate even with the assistance and prevention of Father Donovan. All properties looked better while the real owner had his eye on them. It would be a shame to waste the place at Glandore all for a bit of pride of staying in England. Never a man neglected his patrimony but that it didn't melt down to a kick in the breeches and much trouble in the courts. I perceived, in short, that my Irish lands were in danger. What could endanger them was not quite clear to my eye, but at any rate they must be saved. Moreover it was necessary to take quick measures. I started up from my chair, hastily recounting Jem Bottles's five guineas.

But I bethought me of Lady Mary. She could hardly be my good fairy. She was rather too plump to be a fairy. She was not extremely plump, but when she walked something moved within her skirts. For my part I think little of fairies, who remind me of roasted fowl's wing. Give me the less brittle beauty which is not likely to break in a man's arms.

After all, I reflected, Mickey Clancy could take care quite well of that estate at Glandore; and, if he didn't, Father Donovan would soon bring him to trouble; and, if Father Donovan couldn't, why, the place was worth very little any how. Besides, 'tis a very weak man who cannot throw an estate into the air for a pair of bright eyes.

Aye, and Lady Mary's bright eyes! That was one matter. And there was Forister's bright sword. That was another matter. But to my descendants I declare that my hesitation did not endure an instant. Forister might have an arm so supple and a sword so long that he might be able to touch the nape of his neck with his own point, but I was firm on English soil. I would meet him even if he were a chevaux de frise. Little it mattered to me. He might swing the ten arms of an Indian god; he might yell like a gale at sea; he might be more terrible in appearance than a volcano in its passions; still I would meet him.

There was a knock, and at my bidding a servant approached and said: "A gentleman, Mr. Forister, wishes to see you, sir."

For a moment I was privately in a panic. Should I say that I was ill, and then send for a doctor to prove that I was not ill? Should I run straightway and hide under the bed? No!

"Bid the gentleman enter," said I to the servant.

Forister came in smiling, cool and deadly. "Good day to you, Mr. O'Ruddy," he said, showing me his little teeth. "I am glad to see that you are not for the moment consorting with highwaymen and other abandoned characters who might succeed in corrupting your morals, Mr. O'Ruddy. I have decided to kill you, Mr. O'Ruddy. You may have heard that I am the finest swordsman in England, Mr. O'Ruddy?"

I replied calmly: "I have heard that you are the finest swordsman in England, Mr. Forister, whenever better swordsmen have been traveling in foreign parts, Mr. Forister, and when no visitors of fencing distinction have taken occasion to journey here, Mr. Forister."

This talk did not give him pleasure, evidently. He had entered with brave composure, but now he bit his lip and shot me a glance of hatred. "I only wished to announce," he said savagely, "that I would prefer to kill you in the morning as early as possible."

"And how may I render my small assistance to you, Mr. Forister? Have you come to request me to arise at an untimely hour?"

I was very placid; but it was not for him to be coming to my chamber with talk of killing me. Still, I thought that, inasmuch as he was there, I might do some good to myself by irritating him slightly. I continued:

"I to-day informed my friends—"

"Your friends!" said he.

"My friends," said I. "Colonel Royale in this matter."

"Colonel Royale!" said he.

"Colonel Royale," said I. "And if you are bound to talk more you had best thrust your head from the window and talk to those chimneys there, which will take far more interest in your speech than I can work up. I was telling you that to-day I informed my friends—then you interrupted me. Well, I informed them—but what the devil I informed them of you will not know very soon. I can promise you, however, it was not a thing you would care to hear with your hands tied behind you."

"Here's a cold man with a belly full of ice," said he musingly. "I have wronged him. He has a tongue on him, he has that. And here I have been judging from his appearance that he was a mere common dolt. And, what, Mr. O'Ruddy," he added, "were you pleased to say to the gentlemen which I would not care to hear with my hands tied behind me?"

"I told them why you took that sudden trip to Bristol," I answered softly.

He fairly leaped in a sudden wild rage. "You—told them?" he stuttered. "You poltroon! 'Twas a coward's work!"

"Be easy," said I, to soothe him. "'Tis no more cowardly than it is for the best swordsman in England to be fighting the worst swordsman in Ireland over a matter in which he is entirely in the wrong, although 'tis not me that cares one way or another way. Indeed, I prefer you to be in the wrong, you little black pig."

"Stop," said he, with a face as white as milk. "You told them—you told them about—about the girl at Bristol?"

"What girl at Bristol?" said I innocently. "'Tis not me to be knowing your wenches in Bristol or otherwheres."

A red flush came into the side of his neck and swelled slowly across his cheeks. "If you've told them about Nell!"

"Nell?" said I. "Nell? Yes, that's the name. Nell. Yes, Nell. And if I told them about Nell?"

"Then," he rejoined solemnly, "I shall kill you ten times if I lose my soul in everlasting hell for it."

"But after I have killed you eleven times I shall go to Bristol and have some sweet interviews with fair Nell," said I. This sting I expected to call forth a terrific outburst, but he remained scowling in dark thought. Then I saw where I had been wrong. This Nell was now more a shame than a sweetheart, and he was afraid that word had been passed by me to the brother of—Here was a chance to disturb him. "When I was making my little joke of you and your flame at Bristol," said I thoughtfully, "I believe there were no ladies present. I don't remember quite. Any how we will let that pass. 'Tis of no consequence."

And here I got him in full cry. "God rot you!" he shrieked. His sword sprang and whistled in the air.

"Hold," said I, as a man of peace. "'Twould be murder. My weapon is on the bed, and I am too lazy to go and fetch it. And in the mean time let me assure you that no word has crossed my lips in regard to Nell, your Bristol sweetheart, for the very excellent reason that I never knew of her existence until you yourself told me some moments ago."

Never before had he met a man like me. I thought his under-jaw would drop on the floor.

"Up to a short time ago," said I candidly, "your indecent amours were safe from my knowledge. I can be in the way of putting myself as silent as a turtle when it comes to protecting a man from his folly with a woman. In fact, I am a gentleman. But," I added sternly, "what of the child?"

"The child?" he cried jumping. "May hell swallow you! And what may you know of the child?"

I waved my hand in gentle deprecation of his excitement as I said:

"Peace, Forister; I know nothing of any child. It was only an observation by a man of natural wit who desired to entertain himself. And, pray, how old is the infant?"

He breathed heavily. "You are a fiend," he answered. Keeping his eyes on the floor, he deliberated upon his choice of conduct. Presently he sheathed his sword and turned with some of his old jauntiness toward the door. "Very good," said he. "To-morrow we shall know more of our own affairs."

"True," I replied.

"We shall learn if slyness and treachery are to be defeated by fair-going and honour."

"True," said I.

"We shall learn if a snake in the grass can with freedom bite the foot of a lion."

"True," said I.

There was a loud jovial clamour at the door, and at my cry it flew open. Colonel Royale entered precipitately, beaming with good humour.

"O'Ruddy, you rascal," he shouted, "I commanded you to take much rest, and here I find—" He halted abruptly as he perceived my other visitor. "And here I find," he repeated coldly, "here I find Mr. Forister."

Forister saluted with finished politeness. "My friend and I," he said, "were discussing the probabilities of my killing him in the morning. He seems to think that he has some small chance for his life, but I have assured him that any real betting man would not wager a grain of sand that he would see the sun go down to-morrow."

"Even so," rejoined the Colonel imperturbably.

110

"And I also suggested to my friend," pursued Forister, "that to-morrow I would sacrifice my ruffles for him, although I always abominate having a man's life-blood about my wrists."

"Even so," quoth the undisturbed Colonel.

"And further I suggested to my friend that if he came to the ground with a coffin on his back, it might promote expedition after the affair was over."

Colonel Royale turned away with a gesture of disgust.

I thought it was high time to play an ace at Forister and stop his babble, so I said:

"And when Mr. Forister had finished his graceful remarks we had some talk regarding Mr. Forister's affairs in Bristol, and I confess I was much interested in hearing about the little—"

Here I stopped abruptly, as if I had been interrupted by Forister; but he had given me no sign but a sickly grin.

"Eh, Forister?" said I. "What's that?"

"I was remarking that I had nothing further to say for the present," he replied, with superb insolence. "For the time I am quite willing to be silent. I bid you a good day, sirs."

CHAPTER VIII

As the door closed upon Forister, Colonel Royale beat his hand passionately against the wall. "O'Ruddy," he cried, "if you could severely maim that cold-blooded bully, I would be willing to adopt you as my legitimate grandfather. I would indeed."

"Never fear me," said I. "I shall pink him well."

"Aye," said my friend, looking at me mournfully, "I ever feared your Irish light-heartedness. 'Twill not do to be confident. He is an evil man, but a great swordsman. Now I never liked Ponsonby, and Stewart was the most lovable of men; but in the great duel Ponsonby killed—"

"No," I interrupted, "damn the duel between Ponsonby and Stewart. I'm sick of it. This is to be the duel between The O'Ruddy and Forister, and it won't be like the other."

"Eh, well," said the Colonel good-naturedly; "make your mind easy. But I hope to God you lay him flat."

"After I have finished with him," said I in measured tones, "he will be willing to sell himself as a sailor to go to the Indies; only, poor devil, he won't be able to walk, which is always a drawback after a hard fight, since it leaves one man incapable on the ground and thus discloses strong evidence of a struggle."

I could see that Colonel Royale had no admiration for my bragging air, but how otherwise was I to keep up my spirits? With all my discouragements it seemed to me that I was privileged to do a little fine lying. Had my father been in my place, he would have lied Forister into such a corner that the man would be thinking that he had the devil for an opponent. My father knew more about such matters.

Still I could not help but be thinking how misfortunate it was that I had kicked a great swordsman out of this inn at Bristol when he might have been a harmless shoemaker if I had only decent luck. I must make the best of it, and for this my only method was to talk loudly,—to myself, if need be; to others if I could. I was not the kind that is quite unable to say a good word for itself even if I was not able to lie as well as my father in his prime. In his day he could lie the coat off a man's back, or the patches off a lady's cheek, and he could lie a good dog into howling ominously. Still it was my duty to lie as well as I was able.

After a time Lord Strepp was announced and entered. Both he and Colonel Royale immediately stiffened and decided not to perceive each other. "Sir," said Lord Strepp to me, "I have the honour to present my compliments to you, and to request that you join a friend of mine, Mr. Forister, at dawn to-morrow, in the settlement of a certain small misunderstanding."

"Sir," said I, in the same manner, "I am only too happy to have this little matter adjusted."

"And of course the arrangements, sir?"

"For them I may refer you to my friend Colonel Royale."

"Ah," said the young Lord, as if he had never before seen the Colonel.

"I am at your service, sir," said Colonel Royale as if he never in his whole life had heard of Lord Strepp.

Then these two began to salaam one another, and mouth out fool phrases, and cavort and prance and caracole, until I thought them mad. When they departed there was a dreadful scene. Each refused to go through the door before the other. There was a frightful deadlock. They each bowed and scraped and waved their hands, and surrendered the doorway back and forth, until I thought they were to be in my chamber eternally. Lord Strepp gorgeously presented the right of way to Colonel Royale, and the Colonel gorgeously presented the right of way to Lord Strepp. All this time they were bending their backs at each other.

Finally I could stand it no longer. "In God's name," I shouted, "the door is wide enough for the two of you. Take it together. You will go through like

113

grease. Never fear the door. 'Tis a good wide door."

To my surprise, they turned to glance at me and burst into great laughter. Then they passed out amiably enough together. I was alone.

Well, the first thing I did was to think. I thought with all my force. I fancied the top of my skull was coming off. I thought myself into ten thousand intricacies. I thought myself into doom and out of it, and behind it and below it, but I could not think of anything which was of service to me. It seemed that I had come among a lot of mummers, and one of these mummers was resolved to kill me, although I had never even so much as broken his leg. But I remembered my father's word, who had told me that gentlemen should properly kill each other over a matter of one liking oranges and the other not liking oranges. It was the custom among men of position, he had said, and of course a way was not clear to changing this custom at the time. However, I determined that if I lived I would insist upon all these customs being moderated and re-directed. For my part I was willing that any man should like oranges.

I decided that I must go for a walk. To sit and gloom in my room until the time of the great affair would do me no good in any case. In fact it was likely to do me much harm. I went forth to the garden in the rear of the inn. Here spread a lawn more level than a ballroom floor. There was a summer-house and many beds of flowers. On this day there was nobody abroad in the garden but an atrocious parrot, which, balancing on its stick, called out continually raucous cries in a foreign tongue.

I paced the lawn for a time, and then took a seat in the summer-house. I had been there but a moment when I perceived Lady Mary and the Countess come into the garden. Through the leafy walls of the summer-house I watched them as they walked slowly to and fro on the grass. The mother had evidently a great deal to say to the daughter. She waved her arms and spoke with a keen excitement.

But did I overhear anything? I overheard nothing! From what I knew of the proper conduct of the really thrilling episodes of life I judged that I should have been able to overhear almost every word of this conversation.

Instead, I could only see the Countess making irritated speech to Lady Mary.

Moreover it was legitimate that I should have been undetected in the summer-house. On the contrary, they were perfectly aware that there was somebody there, and so in their promenade they presented it with a distinguished isolation.

No old maid ever held her ears so wide open. But I could hear nothing but a murmur of angry argument from the Countess and a murmur of gentle objection from Lady Mary. I was in possession of an ideal place from which to overhear conversation. Almost every important conversation ever held had been overheard from a position of this kind. It seemed unfair that I, of all men in literature, should be denied this casual and usual privilege.

The Countess harangued in a low voice at great length; Lady Mary answered from time to time, admitting this and admitting that, protesting against the other. It seemed certain to me that talk related to Forister, although I had no real reason for thinking it. And I was extremely angry that the Countess of Westport and her daughter, Lady Mary Strepp, should talk of Forister.

Upon my indignant meditations the parrot interpolated:

"Ho, ho!" it cried hoarsely. "A pretty lady! A pretty lady! A pretty lady! A pretty lady!—"

Lady Mary smiled at this vacuous repetition, but her mother went into a great rage, opening her old jaws like a maddened horse. "Here, landlord! Here, waiter! Here, anybody!"

So people came running from the inn, and at their head was, truly enough, the landlord. "My lady," he cried panting.

She pointed an angry and terrible finger at the parrot. "When I walk in this garden, am I to be troubled with this wretched bird?"

The landlord almost bit the turf while the servants from the inn grovelled near him. "My lady," he cried, "the bird shall be removed at once." He ran forward. The parrot was chained by its leg to a tall perch. As the innkeeper came away with the entire business, the parrot began to shout: "Old harridan! Old harridan! Old harridan!" The innkeeper seemed to me to be about to die of wild terror. It was a dreadful moment. One could not help but feel sorry for this poor wretch, whose sole offence was that he kept an inn and also chose to keep a parrot in his garden.

The Countess sailed grandly toward the door of the hotel. To the solemn protestations of six or seven servants she paid no heed. At the door she paused and turned for the intimate remark. "I cannot endure parrots," she said impressively. To this dictum the menials crouched.

The servants departed: the garden was now empty save for Lady Mary and me. She continued a pensive strolling. Now, I could see plainly that here fate had arranged for some kind of interview. The whole thing was set like a scene in a theatre. I was undoubtedly to emerge suddenly from the summer-house; the lovely maid would startle, blush, cast down her eyes, turn away. Then, when it came my turn, I would doff my hat to the earth and beg pardon for continuing a comparatively futile existence. Then she would slyly murmur a disclaimer of any ability to criticise my continuation of a comparatively futile existence, adding that she was but an inexperienced girl. The ice thus being broken, we would travel by easy stages into more intimate talk.

I looked down carefully at my apparel and flecked a handkerchief over it. I tilted my hat; I set my hip against my harbour. A moment of indecision, of weakness, and I was out of the summer-house. God knows how I hoped that Lady Mary would not run away.

But the moment she saw me she came swiftly to me. I almost lost my wits.

"'Tis the very gentleman I wished to see," she cried. She was blushing, it is true, but it was evident she intended to say nothing about inexperience or mere weak girls. "I wished to see you because—" she hesitated and then rapidly said: "It was about the papers. I wanted to thank you—I—you have no notion how happy the possession of the papers has made my father. It seemed to have given him new life. I—I saw you throw your sword on the floor with the hilt away from you. And—and then you gave me the papers. I knew you were a gallant gentleman."

All this time, I, in my confusion, was bobbing and murmuring pledges of service. But if I was confused, Lady Mary was soon cool enough in the presence of a simple bog-trotter like me. Her beautiful eyes looked at me reflectively.

"There is only one service I can render you, sir," said she softly. "'Tis advice which would have been useful in saving some men's lives if only they had received it. I mean—don't fight with Forister in the morning. 'Tis certain death."

It was now my turn once more. I drew myself up, and for the first time I looked squarely into her bright eyes.

"My lady," said I, with mournful dignity, "I was filled with pride when you said the good word to me. But what am I to think now? Am I, after all, such a poor stick that, to your mind, I could be advised to sell my honour for a mere fear of being killed?"

Even then I remembered my one-time decision to run away from the duel with Forister; but we will not be thinking of that now.

Tears came into Lady Mary's eyes. "Ah, now, I have blundered," she said. "'Tis what you would say, sir. 'Tis what you would do. I have only made matters worse. A woman's meddling often results in the destruction of those she—those she don't care to have killed."

One would think from the look of this last sentence, that with certain reason I could have felt somewhat elated without being altogether a fool. Lady Mary meant nothing of importance by her speech, but it was a little bit for a man who was hungry to have her think of him. But here I was assailed by a very demon of jealousy and distrust. This beautiful witch had some plan in her head which did not concern my welfare at all. Why should she, a great lady, take any trouble for a poor devil who was living at an inn on money borrowed from a highwayman. I had been highly honoured by an indifferent consideration born of a wish to be polite to a man who had eased the mind of her father. No; I would not deceive myself.

But her tears! Were they marking indifferent consideration? For a second I lost myself in a roseate impossible dream. I dreamed that she had spoken to me because she—

Oh, what folly! Even as I dreamed, she turned to me with splendid carriage, and remarked coldly:

"I did not wish you to suppose that I ever failed to pay a debt. I have paid this one. Proceed now, sir, in your glowing stupidity. I have done."

When I recovered myself she was placidly moving away from me toward the door of the inn.

CHAPTER IX

I had better be getting to the story of the duel. I have been hanging back with it long enough, and I shall tell it at once. I remember my father saying that the most aggravating creature in life was one who would be keeping back the best part of a story through mere reasons of trickery, although I have seen himself dawdle over a tale until his friends wished to hurl the decanters at him. However, there can be no doubting of the wisdom of my father's remark. Indeed there can be little doubting of the wisdom of anything that my father said in life, for he was a very learned man. The fact that my father did not invariably defer to his own opinions does not alter the truth of those opinions in my judgment, since even the greatest of philosophers is more likely to be living a life based on the temper of his wife and the advice of his physician than on the rules laid down in his books. Nor am I certain that my father was in a regular habit of delaying a story. I only remember this one incident, wherein he was recounting a stirring tale of a fight with a lancer, and just as the lance was within an inch of the paternal breast my father was reminded, by a sight of the walnuts, that Mickey Clancy was not serving the port with his usual rapidity, and so he addressed him. I remember the words well.

"Mickey, you spalpeen," said my father, "would you be leaving the gentlemen as dry as the bottom of Moses' feet when he crossed the Red Sea? Look at O'Mahoney there! He is as thirsty as a fish in the top of a tree. And Father Donovan has had but two small quarts, and he never takes less than five. Bad luck to you, Mickey, if it was a drink for your own stomach, you would be moving faster. Are you wishing to ruin my reputation for hospitality, you rogue you?"

And my father was going on with Mickey, only that he looked about him at this time and discovered his guests all upon their feet, one with the tongs and one with the poker, others with decanters ready to throw.

"What's this?" said he.

"The lance," said they.

"What lance?" said he.

"The lance of the lancer," said they.

"And why shouldn't he have a lance?" said my father. "'Faith, 'twould be an odd lancer without a lance!"

By this time they were so angry that Mickey, seeing how things were going, and I being a mere lad, took me from the room. I never heard precisely what happened to the lancer, but he must have had the worst of it, for wasn't my father, seated there at the table, telling the story long years after?

Well, as to my duel with Forister: Colonel Royale was an extremely busy man, and almost tired my life out with a quantity of needless attentions. For my part, I thought more of Lady Mary and the fact that she considered me no more than if I had been a spud. Colonel Royale fluttered about me. I would have gruffly sent him away if it were not that everything he did was meant in kindliness and generous feeling. I was already believing that he did not have more than one brain in his head, but I could not be ungrateful for his interest and enthusiasm in getting me out to be hurt correctly. I understood, long years afterward, that he and Lord Strepp were each so particular in the negotiations that no less than eighteen bottles of wine were consumed.

The morning for the duel dawned softly warm, softly wet, softly foggy. The Colonel popped into my room the moment I was dressed. To my surprise, he was now quite mournful. It was I, now, who had to do the cheering.

"Your spirits are low, Colonel?" said I banteringly.

"Aye, O'Ruddy," he answered with an effort, "I had a bad night, with the gout. Heaven help this devil from getting his sword into your bowels."

He had made the appointment with Strepp, of course, and as we walked toward the ground he looked at me very curiously out of the ends of his eyes. "You know—ah, you have the honour of the acquaintance of Lady Mary Strepp, O'Ruddy?" said he suddenly and nervously.

"I have," I answered, stiffening. Then I said: "And you?"

"Her father and I were friends before either of you were born," he said simply. "I was a cornet in his old regiment. Little Lady Mary played at the knee of the poor young subaltern."

"Oh," said I meanly, "you are, then, a kind of uncle."

"Aye," said he, "a kind of uncle. So much of an uncle," he added with more energy, "that when she gave me this note I thought much of acting like a real uncle. From what I have unfortunately overheard, I suspect that the Earl—aw—disagrees with you on certain points."

He averted his face as he handed me the note, and eagerly I tore it open. It was unsigned. It contained but three words: "God spare you!" And so I marched in a tumult of joy to a duel wherein I was expected to be killed.

I glanced at the Colonel. His countenance was deeply mournful. "'Tis for few girls I would become a dove to carry notes between lovers," he said gloomily. "Damn you for it, O'Ruddy!"

"Nay, Colonel," said I. "'Tis no missive of love. Look you!"

But still he kept his eyes averted. "I judge it was not meant for my eyes," he said, still very gloomy.

But here I flamed up in wrath:

"And would the eye of an angel be allowed to rest upon this paper if it were not fit that it should be so?" I demanded in my anger. "Colonel, am I to hear you bleat about doves and lovers when a glance of your eye will disabuse you? Read!"

He read. "'God spare you!'" he repeated tenderly. Then he addressed me with fine candor. "Aye, I have watched her these many years, O'Ruddy. When she was a babe I have seen her in her little bath. When she was a small girl I have seen her asleep with some trinket clasped in her rosy hand on the coverlet. Since she has been a beautiful young lady I have—but no matter. You come along, named nobody, hailing from nowhere; and she—she sends me out to deliver her prayer that God may spare you!"

I was awed by this middle-aged sorrow. But, curse him! when she was a

121

babe he had seen her in her little bath, had he? Damn his eyes! He had seen the baby naked in her tiny tub? Damn his eyes again! I was in such a fury that I longed to fight Royale on the spot and kill him, running my sword through his memory so that it would be blotted out forever, and never, never again, even in Paradise, could he recall the image in the little tub.

But the Colonel's next words took the rage out of me.

"Go in, O'Ruddy," he cried heartily. "There is no truer man could win her. As my lady says, 'God spare you!'"

"And if Forister's blade be not too brisk, I will manage to be spared," I rejoined.

"Oh, there is another thing touching the matter," said the Colonel suddenly. "Forister is your chief rival, although I little know what has passed between them. Nothing important, I think, although I am sure Forister is resolved to have her for a bride. Of that I am certain. He is resolved."

"Is he so?" said I.

I was numb and cold for a moment. Then I slowly began to boil, like a kettle freshly placed on the fire. So I was facing a rival? Well, and he would get such a facing as few men had received. And he was my rival and in the breast of my coat I wore a note—"God spare you!" Ha, ha! He little knew the advantages under which he was to play. Could I lose with "God spare you!" against my heart? Not against three Foristers!

But hold! might it not be that the gentle Lady Mary, deprecating this duel and filled with feelings of humanity, had sent us each a note with this fervid cry for God to spare us? I was forced to concede it possible. After all, I perfectly well knew that to Lady Mary I was a mere nothing. Royale's words had been so many plumes in my life's helmet, but at bottom I knew better than to set great store by them. The whole thing was now to hurry to the duelling-ground and see if I could discover from this black Forister's face if he had received a "God spare you!" I took the Colonel's arm and fairly dragged him.

"Damme, O'Ruddy!" said he, puffing; "this can be nought but genuine eagerness."

When we came to the duelling-place we found Lord Strepp and Forister pacing to and fro, while the top of a near-by wall was crowded with pleasant-minded spectators. "Aye, you've come, have ye, sirs?" called out the rabble. Lord Strepp seemed rather annoyed, and Colonel Royale grew red and stepped peremptorily toward the wall, but Forister and I had eyes only for each other. His eye for me was a glad, cruel eye. I have a dim remembrance of seeing the Colonel take his scabbard and incontinently beat many worthy citizens of Bristol; indeed, he seemed to beat every worthy citizen of Bristol who had not legs enough to get away. I could hear them squeaking out protests while I keenly studied the jubilant Forister.

Aye, it was true. He too had a "God spare you!" I felt my blood begin to run hot. My eyes suddenly cleared as if I had been empowered with miraculous vision. My arm became supple as a whip. I decided upon one thing. I would kill Forister.

I thought the Colonel never would give over chasing citizens, but at last he returned breathless, having scattered the populace over a wide stretch of country. The preliminaries were very simple. In a half-minute Forister and I, in our shirts, faced each other.

And now I passed into such a state of fury that I cannot find words to describe it; but, as I have said, I was possessed with a remarkable clearness of vision and strength of arm. These phenomena amaze me even at this day. I was so airy upon my feet that I might have been a spirit. I think great rages work thus upon some natures. Their competence is suddenly made manifold. They live, for a brief space, the life of giants. Rage is destruction active. Whenever anything in this world needs to be destroyed, nature makes somebody wrathful. Another thing that I recall is that I had not the slightest doubt of my ability to kill Forister. There were no more misgivings: no quakings. I thought of the impending duel with delight.

In all my midnight meditations upon the fight I had pictured myself as lying strictly upon the defensive and seeking a chance opportunity to damage my redoubtable opponent. But the moment after our swords had crossed I was an absolute demon of attack. My very first lunge made him give back a long pace. I saw his confident face change to a look of fierce excitement.

There is little to say of the flying, spinning blades. It is only necessary to remark that Forister dropped almost immediately to defensive tactics before an assault which was not only impetuous but exceedingly brilliant, if I may be allowed to say so. And I know that on my left a certain Colonel Royale was steadily growing happier.

The end came with an almost ridiculous swiftness. The feeling of an ugly quivering wrench communicated itself from the point of my sword to my mind; I heard Strepp and Royale cry "Hold!" I saw Forister fall; I lowered my point and stood dizzily thinking. My sight was now blurred; my arm was weak.

My sword had gone deep into Forister's left shoulder, and the bones there had given that hideous feeling of a quivering wrench. He was not injured beyond repair, but he was in exquisite agony. Before they could reach him he turned over on his elbows and managed in some way to fling his sword at me. "Damn your soul!" he cried, and he gave a sort of howl as Lord Strepp, grim and unceremonious, bounced him over again upon his back. In the mean time Colonel Royale was helping me on with my coat and waistcoat, although I hardly knew that either he or the coat or waistcoat were in existence.

I had my usual inclination to go forward and explain to everybody how it all had happened. But Royale took me forcibly by the arm, and we turned our backs on Strepp and Forister and walked toward the inn.

As soon as we were out of their sight, Colonel Royale clasped my hands with rapture. "My boy," he cried, "you are great! You are renowned! You are illustrious! What a game you could give Ponsonby! You would give him such a stir!"

"Never doubt me," said I. "But I am now your legitimate grandfather, and I should be treated with great respect."

When we came near the inn I began to glance up at the windows. I

124

surely expected to see a face at one of them. Certainly she would care to know who was slain or who was hurt. She would be watching, I fondly hoped, to see who returned on his legs. But the front of the inn stared at us, chilly and vacant, like a prison wall.

When we entered, the Colonel bawled lustily for an immediate bottle of wine, and I joined him in its drinking, for I knew that it would be a bellows to my flagging spirits. I had set my heart upon seeing a face at the window of the inn.

CHAPTER X

And now I found out what it was to be a famous swordsman. All that day the inn seemed to hum with my name. I could not step down a corridor without seeing flocks of servants taking wing. They fled tumultuously. A silly maid coming from a chamber with a bucket saw me and shrieked. She dropped her bucket and fled back into the chamber. A man-servant saw me, gave a low moan of terror, and leaped down a convenient stairway. All attendants scuttled aside.

What was the matter with me? Had I grown in stature or developed a ferocious ugliness? No; I now was a famous swordsman. That was all. I now was expected to try to grab the maids and kiss them wantonly. I now was expected to clout the grooms on their ears if they so much as showed themselves in my sight. In fact, I was now a great blustering, overpowering, preposterous ass.

There was a crowd of people in the coffee-room, but the buzz of talk suddenly ceased as I entered.

"Is this your chair, sir?" said I civilly to a gentleman.

He stepped away from the chair as if it had tried to bite him.

"'Tis at your service, sir!" he cried hastily.

"No," said I, "I would not be taking it if it be yours, for there are just as good chairs in the sea as ever were caught, and it would ill become me to deprive a gentleman of his chair when by exercising a little energy I can gain one for myself, although I am willing to admit that I have a slight hunger upon me. 'Tis a fine morning, sir."

He had turned pale and was edging toward the door. "'Tis at your service, sir," he repeated in a low and frightened voice. All the people were staring at us.

"No, good sir," I remonstrated, stepping forward to explain. "I would not be having you think that I am unable to get a chair for myself, since I am above everything able and swift with my hands, and it is a small thing to get a chair for one's self and not deprive a worthy gentleman of his own."

"I did not think to deprive you, sir," he ejaculated desperately. "The chair is at your service, sir!"

"Plague the man!" I cried, stamping my foot impatiently; and at the stamping of my foot a waiter let fall a dish, some women screamed, three or four people disappeared through the door, and a venerable gentleman arose from his seat in a corner and in a tremulous voice said:

"Sir, let us pray you that there be no bloodshed."

"You are an old fool," said I to him. "How could there be bloodshed with me here merely despising you all for not knowing what I mean when I say it."

"We know you mean what you say, sir," responded the old gentleman. "Pray God you mean peaceably!"

"Hoity-toity!" shouted a loud voice, and I saw a great, tall, ugly woman bearing down upon me from the doorway. "Out of my way," she thundered at a waiter. The man gasped out: "Yes, your ladyship!"

I was face to face with the mother of my lovely Mary.

"Hoity-toity!" she shouted at me again. "A brawler, eh? A lively swordster, hey? A real damn-my-eyes swaggering bully!"

Then she charged upon me. "How dare you brawl with these inoffensive people under the same roof which shelters me, fellow? By my word, I would have pleasure to give you a box on the ear!"

"Madam," I protested hurriedly. But I saw the futility of it. Without devoting further time to an appeal, I turned and fled. I dodged behind three chairs and moved them hastily into a rampart.

"Madam," I cried, feeling that I could parley from my new position, "you labour under a misapprehension."

"Misapprehend me no misapprehensions," she retorted hotly. "How dare you say that I can misapprehend anything, wretch?"

She attacked each flank in turn, but so agile was I that I escaped capture, although my position in regard to the chairs was twice reversed. We performed a series of nimble manœuvres which were characterized on my part by a high degree of strategy. But I found the rampart of chairs an untenable place. I was again obliged hurriedly to retreat, this time taking up a position behind a large table.

"Madam," I said desperately, "believe me, you are suffering under a grave misapprehension."

"Again he talks of misapprehension!"

We revolved once swiftly around the table; she stopped, panting.

"And this is the blusterer! And why do you not stand your ground, coward?"

"Madam," said I with more coolness now that I saw she would soon be losing her wind, "I would esteem it very ungallant behaviour if I endured your attack for even a brief moment. My forefathers form a brave race which always runs away from the ladies."

After this speech we revolved twice around the table. I must in all candour say that the Countess used language which would not at all suit the pages of my true and virtuous chronicle; but indeed it was no worse than I often heard afterward from the great ladies of the time. However, the talk was not always addressed to me, thank the Saints!

After we had made the two revolutions, I spoke reasonably. "Madam," said I, "if we go spinning about the table in this fashion for any length of time, these gawking spectators will think we are a pair of wheels."

"Spectators!" she cried, lifting her old head high. She beheld about seventy-five interested people. She called out loudly to them:

"And is there no gentleman among you all to draw his sword and beat

128

me this rascal from the inn?"

Nobody moved.

"Madam," said I, still reasonable, "would it not be better to avoid a possible scandal by discontinuing these movements, as the tongues of men are not always fair, and it might be said by some—"

Whereupon we revolved twice more around the table.

When the old pelican stopped, she had only enough breath left to impartially abuse all the sight-seers. As her eye fixed upon them, The O'Ruddy, illustrious fighting-man, saw his chance and bolted like a hare. The escape must have formed a great spectacle, but I had no time for appearances. As I was passing out of the door, the Countess, in her disappointed rage, threw a heavy ivory fan after me, which struck an innocent bystander in the eye, for which he apologized.

CHAPTER XI

I wasted no time in the vicinity of the inn. I decided that an interval spent in some remote place would be consistent with the behaviour of a gentleman.

But the agitations of the day were not yet closed for me. Suddenly I came upon a small, slow-moving, and solemn company of men, who carried among them some kind of a pallet, and on this pallet was the body of Forister. I gazed upon his ghastly face; I saw the large blood blotches on his shirt; as they drew nearer I saw him roll his eyes and heard him groan. Some of the men recognized me, and I saw black looks and straight-pointing fingers. At the rear walked Lord Strepp with Forister's sword under his arm. I turned away with a new impression of the pastime of duelling. Forister's pallor, the show of bloody cloth, his groan, the dark stares of men, made me see my victory in a different way, and I even wondered if it had been absolutely necessary to work this mischief upon a fellow-being.

I spent most of the day down among the low taverns of the sailors, striving to interest myself in a thousand new sights brought by the ships from foreign parts.

But ever my mind returned to Lady Mary, and to my misfortune in being pursued around chairs and tables by my angel's mother. I had also managed to have a bitter quarrel with the noble father of this lovely creature. It was hardly possible that I could be joyous over my prospects.

At noon I returned to the inn, approaching with some display of caution. As I neared it, a carriage followed by some horsemen whirled speedily from the door. I knew at once that Lady Mary had been taken from me. She was gone with her father and mother back to London. I recognized Lord Strepp and Colonel Royale among the horsemen.

I walked through the inn to the garden, and looked at the parrot. My senses were all numb. I stared at the bird as it rolled its wicked eye at me.

"Pretty lady! Pretty lady!" it called in coarse mockery.

"Plague the bird!" I muttered, as I turned upon my heel and entered the inn.

"My bill," said I. "A horse for Bath!" said I.

Again I rode forth on a quest. The first had been after my papers. The second was after my love. The second was the hopeless one, and, overcome by melancholy, I did not even spur my horse swiftly on my mission. There was upon me the deep-rooted sadness which balances the mirth of my people,—the Celtic aptitude for discouragement; and even the keening of old women in the red glow of the peat fire could never have deepened my mood.

And if I should succeed in reaching London, what then? Would the wild savage from the rocky shore of Ireland be a pleasing sight to my Lady Mary when once more amid the glamour and whirl of the fashionable town? Besides, I could no longer travel on the guineas of Jem Bottles. He had engaged himself and his purse in my service because I had told him of a fortune involved in the regaining of certain papers. I had regained those papers, and then coolly placed them as a gift in a certain lovely white hand. I had had no more thought of Jem Bottles and his five guineas than if I had never seen them. But this was no excuse for a gentleman. When I was arrived at the rendezvous I must immediately confess to Jem Bottles, the highwayman, that I had wronged him. I did not expect him to demand satisfaction, but I thought he might shoot me in the back as I was riding away.

But Jem was not at the appointed place under the tree. Not puzzled at this behaviour, I rode on. I saw I could not expect the man to stay for ever under a tree while I was away in Bristol fighting a duel and making eyes at a lady. Still, I had heard that it was always done.

At the inn where Paddy holed Forister, I did not dismount, although a hostler ran out busily. "No," said I. "I ride on." I looked at the man. Small, sharp-eyed, weazened, he was as likely a rascal of a hostler as ever helped a highwayman to know a filled purse from a man who was riding to make arrangements with his creditors.

"Do you remember me?" said I.

"No, sir," he said with great promptitude.

"Very good," said I. "I knew you did. Now I want to know if Master Jem Bottles has passed this way to-day. A shilling for the truth and a thrashing for a lie."

The man came close to my stirrup. "Master," he said, "I know you to be a friend of him. Well, in day-time he don't ride past our door. There be lanes. And so he ain't passed here, and that's the truth."

I flung him a shilling. "Now," I said, "what of the red giant?"

The man opened his little eyes in surprise. "He took horse with you gentlemen and rode on to Bristol, or I don't know."

"Very good; now I see two very fine horses champing in the yard. And who owns them?"

If I had expected to catch him in treachery I was wrong.

"Them?" said he, jerking his thumb. He still kept his voice lowered. "They belong to two gentlemen who rode out some hours agone along with some great man's carriage. The officer said some pin-pricks he had gotten in a duel had stiffened him, and made the saddle ill of ease with him, and the young lord said that he would stay behind as a companion. They be up in the Colonel's chamber, drinking vastly. But mind your life, sir, if you would halt them on the road. They be men of great spirit. This inn seldom sees such drinkers."

And so Lord Strepp and Colonel Royale were resting at this inn while the carriage of the Earl had gone on toward Bath? I had a mind to dismount and join the two in their roystering, but my eyes turned wistfully toward Bath.

As I rode away I began to wonder what had become of Jem Bottles and Paddy. Here was a fine pair to be abroad in the land. Here were two jewels to be rampaging across the country. Separately, they were villains enough, but together they would overturn England and get themselves hung for it on twin gibbets. I tried to imagine the particular roguery to which they would first give their attention.

But then all thought of the rascals faded from me as my mind received a vision of Lady Mary's fair face, her figure, her foot. It would not be me to be thinking of two such thieves when I could be dreaming of Lady Mary with her soft voice and the clear depth of her eyes. My horse seemed to have a sympathy with my feeling and he leaped bravely along the road. The Celtic melancholy of the first part of the journey had blown away like a sea-mist. I sped on gallantly toward Bath and Lady Mary.

But almost at the end of the day, when I was within a few miles of Bath, my horse suddenly pitched forward onto his knees and nose. There was a flying spray of muddy water. I was flung out of the saddle, but I fell without any serious hurt whatever. We had been ambushed by some kind of deep-sided puddle. My poor horse scrambled out and stood with lowered head, heaving and trembling. His soft nose had been cut between his teeth and the far edge of the puddle. I led him forward, watching his legs. He was lamed. I looked in wrath and despair back at the puddle, which was as plain as a golden guinea on a platter. I do not see how I could have blundered into it, for the daylight was still clear and strong. I had been gazing like a fool in the direction of Bath. And my Celtic melancholy swept down upon me again, and even my father's bier appeared before me with the pale candle-flames swaying in the gusty room, and now indeed my ears heard the loud wailing keen of the old women.

"Rubbish," said I suddenly and aloud, "and is it one of the best swordsmen in England that is to be beaten by a lame horse?" My spirit revived. I resolved to leave my horse in the care of the people of the nearest house and proceed at once on foot to Bath. The people of the inn could be sent out after the poor animal. Wheeling my eyes, I saw a house not more than two fields away, with honest hospitable smoke curling from the chimneys. I led my beast through a hole in the hedge, and I slowly made my way toward it.

Now it happened that my way led me near a haycock, and as I neared this haycock I heard voices from the other side of it. I hastened forward, thinking to find some yokels. But as I drew very close I suddenly halted and silently listened to the voices on the other side.

"Sure, I can read," Paddy was saying. "And why wouldn't I be able? If we couldn't read in Ireland, we would be after being cheated in our rents, but we never pay them any how, so that's no matter. I would be having you to know we are a highly educated people. And perhaps you would be reading it yourself, my man?"

"No," said Jem Bottles, "I be not a great scholar and it has a look of amazing hardness. And I misdoubt me," he added in a morose and envious voice, "that your head be too full of learning."

"Learning!" cried Paddy. "Why wouldn't I be learned, since my uncle was a sexton and had to know one grave from another by looking at the stones so as never to mix up the people? Learning! says you? And wasn't there a convent at Ballygowagglycuddi, and wasn't Ballygowagglycuddi only ten miles from my father's house, and haven't I seen it many a time?"

"Aye, well, good Master Paddy," replied Jem Bottles, oppressed and sullen, but still in a voice ironic from suspicion, "I never doubt me but what you are a regular clerk for deep learning, but you have not yet read a line from the paper, and I have been waiting this half-hour."

"And how could I be reading?" cried Paddy in tones of indignation. "How could I be reading with you there croaking of this and that and speaking hard of my learning? Bad cess to the paper, I will be after reading it to myself if you are never to stop your clatter, Jem Bottles."

"I be still as a dead rat," exclaimed the astonished highwayman.

"Well, then," said Paddy. "Listen hard, and you will hear such learning as would be making your eyes jump from your head. And 'tis not me either that cares to show my learning before people who are unable to tell a mile-post from a church-tower."

"I be awaiting," said Jem Bottles with a new meekness apparently born

134

of respect for Paddy's eloquence.

"Well, then," said Paddy, pained at these interruptions. "Listen well, and maybe you will gain some learning which may serve you all your life in reading chalk-marks in taprooms; for I see that they have that custom in this country, and 'tis very bad for hard-drinking men who have no learning."

"If you would read from the paper—" began Jem Bottles.

"Now, will you be still?" cried Paddy in vast exasperation.

But here Jem Bottles spoke with angry resolution. "Come, now! Read! 'Tis not me that talks too much, and the day wanes."

"Well, well, I would not be hurried, and that's the truth," said Paddy soothingly. "Listen now." I heard a rustling of paper. "Ahem!" said Paddy, "Ahem! Are ye listening, Jem Bottles?"

"I be," replied the highwayman.

"Ahem!" said Paddy. "Ahem! Are ye listening, Jem Bottles?"

"I be," replied the highwayman.

"Then here's for it," said Paddy in a formidable voice. There was another rustling of paper. Then to my surprise I heard Paddy intone, without punctuation, the following words:

"Dear Sister Mary I am asking the good father to write this because my hand is lame from milking the cows although we only have one and we sold her in the autumn the four shillings you owe on the pig we would like if convenient to pay now owing to the landlord may the plague take him how did your Mickey find the fishing when you see Peggy tell her—"

Here Jem Bottles's voice arose in tones of incredulity.

"And these be the papers of the great Earl!" he cried.

Then the truth flashed across my vision like the lightning. My two madmen had robbed the carriage of the Earl of Westport, and had taken, among other things, the Earl's papers—my papers—Lady Mary's papers. I strode around the haycock.

"Wretches!" I shouted. "Miserable wretches!"

For a time they were speechless. Paddy found his tongue first.

"Aye, 'tis him! 'Tis nothing but little black men and papers with him, and when we get them for him he calls us out of our names in a foreign tongue. 'Tis no service for a bright man," he concluded mournfully.

"Give me the papers," said I.

Paddy obediently handed them. I knew them. They were my papers—Lady Mary's papers.

"And now," said I, eyeing the pair, "what mischief have you two been compassing?"

Paddy only mumbled sulkily. It was something on the difficulties of satisfying me on the subjects of little black men and papers. Jem Bottles was also sulky, but he grumbled out the beginning of an explanation.

"Well, master, I bided under the tree till him here came, and then we together bided. And at last we thought, with the time so heavy, we might better work to handle a purse or two. Thinking," he said delicately, "our gentleman might have need of a little gold. Well, and as we were riding, a good lad from the—your worship knows where—tells us the Earl's carriage is halting there for a time, but will go on later without its escort of two gentlemen; only with servants. And, thinking to do our gentleman a good deed, I brought them to stand on the highway, and then he—"

"And then I," broke in Paddy proudly, "walks up to the carriage-door looking like a king's cruiser, and says I, 'Pray excuse the manners of a self-opinionated man, but I consider your purses would look better in my pocket.' And then there was a great trouble. An old owl of a woman screeched, and was for killing me with a bottle which she had been holding against her nose. But she never dared. And with that an old sick man lifted himself from hundreds of cushions and says he, 'What do you want? You can't have them,' says he, and he keeps clasping his breast. 'First of all,' says I, 'I want what you have there. What I want else I'll tell you at my leisure.' And he was all for mouthing and fuming, but he was that scared he gave me these papers—bad luck to them." Paddy cast an evil eye upon the papers in my hand.

"And then?" said I.

"The driver he tried for to whip up," interpolated Jem Bottles. "He was a game one, but the others were like wet cats."

"And says I," continued Paddy, "'now we will have the gold, if it please you.' And out it came. 'I bid ye a good journey,' says I, and I thought it was over, and how easy it was highwaying, and I liked it well, until the lady on the front seat opens her hood and shows me a prettier face than we have in all Ireland. She clasps two white hands. 'Oh, please Mister Highwayman, my father's papers—' And with that I backs away. 'Let them go,' says I to Jem Bottles, and sick I was of it, and I would be buying masses to-night if I might find a Christian church. The poor lady!"

I was no longer angry with Paddy.

"Aye," said Jem Bottles, "the poor lady was that forlorn!"

I was no longer angry with Jem Bottles.

But I now had to do a deal of thinking. It was plain that the papers were of supreme importance to the Earl. Although I had given them to Lady Mary, they had returned to me. It was fate. My father had taught me to respect these papers, but I now saw them as a sign in the sky.

However, it was hard to decide what to do. I had given the papers to Lady Mary, and they had fled back to me swifter than cormorants. Perhaps it was willed that I should keep them. And then there would be tears in the eyes of Lady Mary, who suffered through the suffering of her father. No; come good, come bad for me, for Jem Bottles, for Paddy, I would stake our fortunes on the act of returning the papers to Lady Mary.

It is the way of Irishmen. We are all of us true philanthropists. That is why we have nothing, although in other countries I have seen philanthropists who had a great deal. My own interest in the papers I staked, mentally, with a glad mind; the minor interests of Jem Bottles and Paddy I staked, mentally, without thinking of them at all. But surely it would be a tribute to fate to give anything to Lady Mary.

I resolved on a course of action. When I aroused to look at my companions I found them seated face to face on the ground like players of draughts. Between them was spread a handkerchief, and on that handkerchief was a heap of guineas. Jem Bottles was saying, "Here be my fingers five times over again." He separated a smaller heap. "Here be my fingers five times over again." He separated another little stack. "And here be my fingers five times over again and two more yet. Now can ye understand?"

"By dad," said Paddy admiringly, "you have the learning this time, Master Bottles. My uncle the sexton could not have done it better."

"What is all this?" said I.

They both looked at me deprecatingly. "'Tis, your honour," began Paddy; "'tis only some little small sum—nothing to be talked of—belonging to the old sick man in the carriage."

"Paddy and Jem Bottles," said I, "I forgive you the taking of the papers. Ye are good men and true. Now we will do great deeds."

CHAPTER XII

My plans were formed quickly. "We now have a treasure chest of no small dimensions," said I, very complacent, naturally. "We can conquer London with this. Everything is before us. I have already established myself as the grandest swordsman in the whole continent of England. Lately we have gained much treasure. And also I have the papers. Paddy, do you take care of this poor horse. Then follow me into Bath. Jem Bottles, do you mount and ride around the town, for I fear your balladists. Meet me on the London road. Ride slowly on the highway to London, and in due time I will overtake you. I shall pocket a few of those guineas, but you yourself shall be the main treasury. Hold! what of Paddy's hair? Did he rob the Earl with that great flame showing? He dare not appear in Bath."

"'Tis small tribute to my wit, sir," answered Jem Bottles. "I would as soon go poaching in company with a lighthouse as to call a stand on the road with him uncovered. I tied him in cloth until he looked no more like himself than he now does look like a parson."

"Aye," said Paddy in some bad humour, "my head was tied in a bag. My mother would not have known me from a pig going to market. And I would not be for liking it every day. My hair is what the blessed Saints sent me, and I see no such fine hair around me that people are free to throw the laugh at me."

"Peace!" said I.

Their horses were tied in an adjacent thicket. I sent Paddy off with my lame mount, giving him full instructions as to his lies. I and Jem Bottles took the other horses and rode toward Bath.

Where a certain lane turned off from the highway I parted with Jem Bottles, and he rode away between the hedges. I cantered into Bath.

The best-known inn was ablaze with fleeting lights, and people were shouting within. It was some time before I could gain a man to look after my horse. Of him I demanded the reason of the disturbance. "The Earl of Westport's carriage has been robbed on the Bristol road, sir," he cried excitedly. "There be parties starting out. I pray they catch him."

"And who would they be catching, my lad," said I.

"Jem Bottles, damn him, sir," answered the man. "But 'tis a fierce time they will have, for he stands no less than eight feet in his boots, and his eyes are no human eyes, but burn blood-red always. His hands are adrip with blood, and 'tis said that he eats human flesh, sir. He surely is a devil, sir."

"From the description I would be willing to believe it," said I. "However, he will be easy to mark. Such a monster can hardly be mistaken for an honest man."

I entered the inn, while a boy staggered under my valises. I had difficulty in finding the landlord. But in the corridor were a number of travellers, and evidently one had come that day from Bristol, for he suddenly nudged another and hurriedly whispered:

"'Tis him! The great Irish swordsman!"

Then the news spread like the wind, apparently, that the man who had beaten the great Forister was arrived in good health at the inn. There were murmurs, and a great deal of attention, and many eyes. I suddenly caught myself swaggering somewhat. It is hard to be a famous person and not show a great swollen chicken-breast to the people. They are disappointed if you do not strut and step high. "Show me to a chamber," said I splendidly. The servants bowed their foreheads to the floor.

But the great hubbub over the Earl's loss continued without abatement. Gentlemen clanked down in their spurs; there was much talk of dragoons; the tumult was extraordinary. Upstairs the landlord led me past the door of a kind of drawing-room. I glanced within and saw the Earl of Westport gesturing and declaiming to a company of gentlemen. He was propped up in a great arm-chair.

"And why would he be waving his hands that way?" said I to two servants

140

who stood without.

"His lordship has lost many valuable papers at the hands of a miscreant, sir," answered one.

"Is it so?" said I. "Well, then, I would see his lordship."

But here this valet stiffened. "No doubt but what his lordship would be happy to see you, sir," he answered slowly. "Unfortunately, however, he has forbidden me to present strangers to his presence."

"I have very important news. Do not be an idiot," said I. "Announce me. The O'Ruddy."

"The O'Ruggy?" said he.

"The O'Ruddy," said I.

"The O'Rudgy?" said he.

"No," said I, and I told him again. Finally he took two paces within the room and sung out in a loud voice:

"The O'Rubby."

I heard the voice of the sick old Earl calling out from his great chair. "Why, 'tis the Irishman. Bid him enter. I am glad—I am always very glad—ahem!—"

As I strode into the room I was aware of another buzz of talk. Apparently here, too, were plenty of people who knew me as the famous swordsman. The Earl moved his jaw and mumbled.

"Aye," said he at last, "here is The O'Ruddy. And, do you know, Mr. O'Ruddy, I have been foully robbed, and, among other things, have lost your worthless papers?"

"I heard that you had lost them," I answered composedly. "But I refuse to take your word that they are worthless."

Many people stared, and the Earl gave me a firm scowl. But after consideration he spoke as if he thought it well to dissemble a great dislike of me. The many candles burned very brightly, and we could all see each other. I thought it better to back casually toward the wall.

"You never accomplish anything," coughed the sick Earl. "Yet you are for ever prating of yourself. I wish my son were here. My papers are gone. I shall never recover them."

"The papers are in the breast of my coat at this moment," said I coolly.

There was a great tumult. The Earl lost his head and cried:

"Seize him!" Two or three young men took steps toward me. I was back to the wall, and in a leisurely and contemptuous way I drew my sword.

"The first gentleman who advances is a dead man," said I pleasantly.

Some drew away quickly; some hesitated, and then withdrew subtilely. In the mean time the screeches of the Earl mocked them all.

"Aye, the wild Irishman brings you up to a stand, he does! Now who will have at him? In all Bath I have no friend with a stout heart?"

After looking them over I said:

"No, my Lord, you have none."

At this insult the aged peer arose from his chair. "Bring me my sword," he cried to his valet. A hush fell upon us all. We were rendered immovable by the solemn dignity of this proceeding.

It was some time before I could find my tongue.

"And if you design to cross blades with me, you will find me a sad renegade," said I. "I am holding the papers for the hands of their true owner."

"And their true owner?" he demanded.

"Lady Mary Strepp," said I.

He sank back into his seat. "This Irishman's impudence is beyond measuring," he exclaimed. The hurrying valet arrived at that moment with a sword. "Take it away! Take it away!" he cried. "Do I wish valets to be handing swords to me at any time of the day or night?"

Here a belligerent red-faced man disengaged himself abruptly from the group of gentlemen and addressed the Earl. "Westport," said he flatly, "I can ill bear your taunt concerning your Bath friends, and this is not to speak of the insolence of the person yonder."

"Oh, ho!" said I. "Well, and the person yonder remains serene in his insolence."

The Earl, smiling slightly, regarded the new speaker.

"Sir Edmund Flixton was ever a dainty swordsman, picking and choosing like a lady in a flower-bed. Perchance he is anxious to fight the gentleman who has just given Reginald Forister something he will not forget?"

At this Flixton actually turned pale and drew back. Evidently he had not yet heard the news. And, mind you, I could see that he would fight me the next moment. He would come up and be killed like a gentleman. But the name of a great conqueror had simply appalled him and smitten him back.

The Earl was gazing at me with an entirely new expression. He had cleverly eliminated all dislike from his eyes. He covered me with a friendly regard.

"O'Ruddy," he said softly, "I would have some private speech with you. Come into my chamber."

The Earl leaned on the shoulder of his valet and a little fat doctor, and walked painfully into another room. I followed, knowing that I was now to withstand a subtle, wheedling, gentle attempt to gain the papers without the name of Lady Mary being mentioned.

The Earl was slowly lowered into a great chair. After a gasp of relief he devoted a brightening attention to me. "You are not a bad fellow, O'Ruddy," he observed. "You remind me greatly of your father. Aye, he was a rare dog, a rare dog!"

"I've heard him say so, many is the day, sir," I answered.

"Aye, a rare dog!" chuckled the old man. "I have in my memory some brisk pictures of your father with his ready tongue, his what-the-devil-does-it-matter-sir, and that extraordinary swordsmanship which you seem to have inherited."

"My father told me you were great friends in France," I answered civilly, "but from some words you let drop in Bristol I judged that he was mistaken."

"Tut," said the Earl. "You are not out of temper with me, are you, O'Ruddy?"

"With me happily in possession of the papers," I rejoined, "I am in good temper with everybody. 'Tis not for me to lose my good nature when I hold all the cards."

The Earl's mouth quickly dropped to a sour expression, but almost as quickly he put on a pleasant smile. "Aye," he said, nodding his sick head. "Always jovial, always jovial. Precisely like his father. In fact it brings back an old affection."

"If the old affection had been brought back a little earlier, sir," said I, "we all would have had less bother. 'Twas you who in the beginning drew a long face and set a square chin over the business. I am now in the mood to be rather airy."

Our glances blazed across each other.

"But," said the Earl in the gentlest of voices, "you have my papers, O'Ruddy, papers entrusted to you by your dying father to give into the hands of his old comrade. Would you betray such a sacred trust? Could you wanton yourself to the base practices of mere thievery?"

"'Tis not I who has betrayed any trust," I cried boldly. "I brought the papers and wished to offer them. They arrived in your possession, and you cried 'Straw, straw!' Did you not?"

"'Twas an expedient, O'Ruddy," said the Earl.

"There is more than one expedient in the world," said I. "I am now using

144

the expedient of keeping the papers."

And in the glance which he gave me I saw that I had been admitted behind a certain barrier. He was angry, but he would never more attempt to overbear me with grand threats. And he would never more attempt to undermine me with cheap flattery. We had measured one against the other, and he had not come away thinking out of his proportion. After a time he said:

"What do you propose to do, Mr. O'Ruddy?"

I could not help but grin at him. "I propose nothing," said I. "I am not a man for meaning two things when I say one."

"You've said one thing, I suppose?" he said slowly.

"I have," said I.

"And the one thing?" said he.

"Your memory is as good as mine," said I.

He mused deeply and at great length. "You have the papers?" he asked finally.

"I still have them," said I.

"Then," he cried with sudden vehemence, "why didn't you read the papers and find out the truth?"

I almost ran away.

"Your—your lordship," I stammered, "I thought perhaps in London—in London perhaps—I might get a—I would try to get a tutor."

CHAPTER XIII

So that is the way of it, is it?" said the Earl, grinning. "And why did you not take it to some clerk?"

"My lord," said I with dignity, "the papers were with me in trust for you. A man may be a gentleman and yet not know how to read and write."

"'Tis quite true," answered he.

"And when I spoke of the tutor in London I did not mean to say that I would use what knowledge he imparted to read your papers. I was merely blushing for the defects in my education, although Father Donovan often said that I knew half as much as he did, poor man, and him a holy father. If you care to so direct me, I can go even now to my chamber and make shift to read the papers."

"The Irish possess a keen sense of honour," said he admiringly.

"We do," said I. "We possess more integrity and perfect sense of honour than any other country in the world, although they all say the same of themselves, and it was my own father who often said that he would trust an Irishman as far as he could see him and no more, but for a foreigner he had only the length of an eyelash."

"And what do you intend with the papers now, O'Ruddy?" said he.

"I intend as I intended," I replied. "There is no change in me."

"And your intentions?" said he.

"To give them into the hands of Lady Mary Strepp and no other," said I boldly.

I looked at him. He looked at me.

"Lady Mary Strepp, my daughter," he said in ironic musing. "Would not her mother do, O'Ruddy?" he asked softly.

I gave a start.

"She is not near?" I demanded, looking from here to there.

He laughed.

"Aye, she is. I can have her here to take the papers in one short moment."

I held up my hands.

"No—no—"

"Peace," said he with a satanic chuckle. "I was only testing your courage."

"My lord," said I gravely, "seeing a bare blade come at your breast is one thing, and running around a table is another, and besides you have no suitable table in this chamber."

The old villain laughed again.

"O'Ruddy," he cried, "I would be a well man if you were always near me. Will I have a table fetched up from below?—'twould be easy."

Here I stiffened.

"My lord, this is frivolity," I declared. "I came here to give the papers. If you do not care to take them in the only way in which I will give them, let us have it said quickly."

"They seem to be safe in your hands at present," he remarked. "Of course after you go to London and get a tutor—ahem!—"

"I will be starting at once," said I, "although Father Donovan always told me that he was a good tutor as tutors went at the time in Ireland. And I want to be saying now, my lord, that I cannot understand you. At one moment you are crying one thing of the papers; at the next moment you are crying another. At this time you are having a laugh with me over them. What do you mean? I'll not stand this shiver-shavering any longer, I'll have you to know. What do you mean?"

He raised himself among his cushions and fixed me with a bony finger.

"What do I mean? I'll tell you, O'Ruddy," said he, while his eyes shone brightly. "I mean that I can be contemptuous of your plot. You will not show these papers to any breathing creature because you are in love with my daughter. Fool, to match your lies against an ex-minister of the King."

My eyes must have almost dropped from my head, but as soon as I recovered from my dumfounderment I grew amazed at the great intellect of this man. I had told nobody, and yet he knew all about it. Yes, I was in love with Lady Mary, and he was as well informed of it as if he had had spies to watch my dreams. And I saw that in many cases a lover was a kind of an ostrich, the bird which buries its head in the sands and thinks it is secure from detection. I wished that my father had told me more about love, for I have no doubt he knew everything of it, he had lived so many years in Paris. Father Donovan, of course, could not have helped me in such instruction. I resolved, any how, to be more cautious in the future, although I did not exactly see how I could improve myself. The Earl's insight was pure mystery to me. I would not be for saying that he practised black magic, but any how, if he had been at Glandore, I would have had him chased through three parishes.

However, the Earl was grinning victoriously, and I saw that I must harden my face to a brave exterior.

"And is it so?" said I. "Is it so?"

"Yes," he said, with his grin.

"And what then?" said I bluntly.

In his enjoyment he had been back again among his cushions.

"'What then? What then?'" he snarled, rearing up swiftly. "Why, then you are an insolent fool: Begone from me! begone! be—" Here some spasm overtook him, a spasm more from rage than from the sickness. He fell back breathless, although his eyes continued to burn at me.

"My lord," said I, bowing, "I will go no poorer than when I came, save that I have lost part of the respect I once had for you."

I turned and left his chamber. Some few gentlemen yet remained in the drawing-room as I passed out into the public part of the inn. I went quietly to a chamber and sat down to think. I was for ever going to chambers and sitting down to think after these talks with the Earl, during which he was for ever rearing up in his chair and then falling back among the cushions.

But here was another tumble over the cliffs, if you like! Here was genuine disaster. I laid my head in my hands and mused before my lonely fire, drinking much and visioning my ruin. What the Earl said was true. There was trouble in the papers for the old nobleman. That he knew. That I knew. And he knew with his devilish wisdom that I would lose my head rather than see her in sorrow. Well, I could bide a time. I would go to London in company with Paddy and Jem Bottles, since they owned all the money, and if three such rogues could not devise something, then I would go away and bury myself in a war in foreign parts, occupying myself in scaling fortresses and capturing guns. These things I know I could have performed magnificently, but from the Earl I had learned that I was an ill man to conduct an affair of the heart.

I do not know how long I meditated, but suddenly there was a great tumult on the stairs near my door. There were the shouts and heavy breathings of men, struggling, and over all rang a screech as from some wild bird. I ran to the door and poked my head discreetly out; for my coat and waistcoat were off as well as my sword, and I wished to see the manner of tumult at a distance before I saw it close. As I thrust forth my head I heard a familiar voice:

"And if ye come closer, ye old hell-cat, 'tis me will be forgetting respect to my four great-grandmothers and braining you. Keep off! Am I not giving ye the word? Keep off!"

Then another familiar voice answered him in a fine high fury. "And you gallows-bird, you gallows-bird, you gallows-bird! You answer me, do you! They're coming, all, even to the hangman! You'll soon know how to dance without a fiddler! Ah, would you? Would you?"

If I had been afflicted with that strange malady of the body which sometimes causes men to fall to the ground and die in a moment without a word, my doom would have been sealed. It was Paddy and Hoity-Toity engaged in animated discussion.

"And if ye don't mind your eye, ye old cormorant—" began Paddy.

"And you would be a highwayman, would you, gallows-bird—" began the Countess.

"Cow—" began Paddy.

Here for many reasons I thought it time to interfere. "Paddy!" I cried. He gave a glance at my door, recognized my face, and, turning quickly, ran through into my chamber. I barred the door even as Hoity-Toity's fist thundered on the oak.

"It's a she-wolf," gasped Paddy, his chest pressing in and out.

"And what did you do to her?" I demanded.

"Nothing but try to run away, sure," said Paddy.

"And why would she be scratching you?"

"She saw me for one of the highwaymen robbing the coach, and there was I, devil knowing what to do, and all the people of the inn trying to put peace upon her, and me dodging, and then—"

"Man," said I, grabbing his arm, "'tis a game that ends on the—"

"Never a bit," he interrupted composedly. "Wasn't the old witch drunk, claws and all, and didn't even the great English lord, or whatever, send his servant to bring her in, and didn't he, the big man, stand in the door and spit on the floor and go in when he saw she was for battering all the servants and using worse talk than the sailors I heard in Bristol? It would not be me they were after, those men running. It would be her. And small power to them, but they were no good at it. I am for taking a stool in my hand—"

"Whist!" said I. "In England they would not be hitting great ladies with stools. Let us hearken to the brawl. She is fighting them finely."

For I had seen that Paddy spoke truth. The noble lady was engaged in battling with servants who had been in pursuit of her when she was in pursuit of Paddy. Never had I seen even my own father so drunk as she was then. But the heart-rending thing was the humble protests of the servants. "Your ladyship! Oh, your ladyship!"—as they came up one by one, or two by two, obeying orders of the Earl, to be incontinently boxed on the ears by a member of a profligate aristocracy. Probably any one of them was strong enough to throw the beldame out at a window. But such was not the manner of the time. One would think they would retreat upon the Earl and ask to be dismissed from his service. But this also was not the manner of the time. No; they marched up heroically and took their cuffs on the head and cried: "Oh, your ladyship! Please, your ladyship!" They were only pretenders in their attacks; all they could do was to wait until she was tired, and then humbly escort her to where she belonged, meanwhile pulling gently at her arms.

"She was after recognizing you then?" said I to Paddy.

"Indeed and she was," said he. He had dropped into a chair and was looking as if he needed a doctor to cure him of exhaustion. "She would be after having eyes like a sea-gull. And Jem Bottles was all for declaring that my disguise was complete, bad luck to the little man."

"Your disguise complete?" said I. "You couldn't disguise yourself unless you stood your head in a barrel. What talk is this?"

"Sure an' I looked no more like myself than I looked like a wild man with eight rows of teeth in his head," said Paddy mournfully. "My own mother would have been after taking me for a horse. 'Tis that old creature with her evil eye who would be seeing me when all the others were blind as bats. I could have walked down the big street in Cork without a man knowing me."

"That you could at any time," said I. The Countess had for some moments ceased to hammer on my door. "Hearken! I think they are managing her."

Either Hoity-Toity had lost heart, or the servants had gained some courage, for we heard them dragging her delicately down the staircase. Presently there was a silence.

After I had waited until this silence grew into the higher silence which seems like perfect safety, I rang the bell and ordered food and drink. Paddy had a royal meal, sitting on the floor by the fireplace and holding a platter on his knee. From time to time I tossed him something for which I did not care. He was very grateful for my generosity. He ate in a barbaric fashion, crunching bones of fowls between his great white teeth and swallowing everything.

I had a mind to discourse upon manners in order that Paddy might not shame me when we came to London; for a gentleman is known by the ways of his servants. If people of quality should see me attended by such a savage they would put me down small. "Paddy," said I, "mend your ways of eating."

"'My ways of eating,' your honour?" said he. "And am I not eating all that I can hold? I was known to be a good man at platter always. Sure I've seen no man in England eat more than me. But thank you kindly, sir."

"You misunderstand me," said I. "I wish to improve your manner of eating. It would not be fine enough for the sight of great people. You eat, without taking breath, pieces as big as a block of turf."

"'Tis the custom in my part of Ireland," answered Paddy.

"I understand," said I. "But over here 'tis only very low people who fall upon their meat from a window above."

"I am not in the way of understanding your honour," said he. "But any how a man may be respectable and yet have a good hunger on him."

CHAPTER XIV

It had been said that the unexpected often happens, although I do not know what learned man of the time succeeded in thus succinctly expressing a great law and any how it matters little, for I have since discovered that these learned men make one headful of brains go a long way by dint of poaching on each other's knowledge. But the unexpected happened in this case, all true enough whatever.

I was giving my man a bit of a warning.

"Paddy," said I, "you are big, and you are red, and you are Irish; but by the same token you are not the great Fingal, son of lightning. I would strongly give you the word. When you see that old woman you start for the open moors."

"Devil fear me, sir," answered Paddy promptly. "I'll not be stopping. I would be swimming to Ireland before she lays a claw on me."

"And mind you exchange no words with her," said I, "for 'tis that which seems to work most wrongfully upon her."

"Never a word out of me," said he. "I'll be that busy getting up the road."

There was another tumult in the corridor, with the same screeches by one and the same humble protests by a multitude. The disturbance neared us with surprising speed. Suddenly I recalled that when the servant had retired after bringing food and drink I had neglected to again bar the door. I rushed for it, but I was all too late. I saw the latch raise. "Paddy!" I shouted wildly. "Mind yourself!" And with that I dropped to the floor and slid under the bed.

Paddy howled, and I lifted a corner of the valance to see what was transpiring. The door had been opened, and the Countess stood looking into the room. She was no longer in a fiery rage; she was cool, deadly determined, her glittering eye fixed on Paddy. She took a step forward.

Paddy, in his anguish, chanted to himself an Irish wail in which he described his unhappiness. "Oh, mother of me, and here I am caught again by the old hell-cat, and sure the way she creeps toward me is enough to put the fear of God in the heart of a hedge-robber, the murdering old witch. And it was me was living so fine and grand in England and greatly pleased with myself. Sorrow the day I left Ireland; it is, indeed."

She was now close to him, and she seemed to be preparing for one stupendous pounce which would mean annihilation to Paddy. Her lean hands were thrust out, with the fingers crooked, and it seemed to me that her fingers were very long. In despair Paddy changed his tune and addressed her.

"Ah, now, alanna. Sure the kind lady would be for doing no harm? Be easy, now, acushla."

But these tender appeals had no effect. Suddenly she pounced. Paddy roared, and sprang backward with splendid agility. He seized a chair.

Now I am quite sure that before he came to England Paddy had never seen a chair, although it is true that at some time in his life he may have had a peep through a window into an Irish gentleman's house, where there might be a chair if the King's officers in the neighbourhood were not very ambitious and powerful. But Paddy handled this chair as if he had seen many of them. He grasped it by the back and thrust it out, aiming all four legs at the Countess. It was a fine move. I have seen a moderately good swordsman fairly put to it by a pack of scoundrelly drawers who assailed him at all points in this manner.

"An you come on too fast," quavered Paddy, "ye can grab two legs, but there will be one left for your eye and another for your brisket."

However she came on, sure enough, and there was a moment of scuffling near the end of the bed out of my sight. I wriggled down to gain another view, and when I cautiously lifted an edge of the valance my eyes met the strangest sight ever seen in all England. Paddy, much dishevelled and panting like a hunt-dog, had wedged the Countess against the wall. She was pinioned by the four legs of the chair, and Paddy, by dint of sturdily pushing at the chair-back, was keeping her in a fixed position.

In a flash my mind was made up. Here was the time to escape. I scrambled quickly from under the bed. "Bravo, Paddy!" I cried, dashing about the room after my sword, coat, waistcoat, and hat. "Devil a fear but you'll hold her, my bucko! Push hard, my brave lad, and mind your feet don't slip!"

"If your honour pleases," said Paddy, without turning his eyes from his conquest, "'tis a little help I would be wishing here. She would be as strong in the shoulder as a good plough-horse and I am not for staying here for ever."

"Bravo, my grand lad!" I cried, at last finding my hat, which had somehow gotten into a corner. From the door I again addressed Paddy in encouraging speech. "There's a stout-hearted boy for you! Hold hard, and mind your feet don't slip!"

He cast a quick agonized look in my direction, and, seeing that I was about basely to desert him, he gave a cry, dropped the chair, and bolted after me. As we ran down the corridor I kept well in advance, thinking it the best place in case the pursuit should be energetic. But there was no pursuit. When Paddy was holding the Countess prisoner she could only choke and stammer, and I had no doubt that she now was well mastered by exhaustion.

Curiously there was little hubbub in the inn. The fact that the Countess was the rioter had worked in a way to cause people to seek secluded and darkened nooks. However, the landlord raised his bleat at me. "Oh, sir, such a misfortune to befall my house just when so many grand ladies and gentlemen are here."

I took him quietly by the throat and beat his head against the wall, once, twice, thrice.

"And you allow mad ladies to molest your guests, do you?" said I.

"Sir," he stuttered, "could I have caused her to cease?

"True," I said, releasing him. "But now do as I bid you and quickly. I am away to London. I have had my plenty of you and your mad ladies."

We started bravely to London, but we only went to another and quieter inn, seeking peace and the absence of fear. I may say we found it, and, in a chair before a good fire, I again took my comfort. Paddy sat on the floor, toasting his shins. The warmth passed him into a reflective mood.

"And I know all I need of grand ladies," he muttered, staring into the fire. "I thought they were all for riding in gold coaches and smelling of beautiful flowers, and here they are mad to be chasing Irishmen in inns. I remember old Mag Cooligan fought with a whole regiment of King's troops in Bantry, and even the drums stopped beating, the soldiers were that much interested. But, sure, everybody would be knowing that Mag was no grand lady, although Pat Cooligan, her brother, was pig-killer to half the country-side. I am thinking we were knowing little about grand ladies. One of the soldiers had his head broke by a musket because the others were so ambitious to destroy the old lady, and she scratching them all. 'Twas long remembered in Bantry."

"Hold your tongue about your betters," said I sharply. "Don't be comparing this Mag Cooligan with a real Countess."

"There would be a strange similarity any how," said he. "But, sure, Mag never fought in inns, for the reason that they would not be letting her inside."

"Remember how little you are knowing of them, Paddy," said I. "'Tis not for you to be talking of the grand ladies when you have seen only one, and you would not be knowing another from a fish. Grand ladies are eccentric, I would have you to know. They have their ways with them which are not for omadhauns like you to understand."

"Eccentric, is it?" said he. "I thought it would be some such devilment."

"And I am knowing," said I with dignity, "of one lady so fine that if you don't stop talking that way of ladies I will break your thick skull for you, and it would matter to nobody."

"'Tis an ill subject for discussion, I am seeing that," said Paddy. "But, faith, I could free Ireland with an army of ladies like one I've seen."

"Will you be holding your tongue?" I cried wrathfully.

Paddy began to mumble to himself,—"Bedad, he was under the bed fast enough without offering her a stool by the fire and a small drop of drink which would be no more than decent with him so fond of her. I am not knowing the ways of these people."

In despair of his long tongue I made try to change the talking.

"We are off for London, Paddy. How are you for it?"

"London, is it?" said he warily. "I was hearing there are many fine ladies there."

For the second time in his life I cuffed him soundly on the ear.

"Now," said I, "be ringing the bell. I am for buying you a bit of drink; but if you mention the gentry to me once more in that blackguard way I'll lather you into a resemblance to your grandfather's bones."

After a pleasant evening I retired to bed leaving Paddy snug asleep by the fire. I thought much of my Lady Mary, but with her mother stalking the corridors and her knowing father with his eye wide open, I knew there was no purpose in hanging about a Bath inn. I would go to London, where there were gardens, and walks in the park, and parties, and other useful customs. There I would win my love.

The following morning I started with Paddy to meet Jem Bottles and travel to London. Many surprising adventures were in store for us, but an account of these I shall leave until another time, since one would not be worrying people with too many words, which is a great fault in a man who is recounting his own affairs.

CHAPTER XV

As we ambled our way agreeably out of Bath, Paddy and I employed ourselves in worthy speech. He was not yet a notable horseman, but his Irish adaptability was so great that he was already able to think he would not fall off so long as the horse was old and tired.

"Paddy," said I, "how would you like to be an Englishman? Look at their cities. Sure, Skibbereen is a mud-pond to them. It might be fine to be an Englishman."

"I would not, your honour," said Paddy. "I would not be an Englishman while these grand—But never mind; 'tis many proud things I will say about the English considering they are our neighbours in one way; I mean they are near enough to come over and harm us when they wish. But any how they are a remarkable hard-headed lot, and in time they may come to something good."

"And is a hard head such a qualification?" said I.

Paddy became academic. "I have been knowing two kinds of hard heads," he said. "Mickey McGovern had such a hard skull on him no stick in the south of Ireland could crack it, though many were tried. And what happened to him? He died poor as a rat. 'Tis not the kind of hard head I am meaning. I am meaning the kind of hard head which believes it contains all the wisdom and honour in the world. 'Tis what I mean. If you have a head like that, you can go along blundering into ditches and tumbling over your own shins, and still hold confidence in yourself. 'Tis not very handsome for other men to see; but devil a bit care you, for you are warm inside with complacence."

"Here is a philosopher, in God's truth," I cried. "And where were you learning all this? In Ireland?"

"Your honour," said Paddy firmly, "you yourself are an Irishman. You are not for saying there is no education in Ireland, for it educates a man to see burning thatches and such like. One of them was my aunt's, Heaven rest her!"

"Your aunt?" said I. "And what of your aunt? What have the English to do with your aunt?"

"That's what she was asking them," said Paddy; "but they burned her house down over a little matter of seventeen years' rent she owed to a full-blooded Irishman, may the devil find him!"

"But I am for going on without an account of your burnt-thatch education," said I. "You are having more than two opinions about the English, and I would be hearing them. Seldom have I seen a man who could gain so much knowledge in so short a space. You are interesting me."

Paddy seemed pleased. "Well, your honour," said he confidentially, "'tis true for you. I am knowing the English down to their toes."

"And if you were an Englishman, what kind of an Englishman would you like to be?" said I.

"A gentleman," he answered swiftly. "A big gentleman!" Then he began to mimic and make gestures in a way that told me he had made good use of his eyes and of the society of underlings in the various inns. "Where's me man? Send me man! Oh, here you are! And why didn't you know I wanted you? What right have you to think I don't want you? What? A servant dead? Pah! Send it down the back staircase at once and get rid of it. Bedad!" said Paddy enthusiastically, "I could do that fine!" And to prove what he said was true, he cried "Pah!" several times in a lusty voice.

"I see you have quickly understood many customs of the time," said I. "But 'tis not all of it. There are many quite decent people alive now."

"'Tis strange we have never heard tell of them," said Paddy musingly. "I have only heard of great fighters, blackguards, and beautiful ladies, but sure, as your honour says, there must be plenty of quiet decent people somewhere."

"There is," said I. "I am feeling certain of it, although I am not knowing exactly where to lay my hand upon them."

"Perhaps they would be always at mass," said Paddy, "and in that case your honour would not be likely to see them."

"Masses!" said I. "There are more masses said in Ireland in one hour than here in two years."

"The people would be heathens, then?" said Paddy, aghast.

"Not precisely," said I. "But they have reformed themselves several times, and a number of adequate reformations is a fine thing to confuse the Church. In Ireland we are all for being true to the ancient faith; here they are always for improving matters, and their learned men study the Sacred Book solely with a view to making needed changes."

"'Tis heathen they are," said Paddy with conviction. "I was knowing it. Sure, I will be telling Father Corrigan the minute I put a foot on Ireland, for nothing pleases him so much as a good obstinate heathen, and he very near discourses the hair off their heads."

"I would not be talking about such matters," said I. "It merely makes my head grow an ache. My father was knowing all about it; but he was always claiming that if a heathen did his duty by the poor he was as good as anybody, and that view I could never understand."

"Sure, if a heathen gives to the poor, 'tis poison to them," said Paddy. "If it is food and they eat it, they turn black all over and die the day after. If it is money, it turns red-hot and burns a hole in their hand, and the devil puts a chain through it and drags them down to hell, screeching."

"Say no more," said I. "I am seeing you are a true theologian of the time. I would be talking on some more agreeable topic, something about which you know less."

"I can talk of fishing," he answered diffidently. "For I am a great fisherman, sure. And then there would be turf-cutting, and the deadly stings given to men by eels. All these things I am knowing well."

"'Tis a grand lot to know," said I, "but let us be talking of London. Have you been hearing of London?"

"I have been hearing much about the town," said Paddy. "Father

Corrigan was often talking of it. He was claiming it to be full of loose women, and sin, and fighting in the streets during mass."

"I am understanding something of the same," I replied. "It must be an evil city. I am fearing something may happen to you, Paddy,—you with your red head as conspicuous as a clock in a tower. The gay people will be setting upon you and carrying you off. Sure there has never been anything like you in London."

"I am knowing how to be dealing with them. It will be all a matter of religious up-bringing, as Father Corrigan was saying. I have but to go to my devotions, and the devil will fly away with them."

"And supposing they have your purse?" said I. "The devil might fly away with them to an ill tune for you."

"When they are flying away with my purse," he replied suggestively, "they will be flying away with little of what could be called my ancestral wealth."

"You are natural rogues," said I, "you and Jem Bottles. And you had best not be talking of religion."

"Sure a man may take the purse of an ugly old sick monkey like him, and still go with an open face to confession," rejoined Paddy, "and I would not be backward if Father Corrigan's church was a mile beyond."

"And are you meaning that Father Corrigan would approve you in this robbery?" I cried.

"Devil a bit he would, your honour," answered Paddy indignantly. "He would be saying to me: 'Paddy, you limb of Satan, and how much did you get?' I would be telling him. 'Give fifteen guineas to the Church, you mortal sinner, and I will be trying my best for you,' he would be saying. And I would be giving them."

"You are saved fifteen guineas by being in England, then," said I, "for they don't do that here. And I am thinking you are traducing your clergy, you vagabond."

161

"Traducing?" said he. "That would mean giving them money. Aye, I was doing it often. One year I gave three silver shillings."

"You're wrong," said I. "By 'traducing' I mean speaking ill of your priest."

"'Speaking ill of my priest'?" cried Paddy, gasping with amazement. "Sure, my own mother never heard a word out of me!"

"However," said I, "we will be talking of other things. The English land seems good."

Paddy cast his eye over the rainy landscape. "I am seeing no turf for cutting," he remarked disapprovingly, "and the potatoes would not be growing well here. 'Tis a barren country."

At nightfall we came to a little inn which was ablaze with light and ringing with exuberant cries. We gave up our horses and entered. To the left was the closed door of the taproom, which now seemed to furnish all the noise. I asked the landlord to tell me the cause of the excitement.

"Sir," he answered, "I am greatly honoured to-night. Mr. O'Ruddy, the celebrated Irish swordsman, is within, recounting a history of his marvellous exploits."

"Indeed!" said I.

"Bedad!" said Paddy.

CHAPTER XVI

Paddy was for opening his mouth wide immediately, but I checked him. "I would see this great man," said I to the landlord, "but I am so timid by nature I fear to meet his eagle eye. Is there no way by which we could observe him in secret at our leisure?"

"There be one way," remarked the landlord after deliberation. I had passed him a silver coin. He led us to a little parlour back of the taproom. Here a door opened into the tap itself, and in this door was cut a large square window so that the good man of the inn could sometimes sit at his ease in his great chair in the snug parlour and observe that his customers had only that for which they were paying. It is a very good plan, for I have seen many a worthy man become a rogue merely because nobody was watching him. My father often was saying that if he had not been narrowly eyed all his young life, first by his mother and then by his wife, he had little doubt but what he might have been engaged in dishonest practices sooner or later.

A confident voice was doing some high talking in the taproom. I peered through the window, but at first I saw only a collection of gaping yokels, poor bent men with faces framed in straggly whiskers. Each had a pint pot clutched with a certain air of determination in his right hand.

Suddenly upon our line of vision strode the superb form of Jem Bottles. A short pipe was in his mouth, and he gestured splendidly with a pint pot. "More of the beer, my dear," said he to a buxom maid. "We be all rich in Ireland. And four of them set upon me," he cried again to the yokels. "All noblemen, in fine clothes and with sword-hilts so flaming with jewels an ordinary man might have been blinded. 'Stop!' said I. 'There be more of your friends somewhere. Call them.' And with that—"

"'And with that'?" said I myself, opening the door and stepping in upon him. "'And with that'?" said I again. Whereupon I smote him a blow which staggered him against the wall, holding his crown with both hands while his broken beer-pot rolled on the floor. Paddy was dancing with delight at seeing some other man cuffed, but the landlord and the yokels were nearly dead of terror. But they made no sound; only the buxom girl whimpered.

"There is no cause for alarm," said I amiably. "I was only greeting an old friend. 'Tis a way I have. And how wags the world with you, O'Ruddy?"

"I am not sure for the moment," replied Jem Bottles ruefully. "I must bide till it stops spinning."

"Truth," cried I. "That would be a light blow to trouble the great O'Ruddy. Come now; let us have the pots filled again, and O'Ruddy shall tell us more of his adventures. What say you, lads?"

The yokels had now recovered some of their senses, and they greeted my plan with hoarse mutterings of hasty and submissive assent.

"Begin," said I sternly to the highwayman. He stood miserably on one foot. He looked at the floor; he looked at the wall; from time to time he gave me a sheep's glance. "Begin," said I again. Paddy was wild with glee. "Begin," said I for the third time and very harshly.

"I—" gulped out the wretched man, but he could get no further.

"I am seeing I must help you," said I. "Come now, when did you learn the art of sticadoro proderodo sliceriscum fencing?"

Bottles rolled the eyes of despair at me, but I took him angrily by the shoulder. "Come now; when did you learn the art of sticadoro proderodo sliceriscum fencing?"

Jem Bottles staggered, but at last he choked out: "My mother taught me." Here Paddy retired from the room, doubled in a strong but soundless convulsion.

"Good," said I. "Your mother taught you. We are making progress any how. Your mother taught you. And now tell me this: When you slew Cormac of the Cliffs, what passado did you use? Don't be stuttering. Come now; quick with you; what passado did you use? What passado?"

With a heroism born of a conviction that in any event he was a lost man, Jem Bottles answered: "A blue one."

"Good," I cried cheerfully. "'A blue one'! We are coming on fine. He killed Cormac with a blue passado. And now I would be asking you—"

"Master," interrupted the highwayman with sudden resolution. "I will say no more. I have done. You may kill me an it pleases you."

Now I saw that enough was enough. I burst into laughter and clapped him merrily on the shoulder. "Be cheery, O'Ruddy," I cried. "Sure an Irishman like you ought to be able to look a joke in the face." He gave over his sulks directly, and I made him buy another pint each for the yokels. "'Twas dry work listening to you and your exploits, O'Ruddy," said I.

Later I went to my chamber, attended by my followers, having ordered roast fowls and wine to be served as soon as possible. Paddy and Jem Bottles sat on stools one at each side of the fireplace, and I occupied a chair between them.

Looking at my two faithful henchmen, I was suddenly struck by the thought that they were not very brisk servants for a gentleman to take to fashionable London. I had taken Paddy out of his finery and dressed him in a suit of decent brown; but his hair was still unbarbered, and I saw that unless I had a care his appearance would greatly surprise and please London. I resolved to have him shorn at the first large town.

As for Jem Bottles, his clothes were well enough, and indeed he was passable in most ways unless it was his habit, when hearing a sudden noise, to take a swift dark look to the right and to the left. Then, further, people might shrewdly note his way of always sitting with his back to the wall and his face to the door. However, I had no doubt of my ability to cure him of these tricks as soon as he was far enough journeyed from the scenes of his earlier activity.

But the idea I entertained at this moment was more to train them to be fine grand servants, such as I had seen waiting on big people in Bath. They were both willing enough, but they had no style to them. I decided to begin at once and see what I could teach them.

"Paddy," said I, taking off my sword and holding it out to him. "My sword!"

Paddy looked at it. "It is, sir," he answered respectfully.

"Bad scran to you, Paddy!" I cried angrily. "I am teaching you your duties. Take the sword! In both hands, mind you! Now march over and lay it very tenderly on the stand at the head of the bed. There now!"

I now turned my attention to Jem Bottles.

"Bottles," said I peremptorily, "my coat and waistcoat."

"Yes, sir," replied Bottles quickly, profiting by Paddy's lesson.

"There now," said I, as Bottles laid the coat and waistcoat on a dresser. "'Tis a good beginning. When supper comes I shall teach you other duties."

The supper came in due course, and after the inn's man had gone I bid Jem and Paddy stand one on either side of my chair and a little way back. "Now," said I, "stand square on your feet, and hold your heads away high, and stick your elbows out a little, and try to look as if you don't know enough to tell fire from water. Jem Bottles has it. That's it! Bedad! look at the ignorance on him! He's the man for you, Paddy! Wake up now, and look stupid. Am I not telling you?"

"Begor!" said Paddy dejectedly, "I feel like the greatest omadhaun in all the west country, and if that is not being stupid enough for your honour I can do no better."

"Shame to you, Paddy, to let an Englishman beat you so easily," said I. "Take that grin off your face, you scoundrel! Now," I added, "we are ready to begin. Wait, now. You must each have something to hold in your fist. Let me be thinking. There's only one plate and little of anything else. Ah, I have it! A bottle! Paddy, you shall hold one of the bottles. Put your right hand underneath it, and with your left hand hold it by the neck. But keep your elbows out. Jem, what the devil am I to give you to hold? Ah, I have it! Another bottle! Hold it the same as Paddy. Now! Stand square on your feet, and hold your heads away high, and stick your elbows out a little, and look

166

stupid. I am going to eat my supper."

I finished my first and second bottles with the silence only broken by the sound of my knife-play and an occasional restless creaking of boots as one of my men slyly shifted his position. Wishing to call for my third bottle, I turned and caught them exchanging a glance of sympathetic bewilderment. As my eye flashed upon them, they stiffened up like grenadier recruits.

But I was not for being too hard on them at first. "'Tis enough for one lesson," said I. "Put the bottles by me and take your ease."

With evident feelings of relief they slunk back to the stools by the fire, where they sat recovering their spirits.

After my supper I sat in the chair toasting my shins and lazily listening to my lads finishing the fowls. They seemed much more like themselves, sitting there grinding away at the bones and puffing with joy. In the red firelight it was such a scene of happiness that I misdoubted for a moment the wisdom of my plan to make them into fine grand numskulls.

I could see that all men were not fitted for the work. It needed a beefy person with fat legs and a large amount of inexplicable dignity, a regular God-knows-why loftiness. Truth, in those days, real talent was usually engaged in some form of rascality, barring the making of books and sermons. When one remembers the impenetrable dulness of the great mass of the people, the frivolity of the gentry, the arrogance and wickedness of the court, one ceases to wonder that many men of taste took to the highway as a means of recreation and livelihood. And there I had been attempting to turn my two frank rascals into the kind of sheep-headed rubbish whom you could knock down a great staircase, and for a guinea they would say no more. Unless I was the kicker, I think Paddy would have returned up the staircase after his assailant. Jem Bottles probably would have gone away nursing his wrath and his injury, and planning to waylay the kicker on a convenient night. But neither would have taken a guinea and said no more. Each of these simple-hearted reprobates was too spirited to take a guinea for a kick down a staircase.

Any how I had a mind that I could be a gentleman true enough without the help of Jem and Paddy making fools of themselves. I would worry them no more.

As I was musing thus my eyes closed from a sense of contented weariness, but I was aroused a moment later by hearing Paddy address Jem Bottles in a low voice. "'Tis you who are the cool one, Jem!" said he with admiration, "trying to make them think you were him!" Here I was evidently indicated by a sideways bob of the head. "Have you not been seeing the fine ways of him? Sure, be looking at his stride and his habit of slatting people over the head, and his grand manners with his food. You are looking more like a candlestick than you are looking like him. I wonder at you."

"But I befooled them," said Bottles proudly. "I befooled them well. It was Mr. O'Ruddy here, and Mr. O'Ruddy there, and the handsome wench she gave me many a glance of her eye, she did."

"Sorrow the day for her, then," responded Paddy, "and if you would be cozening the girls in the name of him there, he will be cozening you, and I never doubt it."

"'Twas only a trick to make the time go easy, it was," said Bottles gloomily. "If you remember, Master Paddy, I have spent the most of my new service waiting under oak-trees; and I will not be saying that it rained always, but oft-times it did rain most accursedly."

CHAPTER XVII

We rode on at daybreak. At the first large village I bid a little man cut Paddy's hair, and although Paddy was all for killing the little man, and the little man twice ran away, the work was eventually done, for I stood over Paddy and threatened him. Afterward the little boys were not so anxious to hoot us through the streets, calling us Africans. For it must be recalled that at this time there was great curiosity in the provinces over the Africans, because it was known that in London people of fashion often had African servants; and although London cared nothing for the provinces, and the provinces cared nothing for London, still the rumour of the strange man interested the country clodhopper so greatly that he called Paddy an African on principle, in order that he might blow to his neighbours that he had seen the fascinating biped. There was no general understanding that the African was a man of black skin; it was only understood that he was a great marvel. Hence the urchins in these far-away villages often ran at the heels of Paddy's horse, yelling.

In time the traffic on the highway became greatly thickened, and several times we thought we were entering London because of the large size and splendour of the towns to which we came. Paddy began to fear the people had been deceiving us as to the road, and that we had missed London entirely. But finally we came to a river with hundreds of boats upon it, and there was a magnificent bridge, and on the other bank was a roaring city, and through the fog the rain came down thick as the tears of the angels. "That's London," said I.

We rode out upon the bridge, all much interested, but somewhat fearful, for the noise of the city was terrible. But if it was terrible as we approached it, I hesitate to say what it was to us when we were once fairly in it. "Keep close to me," I yelled to Paddy and Jem, and they were not unwilling. And so we rode into this pandemonium, not having the least idea where we were going.

As we progressed I soon saw what occasioned the major part of the noise. Many heavy carts thundered slowly through the narrow, echoing streets, bumping their way uproariously over a miserable pavement. Added to this, of course, were the shrill or hoarse shouts of the street vendors and the apprentices at the shop-doors. To the sky arose an odour almost insupportable, for it was new to us all.

The eaves of the houses streamed with so much water that the sidewalks were practically untenable, although here and there a hardy wayfarer strode on regardless of a drenched cloak, probably being too proud to take to the street. Once our travel was entirely blocked by a fight. A butcher in a bloody apron had dashed out of his shop and attacked the driver of a brewer's sledge. A crowd gathered miraculously and cheered on this spectacle; women appeared at all the windows; urchins hooted; mongrel dogs barked. When the butcher had been worsted and chased back into his shop by the maddened brewer we were allowed to pursue our journey.

I must remark that neither of these men used aught but his hands. Mostly their fists were doubled, and they dealt each other sounding, swinging blows; but there was some hair-pulling, and when the brewer had the butcher down I believe the butcher tried to bite his opponent's ear. However they were rather high-class for their condition. I found out later that at this time in the darker parts of London the knife was a favourite weapon of the English and was as rampant as ever it is in the black alleys of an Italian city. It was no good news for me, for the Irish had long been devoted to the cudgel.

When I wish for information I always prefer making the request to a gentleman. To have speech of a boor is well enough if he would not first study you over to find, if he can, why you want the information, and, after a prolonged pause, tell you wrong entirely. I perceived a young gentleman standing in under a porch and ogling a window on the opposite side of the way. "Sir," said I, halting my horse close to him, "would you be so kind as to point to a stranger the way to a good inn?" He looked me full in the face, spat meaningly in the gutter, and, turning on his heel, walked away. And I will give oath he was not more than sixteen years old.

I sat stiff in the saddle; I felt my face going hot and cold. This new-feathered bird with a toy sword! But to save me, as it happened, from a preposterous quarrel with this infant, another man came along the sidewalk. He was an older man, with a grave mouth and a clean-cut jowl. I resolved to hail him. "And now my man," said I under my breath, "if you are as bad as the other, by the mass, I'll have a turnover here with you, London or no London."

Then I addressed him. "Sir—" I began. But here a cart roared on my other side, and I sat with my mouth open, looking at him. He smiled a little, but waited courteously for the hideous din to cease. "Sir," I was enabled to say at last, "would you be so kind as to point to a stranger the way to a good inn?" He scanned me quietly, in order, no doubt, to gain an idea what kind of inn would suit my condition. "Sir," he answered, coming into the gutter and pointing, "'tis this way to Bishopsgate Street, and there you will see the sign of the 'Pig and Turnip,' where there is most pleasurable accommodation for man and beast, and an agreeable host." He was a shop-keeper of the city of London, of the calm, steady breed that has made successive kings either love them or fearingly hate them,—the bone and the sinew of the great town.

I thanked him heartily, and we went on to the "Pig and Turnip." As we clattered into the inn yard it was full of people mounting and dismounting, but there seemed a thousand stable-boys. A dozen flung themselves at my horse's head. They quite lifted me out of the saddle in their great care that I should be put to no trouble. At the door of the inn a smirking landlord met me, bowing his head on the floor at every backward pace, and humbly beseeching me to tell how he could best serve me. I told him, and at once there was a most pretentious hubbub. Six or eight servants began to run hither and yon. I was delighted with my reception, but several days later I discovered they had mistaken me for a nobleman of Italy or France, and I was expected to pay extravagantly for graceful empty attentions rather than for sound food and warm beds.

This inn was so grand that I saw it would no longer do for Paddy and Jem to be sleeping in front of my fire like big dogs, so I nodded assent when the landlord asked if he should provide lodgings for my two servants. He packed them off somewhere, and I was left lonely in a great chamber. I had some fears having Paddy long out of my sight, but I assured myself that London had such terrors for him he would not dare any Irish mischief. I could trust Jem Bottles to be discreet, for he had learned discretion in a notable school.

Toward the close of the afternoon, the rain ceased, and, attiring myself for the street and going to the landlord, I desired him to tell me what interesting or amusing walk could now conveniently be taken by a gentleman who was a stranger to the sights of London. The man wagged his head in disapproval.

"'Twill be dark presently, sir," he answered, "and I would be an ill host if I did not dissuade a perfect stranger from venturing abroad in the streets of London of a night-time."

"And is it as bad as that?" I cried, surprised.

"For strangers, yes," said he. "For they be for ever wandering, and will not keep to the three or four streets which be as safe as the King's palace. But if you wish, sir, I will provide one man with a lantern and staff to go before you, and another man with lantern and staff to follow. Then, with two more stout lads and your own servants, I would venture—"

"No, no!" I cried, "I will not head an army on a night march when I intended merely an evening stroll. But how, pray you, am I to be entertained otherwise than by going forth?"

The innkeeper smiled with something like pity.

"Sir, every night there meets here such a company of gay gentlemen, wits and poets, as would dazzle the world did it but hear one half of what they say over their pipes and their punch. I serve the distinguished company myself, for I dare trust nobody's care in a matter so important to my house; and I assure you, sir, I have at times been so doubled with mirth there was no life in me. Why, sir, Mr. Fullbil himself comes here at times!"

"Does he, indeed?" I cried, although I never had heard of the illustrious man.

"Indeed and he does, sir," answered the innkeeper, pleased at my quick appreciation of this matter. "And then there is goings on, I warrant me. Mr. Bobbs and the other gentlemen will be in spirits."

172

"I never doubt you," said I. "But is it possible for a private gentleman of no wit to gain admittance to this distinguished company?"

"Doth require a little managing, sir," said he, full of meaning.

"Pray you manage it then," said I, "for I have nought to do in London for at least two days, and I would be seeing these famous men with whose names my country rings."

Early in the evening the innkeeper came to me, much pleased. "Sir, the gentlemen bid me bring you their compliments, and I am to say they would be happy to have a pleasure in the honour of your presence. Mr. Fullbil himself is in the chair to-night. You are very fortunate, sir."

"I am," said I. "Lead away, and let us hope to find the great Fullbil in high feather."

CHAPTER XVIII

The innkeeper led me down to a large room the door of which he had flung open with a flourish. "The furrin' gentleman, may it please you, sirs," he announced, and then retired.

The room was so full of smoke that at first I could see little, but soon enough I made out a long table bordered with smoking and drinking gentlemen. A hoarse voice, away at the head of the board, was growling some words which convulsed most of the gentlemen with laughter. Many candles burned dimly in the haze.

I stood for a moment, doubtful as to procedure, but a gentleman near the foot of the table suddenly arose and came toward me with great frankness and good nature. "Sir," he whispered, so that he would not interrupt the growls at the farther end of the room, "it would give me pleasure if you would accept a chair near me."

I could see that this good gentleman was moved solely by a desire to be kind to a stranger, and I, in another whisper, gave my thanks and assent to his plan. He placed me in a chair next his own. The voice was still growling from the head of the table.

Very quickly my eyes became accustomed to the smoke, especially after I was handed a filled clay pipe by my new and excellent friend. I began to study the room and the people in it. The room was panelled in new oak, and the chairs and table were all of new oak, well carved. It was the handsomest room I had ever been in.

Afterward I looked toward the growl. I saw a little old man in a chair much too big for him, and in a wig much too big for him. His head was bent forward until his sharp chin touched his breast, and out from under his darkling brows a pair of little eyes flashed angrily and arrogantly. All faces were turned toward him, and all ears were open to his growls. He was the king; it was Fullbil.

His speech was all addressed to one man, and I looked at the latter. He was a young man with a face both Roman and feminine; with that type of profile which is possessed by most of the popular actors in the reign of His Majesty of to-day. He had luxuriant hair, and, stung by the taunts of Fullbil, he constantly brushed it nervously from his brow while his sensitive mouth quivered with held-in retorts. He was Bobbs, the great dramatist.

And as Fullbil growled, it was a curiously mixed crowd which applauded and laughed. There were handsome lordlings from the very top of London cheek by cheek with sober men who seemed to have some intellectual occupation in life. The lordlings did the greater part of the sniggering. In the meantime everybody smoked hard and drank punch harder. During occasional short pauses in Fullbil's remarks, gentlemen passed ecstatic comments one to another.—"Ah, this is indeed a mental feast!"—"Did ye ever hear him talk more wittily?"—"Not I, faith; he surpasses even himself!"—"Is it not a blessing to sit at table with such a master of learning and wit?"—"Ah, these are the times to live in!"

I thought it was now opportune to say something of the same kind to my amiable friend, and so I did it. "The old corpse seems to be saying a prayer," I remarked. "Why don't he sing it?"

My new friend looked at me, all agape, like a fish just over the side of the boat. "'Tis Fullbil, the great literary master—" he began; but at this moment Fullbil, having recovered from a slight fit of coughing, resumed his growls, and my friend subsided again into a worshipping listener.

For my part I could not follow completely the words of the great literary master, but I construed that he had pounced upon the drama of the time and was tearing its ears and eyes off.

At that time I knew little of the drama, having never read or seen a play in my life; but I was all for the drama on account of poor Bobbs, who kept chewing his lip and making nervous movements until Fullbil finished, a thing which I thought was not likely to happen before an early hour of the morning. But finish he did, and immediately Bobbs, much impassioned, brought his glass heavily down on the table in a demand for silence. I thought he would get little hearing, but, much to my surprise, I heard again the ecstatic murmur: "Ah, now, we shall hear Bobbs reply to Fullbil!"—"Are we not fortunate?"—"Faith, this will be over half London to-morrow!"

Bobbs waited until this murmur had passed away. Then he began, nailing an impressive forefinger to the table:

"Sir, you have been contending at some length that the puzzling situations which form the basis of our dramas of the day could not possibly occur in real life because five minutes of intelligent explanation between the persons concerned would destroy the silly mystery before anything at all could happen. Your originality, sir, is famous—need I say it?—and when I hear you champion this opinion in all its majesty of venerable age and general acceptance I feel stunned by the colossal imbecile strength of the whole proposition. Why, sir, you may recall all the mysterious murders which occurred in England since England had a name. The truth of them remains in unfathomable shadow. But, sir, any one of them could be cleared up in five minutes' intelligent explanation. Pontius Pilate could have been saved his blunder by far, far, far less than five minutes of intelligent explanation. But—mark ye!—but who has ever heard five minutes of intelligent explanation? The complex interwoven mesh of life constantly, eternally, prevents people from giving intelligent explanations. You sit in the theatre, and you say to yourself: 'Well, I could mount the stage, and in a short talk to these people I could anticipate a further continuation of the drama.' Yes, you could; but you are an outsider. You have no relations with these characters. You arise like an angel. Nobody has been your enemy; nobody has been your mistress. You arise and give the five minutes' intelligent explanation; bah! There is not a situation in life which does not need five minutes' intelligent explanation; but it does not get it."

It could now be seen that the old man Fullbil was simply aflame with a destructive reply, and even Bobbs paused under the spell of this anticipation of a gigantic answering. The literary master began very deliberately.

"My good friend Bobbs," said he, "I see your nose gradually is turning red."

176

The drama immediately pitched into oblivion. The room thundered with a great shout of laughter that went to the ceiling. I could see Bobbs making angry shouts against an invulnerable bank of uncontrolled merriment. And amid his victory old Fullbil sat with a vain smile on his cracked lips.

My excellent and adjacent friend turned to me in a burst of enthusiasm.

"And did you ever hear a thing so well turned? Ha, ha! 'My good friend Bobbs,' quoth he, 'I see your nose gradually is turning red.' Ha, ha, ha! By my King, I have seldom heard a wittier answer."

"Bedad!" said I, somewhat bewildered, but resolved to appreciate the noted master of wit, "it stamped the drama down into the ground. Sure, never another play will be delivered in England after that tremendous overthrow."

"Aye," he rejoined, still shuddering with mirth, "I fail to see how the dramatists can survive it. It was like the wit of a new Shakespeare. It subsided Bobbs to nothing. I would not be surprised at all if Bobbs now entirely quit the writing of plays, since Fullbil's words so closely hit his condition in the dramatic world. A dangerous dog is this Fullbil."

"It reminds me of a story my father used to tell—" I began.

"Sir," cried my new friend hastily, "I beg of you! May I, indeed, insist? Here we talk only of the very deepest matters."

"Very good, sir," I replied amiably. "I will appear better, no doubt, as a listener; but if my father was alive—"

"Sir," beseeched my friend, "the great Fancher, the immortal critic, is about to speak."

"Let him," said I, still amiable.

A portly gentleman of middle age now addressed Bobbs amid a general and respectful silence.

"Sir," he remarked, "your words concerning the great age of what I shall call the five-minutes-intelligent-explanation theory was first developed by the Chinese, and is contemporaneous, I believe, with their adoption of the custom of roasting their meat instead of eating it raw."

"Sir, I am interested and instructed," rejoined Bobbs.

Here old Fullbil let go two or three growls of scornful disapproval.

"Fancher," said he, "my delight in your company is sometimes dimmed by my appreciation of your facilities for being entirely wrong. The great theory of which you speak so confidently, sir, was born no earlier than seven o'clock on the morning of this day. I was in my bed, sir; the maid had come in with my tea and toast. 'Stop,' said I, sternly. She stopped. And in those few moments of undisturbed reflection, sir, the thought came to life, the thought which you so falsely attribute to the Chinese, a savage tribe whose sole distinction is its ability to fly kites."

After the murmurs of glee had died away, Fancher answered with spirit:

"Sir, that you are subject to periods of reflection I will not deny, I cannot deny. Nor can I say honourably that I give my support to our dramatic friend's defence of his idea. But, sir, when you refer to the Chinese in terms which I cannot but regard as insulting, I am prepared, sir, to—"

There were loud cries of "Order! Order! Order!" The wrathful Fancher was pulled down into his chair by soothful friends and neighbours, to whom he gesticulated and cried out during the uproar.

I looked toward old Fullbil, expecting to see him disturbed, or annoyed, or angry. On the contrary he seemed pleased, as a little boy who had somehow created a row.

"The excellent Fancher," said he, "the excellent Fancher is wroth. Let us proceed, gentlemen, to more friendly topics. You, now, Doctor Chord, with what new thing in chemics are you ready to astound us?"

The speech was addressed to a little man near me, who instantly blushed crimson, mopping his brow in much agitation, and looked at the table, unable for the moment to raise his eyes or speak a word.

"One of the greatest scientists of the time," said my friend in my ear.

"Sir," faltered the little man in his bashfulness, "that part of the discourse which related to the flying of kites has interested me greatly, and I am ready to contend that kites fly, not, as many say, through the influence of a demon or spirit which inhabits the materials, but through the pressure of the wind itself."

Fancher, now himself again, said:

"I wish to ask the learned doctor whether he refers to Chinese kites?"

The little man hurriedly replied that he had not Chinese kites in his mind at all.

"Very good, then," said the great critic. "Very good."

"But, sir," said Fullbil to little Chord, "how is it that kites may fly without the aid of demons or spirits, if they are made by man? For it is known, sir, that man may not move in the air without the aid of some devilish agency, and it is also known that he may not send aloft things formed of the gross materials of the earth. How, then, can these kites fly virtuously?"

There was a general murmur of approbation of Fullbil's speech, and the little doctor cast down his eyes and blushed again, speechless.

It was a triumph for Fullbil, and he received the congratulations of his friends with his faint vain smile implying that it was really nothing, you know, and that he could have done it much better if he had thought that anybody was likely to heed it.

The little Doctor Chord was so downtrodden that for the remainder of the evening he hardly dared to raise his eyes from the table, but I was glad to see him apply himself industriously to the punch.

To my great alarm Fullbil now said: "Sirs, I fear we have suffered ourselves to forget we have with us to-night a strange gentleman from foreign parts. Your good fortune, sir," he added, bowing to me over his glass. I bowed likewise, but I saw his little piggish eyes looking wickedly at me. There went a titter around the board, and I understood from it that I was the next victim of the celebrated Fullbil.

"Sir," said he, "may I ask from what part of Italy do you come?"

"I come from Ireland, sir," I answered decently.

He frowned. "Ireland is not in Italy, sir," said he. "Are you so good as to trifle with me, sir?"

"I am not, sir," said I.

All the gentlemen murmured; some looked at me with pity, some with contempt. I began to be frightened until I remembered that if I once drew my sword I could chase the whole roomful of philosophy into the next parish. I resolved to put on a bold front.

"Probably, sir," observed Fullbil, "the people of Ireland have heard so much of me that I may expect many visits from Irish gentlemen who wish to hear what my poor mind may develop in regard to the only true philosophy of life?"

"Not in the least, sir," I rejoined. "Over there they don't know you are alive, and they are not caring."

Consternation fell upon that assembly like snow from a roof. The gentlemen stared at me. Old Fullbil turned purple at first, but his grandeur could not be made to suffer long or seriously from my impudence. Presently he smiled at me,—a smile confident, cruel, deadly.

"Ireland is a great country, sir," he observed.

"'Tis not so great as many people's ignorance of it," I replied bluntly, for I was being stirred somewhat.

"Indeed!" cried Fullbil. Then he triumphantly added: "Then, sir, we are proud to have among us one so manifestly capable of giving us instruction."

There was a loud shout of laughter at this sally, and I was very uncomfortable down to my toes; but I resolved to hold a brave face, and pretended that I was not minding their sneers. However, it was plain enough that old Fullbil had made me the butt of the evening.

"Sir," said the dramatist Bobbs, looking at me, "I understand that in

Ireland pigs sit at table with even the best families."

"Sir," said the critic, Fancher, looking at me, "I understand that in Ireland the chastity of the women is so great that no child is born without a birthmark in the shape of the initials of the legal husband and father."

"Sir," said old Fullbil, "I understand that in Ireland people go naked when it rains, for fear of wetting their clothes."

Amid the uproarious merriment provoked by their speeches I sat in silence. Suddenly the embarrassed little scientist, Doctor Chord, looked up at me with a fine friendly sympathy. "A glass with you, sir," he said, and as we nodded our heads solemnly over the rims I felt that there had come to my help one poor little frightened friend. As for my first acquaintance, he, seeing me attacked not only by the redoubtable Fullbil, but also by the formidable Bobbs and the dangerous Fancher, had immediately begun to pretend that never in his life had he spoken to me.

Having a great knowledge of Irish character I could see that trouble was brewing for somebody, but I resolved to be very backward, for I hesitated to create a genuine disturbance in these philosophical circles. However, I was saved this annoyance in a strange manner. The door opened, and a newcomer came in, bowing right and left to his acquaintances, and finally taking a seat near Fullbil. I recognized him instantly; he was Sir Edmund Flixton, the gentleman who had had some thought of fighting me in Bath, but who had refrained from it upon hearing that I had worsted Forister.

However, he did not perceive me at that time. He chattered with Fullbil, telling him evidently some very exciting news, for I heard the old man ejaculate. "By my soul, can it be possible?" Later Fullbil related some amusing things to Flixton, and, upon an inquiry from Flixton, I was pointed out to him. I saw Flixton's face change; he spoke hastily to old Fullbil, who turned pale as death. Swiftly some bit of information flashed around the board, and I saw men's eyes open wide and white as they looked at me.

I have said it was the age of bullies. It was the age when men of physical prowess walked down the street shouldering lesser men into the gutter, and the lesser men had never a word to say for themselves. It was the age when if you expressed opinions contrary to those of a bully he was confidently expected to kill you or somehow maltreat you.

Of all that company of genius there now seemed to be only one gentleman who was not a-tremble. It was the little scientist Doctor Chord. He looked at me with a bright and twinkling eye; suddenly he grinned broadly. I could not but burst into laughter when I noted the appetite with which he enjoyed the confusion and alarm of his friends.

"Come, Fullbil! Come, Bobbs! Come, Fancher! Where are all your pretty wits?" he cried; for this timid little man's impudence increased mightily amid all this helpless distress. "Here's the dignity and power of learning of you, in God's truth. Here's knowledge enthroned, fearless, great! Have ye all lost your tongues?"

And he was for going on to worry them, but that I called out to him,—

"Sir," said I mildly, "if it please you, I would not have the gentlemen disturbed over any little misunderstanding of a pleasant evening. As regards quarrelling, I am all milk and water myself. It reminds me of an occasion in Ireland once when—" Here I recounted a story which Father Donovan always began on after more than three bottles, and to my knowledge he had never succeeded in finishing it. But this time I finished it. "And," said I, "the fellow was sitting there drinking with them, and they had had good fun with him, when of a sudden he up and spoke. Says he: ''Tis God's truth I never expected in all my life to be an evening in the company of such a lot of scurvy rat-eaters,' he says to them. 'And,' says he, 'I have only one word for that squawking old masquerading peacock that sits at the head of the table,' says he. 'What little he has of learning I could put in my eye without going blind,' says he. 'The old curmudgeon!' says he. And with that he arose and left the room, afterward becoming the King of Galway and living to a great age."

This amusing tale created a sickly burst of applause, in the midst of which I bowed myself from the room.

CHAPTER XIX

On my way to my chamber I met the innkeeper and casually asked him after Paddy and Jem. He said that he would send to have word of them and inform me as soon as possible. Later a drawer came to my door and told me that Paddy and Jem, with three men-servants of gentlemen sleeping at the inn, had sallied out to a mug-house.

"Mug-house?" said I. "What in the devil's name is a mug-house?"

"Mug-house, sir?" said the man, staring. "Mug-house? Why, sir, 'tis—'tis a form of amusement, sir."

"It is, is it?" said I. "Very good. And does any one here know to what mug-house they went?"

"The 'Red Slipper,' I think, sir," said the man.

"And how do I get to it?" said I.

"Oh, sir," he cried, "'tis impossible!"

"Is it?" said I. "And why is it? The innkeeper said the same to me, and I would like to hear all the reasons."

"Sir," said the man, "when it becometh dark in London there walk abroad many men of evil minds who are no respecters of persons, but fall upon whomsoever they, may, beating them sorely, having no regard for that part of the Holy Book in which it is written—"

"Let go," said I. "I see what you mean." I then bade him get for me a stout lad with a cudgel and a lantern and a knowledge of the whereabouts of the "Red Slipper."

I, with the stout lad, had not been long in the street before I understood what the landlord and the waiter had meant. In fact we were scarce out of the door before the man was menacing with his cudgel two human vultures who slunk upon us out of the shadow. I saw their pale, wicked, snarling faces in the glow of the lantern.

A little later a great shindy broke out in the darkness, and I heard voices calling loudly for a rally in the name of some guild or society. I moved closer, but I could make out little save that it was a very pretty fight in which a company of good citizens were trying to put to flight a band of roughs and law-breakers. There was a merry rattling of sticks. Soon enough, answering shouts could be heard from some of the houses, and with a great slamming of doors men rushed out to do battle for the peace of the great city. Meanwhile all the high windows had been filled with night-capped heads, and some of these people even went so far as to pour water down upon the combatants. They also sent down cat-calls and phrases of witty advice. The sticks clattered together furiously; once a man with a bloody face staggered past us; he seemed to have been whacked directly on the ear by some uneducated person. It was as fine a shindy as one could hope to witness, and I was deeply interested.

Then suddenly a man called out hoarsely that he had been stabbed—murdered. There were yells from the street and screams from the windows. My lantern-bearer plucked me madly by the sleeve. I understood him, and we hastily left the neighbourhood.

I may tell now what had happened and what followed this affair of the night. A worthy citizen had been stabbed to death indeed. After further skirmishes his comrade citizens had taken several wretches into custody. They were tried for the murder and all acquitted save one. Of this latter it was proven that the brawl had started through his attempt to gain the purse of a passing citizen, and forthwith he was sentenced to be hanged for murder. His companion rascals were sent to prison for long terms on the expectation that one of them really might have been the murderer.

We passed into another street, where each well-lighted window framed one or more painted hussies who called out in jocular obscenity, but when we marched stiffly on without replying their manner changed, and they delivered at us volley after volley of language incredibly foul. There were only two of these creatures who paid no heed, and their indifference to us was due to the fact that they were deeply engaged in a duel of words, exchanging the most frightful, blood-curdling epithets. Confident drunken men jostled us from time to time, and frequently I could see small, ashy-faced, ancient-eyed youths dodging here and there with food and wine. My lantern-bearer told me that the street was not quite awake; it was waiting for the outpourings from the taverns and mug-houses. I bade him hurry me to the "Red Slipper" as soon as possible, for never have I had any stomach for these tawdry evils, fit as they are only for clerks and sailors.

We came at length to the creaking sign of the "Red Slipper." A great noise came from the place. A large company was roaring out a chorus. Without many words I was introduced into the room in which the disturbance was proceeding. It was blue with smoke, and the thundering chorus was still unfinished. I sank unnoticed into a quiet corner.

I was astonished at the appearance of the company. There were many men who looked like venerable prelates, and many men who looked like the heads of old and noble houses. I laughed in my sleeve when I remembered I had thought to find Paddy and Jem here. And at the same time I saw them up near the head of the table, if it please you. Paddy had his hand on the shoulder of a bishop, and Jem was telling some tale into the sympathetic ear of a marquis. At least this is the way matters appeared to my stupefied sense.

The singing ceased, and a distinguished peer at my elbow resumed a talk which evidently had been broken by the chorus:

"And so the Duke spoke with somewhat more than his accustomed vigour," said the distinguished peer.

My worst suspicions were confirmed. Here was a man talking of what had been said by a duke. I cast my eye toward my happy pair of rogues and wondered how I could ever extricate them from their position.

Suddenly there was a loud pounding upon the table, and in the ensuing quiet the grave and dignified voice of the chairman could be heard:

"Gentlemen," he said, "we crave your attention to a song by Mr. John Snowden."

Whereupon my very own Jem Bottles arose amid a burst of applause,

185

and began to sing a ballad which had been written in Bristol or Bath in celebration of the notorious scoundrel Jem Bottles.

Here I could see that if impudence could serve us we would not lack success in England. The ballad was answered with wild cheers of appreciation. It was the great thing of the evening. Jem was strenuously pressed to sing again, but he buried his face in his mug and modestly refused. However, they devoted themselves to his chorus and sang it over and over with immense delight. I had never imagined that the nobility were so free and easy.

During the excitement over Jem's ballad I stole forward to Paddy. "Paddy," I whispered, "come out of this now. 'Tis no place for you here among all these reverend fathers and gentlemen of title. Shame on you!"

He saw my idea in a flash.

"Whist, sir," he answered. "There are being no reverend fathers or gentlemen of title here. They are all after being footmen and valets."

I was extremely vexed with myself. I had been in London only a brief space; and Paddy had been in the city no longer. However, he had already managed his instruction so well that he could at once tell a member of the gentry from a servant. I admired Paddy's cleverness, but at the same time I felt a certain resentment against the prelates and nobles who had so imposed upon me.

But, to be truthful, I have never seen a finer display of manners. These menials could have put courtiers to the blush. And from time to time somebody spoke out loud and clear an opinion pilfered verbatim from his master. They seldom spoke their own thoughts in their own way; they sent forth as their own whatever they could remember from the talk of their masters and other gentlemen. There was one man who seemed to be the servant of some noted scholar, and when he spoke the others were dumfounded into quiet.

"The loriot," said he with a learned frown, "is a bird. If it is looked upon by one who has the yellow jaundice, the bird straightway dies, but the sick person becomes well instantly. 'Tis said that lovage is used, but I would be luctuous to hear of anybody using this lothir weed, for 'tis no pentepharmacon, but a mere simple and not worth a caspatory."

This utterance fairly made their eyes bulge, and they sat in stunned silence. But I must say that there was one man who did not fear.

"Sir," said Paddy respectfully, but still with his own dignity, "I would be hearing more of this bird, and we all would be feeling honoured for a short description."

"In color he is ningid," said the learned valet.

"Bedad!" cried Paddy. "That's strange!"

"'Tis a question full of tenebrosity," remarked the other leaning back in his chair. "We poor scholars grow madarosis reflecting upon it. However, I may tell you that the bird is simous; yblent in the sunlight, but withal strenuous-eyed; its blood inclined to intumescence. However, I must be breviloquent, for I require an enneadecaterides to enumerate the true qualities of the loriot."

"By gor!" said Paddy, "I'll know that bird if I see him ten years from now. Thank you kindly, sir. But we would be late for breakfast if you took the required time; and that's true for me."

Afterward I reflected that I had attended the meetings of two scholarly bodies in this one evening, but for the life of me I couldn't decide which knew the least.

CHAPTER XX

By the following Sunday I judged that the Earl of Westport and his family had returned to London, and so I walked abroad in the hopes of catching a glimpse of some of them among the brilliant gentry who on this day thronged the public gardens. I had both Jem Bottles and Paddy accompany me, for I feared that they would get into mischief if I left them to themselves. The innkeeper had told me that Kensington Gardens was the place where the grand people mostly chose to walk and flirt and show their clothes on a clear Sunday. It was a long way to these Gardens, but we footed out bravely, although we stopped once to see a fight between five drunken apprentices, as well as several times for much-needed refreshment.

I had no idea that the scene at the Gardens would be so splendid. Outside, the road was a block of gleaming chariots and coaches with servants ablaze in their liveries. Here I left Paddy and Jem to amuse themselves as suited them.

But the array of carriages had been only a forecast of what my eyes would encounter in the Garden itself. I was involved at once in a swarm of fashionable people. My eyes were dazzled with myriad colours, and my nostrils, trained as they were to peat smoke, were saluted by a hundred delicious perfumes. Priceless silks and satins swept against my modest stockings.

I suffered from my usual inclination to run away, but I put it down with an iron will. I soon found a more retired spot from which I could review the assemblage at something like my leisure. All the highly fashionable flock knew each other intimately, it appeared, and they kept off with figurative pikes attempts of a certain class not quite so high and mighty, who seemed for ever trying to edge into situations which would benefit them on the social ladder. Their failures were dismal, but not so dismal as the heroic smiles with which they covered their little noiseless defeats.

I saw a lady, sumptuously arrayed, sweep slowly along with her daughter, a beautiful girl who greatly wished to keep her eyes fixed on the ground. The mother glanced everywhere with half-concealed eagerness and anxiety. Once she bowed impressively to a dame with a cold, pale aristocratic face, around whom were gathered several officers in the uniform of His Majesty's Guards. The grand dame lifted her lorgnette and stared coolly at that impressive bow; then she turned and said something amusing to one of the officers, who smilingly answered. The mother, with her beautiful daughter, passed on, both pairs of eyes now on the ground.

I had thought the rebuff would settle this poor misguided creature, but in the course of an hour I saw three more of her impressive bows thrown away against the icy faces of other women. But as they were leaving the Gardens they received attention from members of the very best society. One lordling nudged another lordling, and they stared into the face of the girl as if she had been a creature of the street. Then they leisurely looked her up and down from head to toe. No tailor could have taken her measurements so completely. Afterward they grinned at each other, and one spoke behind his hand, his insolent speculative eyes fixed on the retiring form of the girl. This was the social reward of the ambitious mother.

It has always been clear to me why the women turn out in such cohorts to any sort of a function. They wish to see the frocks, and they are insistent that their own frocks shall be seen. Moreover they take great enjoyment in hating such of their enemies as may come under their notice. They never have a really good time; but of this fact they are not aware, since women are so constituted that they are able to misinterpret almost every one of their emotions.

The men, knowing something of their own minds at times, stealthily avoid such things unless there are very special reasons. In my own modest experience I have seen many a popular hostess hunting men with a net. However it was plain why so many men came to Kensington Gardens on a Sunday afternoon. It was the display of feminine beauty. And when I say "display" I mean it. In my old age the fashion balloons a lady with such a sweep of wires and trellises that no Irishman could marry her because there is never a door in all Ireland through which his wife could pass. In my youth, however, the fashion required all dresses to be cut very low, and all skirts to cling so that if a four-legged woman entered a drawing-room everybody would know it. It would be so easy to count them. At present a woman could have eight legs and nobody be the wiser.

It was small wonder that the men came to ogle at Kensington Gardens on a fine Sunday afternoon. Upon my word, it was worth any young gentleman's time. Nor did the beauties blush under the gaze of banks of fastidious beaus who surveyed them like men about to bid at a horse-fair. I thought of my father and how he would have enjoyed the scene. I wager he would have been a gallant with the best of them, bowing and scraping, and dodging ladies' skirts. He would have been in his very element.

But as for me I had come to gain a possible glimpse of Lady Mary. Beyond that I had no warm interest in Kensington Gardens. The crowd was too high and fine; many of the people were altogether too well bred. They frightened me.

However, I turned my head by chance to the left, and saw near me a small plain man who did not frighten me at all. It was Doctor Chord, the little scientist. He was alone and seemed to be occupied in studying the crowd. I moved over to him.

"A good day to you, sir," I said, extending my hand.

When he recognized me, his face broke into a beaming smile.

"Why, sir," he cried, "I am very glad to see you, sir. Perchance, like me, you have come here for an hour's quiet musing on fashionable folly."

"That's it, sir," said I. "You've hit it exactly."

I have said that he was a bashful man, but it seemed that his timidity was likely to show itself only in the presence of other great philosophers and scientists. At any rate, he now rattled on like a little engine, surveying the people keenly and discoursing upon their faults.

"There's the old Marquis of Stubblington," observed my friend. "He beats his wife with an ebony stick. 'Tis said she always carries a little bottle of liniment in the pocket of her skirt. Poor thing, her only pleasure in life is to talk scandal; but this she does on such a heroic scale that it occupies her time completely. There is young Lord Gram walking again with that soap-boiler and candle-maker. 'Tis disgraceful! The poor devil lends Gram money, and Gram repays him by allowing him to be seen in his company. Gram gambles away the money, but I don't know what the soap-boiler does with his distinguished honours. However, you can see that the poor wretch is delighted with his bargain. There are the three Banellic girls, the most ill-tempered, ugly cats in England. But each will have a large marriage portion, so they have no fears, I warrant me. I wonder the elder has the effrontery to show her face here so soon if it is true that the waiting-woman died of her injuries. Little Wax is talking to them. He needs one of those marriage portions. Aye, he needs all three, what with his very boot-maker almost inclined to be insolent to him. I see that foreign count is talking to the Honourable Mrs. Trasky. He is no more nor less than a gambler by trade, and they say he came here from Paris because he was caught cheating there, and was kicked and caned with such intense publicity that he was forced to leave in the dead of night. However, he found many young birds here eager to be plucked and devoured. 'Tis little they care, so long as they may play till dawn. Did you hear about Lady Prefent? She went after her son to the Count's rooms at night. In her younger days she lived rather a gay life herself, 'tis rumoured, and so she was not to be taken by her son's lies as to where he spent his evenings and his money. Ha, I see the Countess Cheer. There is a citadel of virtue! It has been stormed and taken so many times that I wonder it is not in ruins, and yet here it is defiant, with banners flying. Wonderful. She—"

"Hold!" I cried. "I have enough. I would have leave to try and collect my wits. But one thing I would know at once. I thought you were a shy scholar, and here you clatter away with the tongue of an old rake. You amaze me. Tell me why you do this? Why do you use your brain to examine this muck?"

"'Tis my recreation," he answered simply. "In my boyhood I was allowed no games, and in the greater part of my manhood I have been too busy. Of late years I have more leisure, and I often have sought here a little innocent amusement, something to take one's mind off one's own affairs, and yet not

191

of such an arduous nature as would make one's head tired."

"By my faith, it would make my head tired," I said. "What with remembering the names of the people and all the different crimes, I should go raving mad." But what still amazed me was the fact that this little man, habitually meek, frightened and easily trodden down in most ordinary matters, should be able to turn himself upon occasion into a fierce and howling wolf of scandal, baying his betters, waiting for the time when an exhausted one fell in the snow, and then burying his remorseless teeth in him. What a quaint little Doctor Chord.

"But tell me truly," said I. "Is there no virtuous lady or honest gentleman in all this great crowd?"

He stared, his jaw dropping. "Strap me, the place is full of them," he ejaculated. "They are as thick as flies in a fish-market."

"Well, then," said I, "let us talk of them. 'Tis well to furbish and burnish our minds with tales of rectitude and honour."

But the little Doctor was no longer happy. "There is nought to say," he answered gloomily. "They are as quiet as Bibles. They make no recreation for me. I have scant interest in them."

"Oh, you little rogue, you!" I cried. "What a precious little bunch of evil it is! 'They make no recreation for me,' quoth he. Here's a great, bold, outspoken monster. But, mark you, sir, I am a younger man, but I too have a bold tongue in my head, and I am saying that I have friends among ladies in London, and if I catch you so much as whispering their names in your sleep, I'll cut off your ears and eat them. I speak few words, as you may have noted, but I keep my engagements, you little brew of trouble, you!"

"Strap me," whimpered the little Doctor, plucking feverishly at the buttons of his coat, rolling his eyes wildly, not knowing at all what he did. "The man's mad! The man's mad!"

"No," said I, "my blood is cold, very cold."

The little Doctor looked at me with the light of a desperate inspiration

192

in his eye. "If your blood is cold, sir," said he, "I can recommend a gill of port wine."

I needs must laugh. "Good," I cried, "and you will join me."

CHAPTER XXI

I don't know if it was the gill of comforting port, but at any rate I was soon enough convinced that there was no reason for speaking harshly to Doctor Chord. It served no purpose; it accomplished nothing. The little old villain was really as innocent as a lamb. He had no dream of wronging people. His prattle was the prattle of an unsophisticated maiden lady. He did not know what he was talking. These direful intelligences ran as easily off his tongue as water runs off the falling wheel. When I had indirectly informed him that he was more or less of a dangerous scandal-monger, he had cried: "The man is mad!" Yes; he was an innocent old thing.

But then it is the innocent old scandal-mongers, poor placid-minded well-protected hens, who are often the most harmful. The vicious gabblers defeat themselves very often. I remember my father once going to a fair and kissing some girls there. He kissed them all turn by turn, as was his right and his duty, and then he returned to a girl near the head of the list and kissed her five times more because she was the prettiest girl in all Ireland, and there is no shame to him there. However, there was a great hullabaloo. The girls who had been kissed only once led a regular crusade against the character of this other girl, and before long she had a bad name, and the odious sly lads with no hair on their throats winked as she passed them, and numerous mothers thanked God that their daughters were not fancied by the lord of that region. In time these tales came to the ears of my father, and he called some of his head men to meet him in the dining-room.

"I'll have no trifling," said he. "The girl is a good girl for all I know, and I have never seen her before or since. If I can trace a bad word to any man's mouth, I'll flog him till he can't move. 'Tis a shame taking away the girl's name for a few kisses by the squire at a fair with everybody looking on and laughing. What do you blackguards mean?"

Every man in the dining-room took oath he had never said a word, and they all spoke truth. But the women clamoured on without pausing for wind, and refused to take word of the men-folk, who were gifted with the power of reason. However, the vicious people defeated themselves in time. People began to say to a lass who had been kissed only once: "Ah, now, you would be angry because you were not getting the other five." Everything seemed to grow quiet, and my father thought no more about it, having thought very little about it in the first place save enough to speak a few sharp words. But, would you believe it, there was an old woman living in a hovel not a mile from the castle, who kept up the scandal for twelve more months. She had never been married, and, as far as any one knew, she had never wished to be. She had never moved beyond Father Donovan's church in one direction and a little peat-heap in the other direction. All her days she had seen nothing but the wind-swept moors, and heard nothing but the sea lashing the black rocks. I am mistaken; once she came to the castle, hearing that my mother was ill. She had a remedy with her, poor soul, and they poured it in the ashes when her back was turned. My mother bade them give her some hot porridge and an old cloth gown of her own to take home. I remember the time distinctly. Well, this poor thing couldn't tell between a real sin and an alligator. Bony, withered, aged, this crone might have been one of the highest types of human perfection. She wronged nobody; she had no power to wrong. Nobody wronged her; it was never worth it. She really was at peace with all the world. This obeys the most exalted injunctions. Every precept is kept here. But this tale of the Squire and the girl took root in her head. She must have been dazzled by the immensity of the event. It probably appealed to her as would a grand picture of the burning of Rome or a vivid statue of Lot's wife turning to look back. It reached the dimensions of great history. And so this old woman, who had always lived the life of a nun, dreamed of nothing but the colossal wrong which had come within her stunted range of vision. Before and after church she talked of no other thing for almost eighteen months. Finally my father in despair rode down to her little cottage.

"Mollie," said he, calling from the road, "Mollie, come out." She came out.

"Mollie," said my father, "you know me?"

"Ay," said she, "you are The O'Ruddy, and you are a rogue."

"True for you, Mollie," said my father pleasantly. "You know it and I know it. I am indeed a grand rogue. But why would you be tearing to tatters the name of that poor girl in Ballygoway?"

"'Tis not me that has said more than three words," she cried, astonished, "and before I speak ill of anybody I hope the devil flies away with me."

Well, my father palavered on for a long time, telling her that he would take away the pension of twenty-five shillings a year which he had given her because he by accident had shot her second cousin in the leg twelve years before that time. She steadfastly answered that she would never speak ill of anybody; but the girl was a brazen-faced wench, and he was no better. My father came away, and I have no doubt the scandal would still be alive if the old woman had not died, may the saints rest her!

And so I was no longer angry with Doctor Chord, but spoke to him pleasantly.

"Come," said I, "I would have you point me out the great swordsmen, if it pleases you. I am eager to see them, and the talk will be cleanly, also."

"Aye," said my friend. "Nothing could give me more pleasure. And now, look you! The tall, straight, grave young man there is Ponsonby, who flashes the wisest blade in England unless Reginald Forister is better. Any how, Forister is not here to-day. At least I don't see him. Ponsonby fought his last duel with a gentleman named Vellum because Vellum said flatly that Mrs. Catherine Wainescorte was a—"

"Stop there," said I, "and get to the tale of the fighting."

"Well, Ponsonby won without difficulty," said the Doctor; "but it is said that he took an unfair advantage—"

"Stop again!" I cried. "Stop again! We will talk no more of swordsmen. Somehow I have lost my interest. I am put to it to think of a subject for talk, and we may have to do with a period of silence, but that will do your jaw no injury at any rate."

But I was mistaken in thinking that the little man could forego his recreation for more than a moment. Suddenly he burst out with a great spleen:

"Titles!" he cried. "Empty titles! husks, husks, husks! 'Tis all they care for, this mob! Honourable manhood goes a-begging while the world worships at the feet of pimply lords! Pah! Lovely girls, the making of fine wives and mothers, grow old while the world worships at the feet of some old horse-headed duchess! Pah! Look at those pick-thanks and flatterers, cringing at the boots of the people of fashion. Upon my life, before I would so demean myself, I—" he ceased suddenly, his eye having caught sight of some people in the crowd. "Ah," said he, while a singularly vain and fatuous smile settled upon his countenance. "Ah, the Countess of Westport and her charming daughter, the Lady Mary, have arrived. I must go and speak to them." My eye had followed his glance quickly enough you may be sure. There, true enough, was the formidable figure of the old Countess, and at her side was the beautiful Lady Mary.

With an absent-minded murmur of apology, Doctor Chord went mincing toward them, his face still spread with its idiotic smile.

He cantered up to them with the grace of a hobbled cow. I expected him to get a rebuff that would stun him into the need of a surgeon, but to my surprise the Countess received him affably, bending her head to say some gracious words. However, I had more eyes for Lady Mary than for the capers of little Chord.

It was a great joy to be able to look at her. I suffered from a delicious trembling, and frequently my vision became dim purely from the excitement. But later I was moved by another profound emotion. I was looking at her; I must have her look at me. I must learn if her eye would light, if her expression would change, when she saw me. All this sounds very boyish, but it is not necessary to leave it out for that reason, because, as my father often said, every Irishman is a boy until he has grandchildren. I do not know if he was perfectly right in this matter, but it is a certain advantage in a love affair to have the true boyish ardour which is able to enshrine a woman in one's heart to the exclusion of everything, believing her to be perfection and believing life without her a hell of suffering and woe. No man of middle-aged experience can ever be in love. He may have his illusions. He may think he is in love. A woman may gain the power to bind him hand and foot and drag him wherever she listeth, but he is not in love. That is his mistaken idea. He is only misinterpreting his feelings. But, as my father said, it is very different with Irishmen, who are able to remain in love to a very great age. If you will note, too, climatic conditions and other unpleasant matters have practically no effect upon them; so little, indeed, that you may find streets named after the main Italian cities, and many little German children speak with a slight brogue. My father often said that one great reason for an Irishman's successes with the ladies was his perfect willingness to get married. He was seldom to be seen scouting for advantages in intrigue. If the girl be willing, be she brown, yellow, or white, he was always for the priest and the solemn words. My father also contended that in every marriage contracted on the face of the earth in which neither maid nor man could understand the other's national speech, the bridegroom was an Irishman. He was the only man who was able to make delightful love with the aid of mere signals.

However I must be going on with my story, although it is a great pleasure to talk of my country-men. They possess a singular fascination for me. I cannot forget that I too am an Irishman.

The little Doctor was still saying agreeable things; Lady Mary was smiling in gentle amusement. As I moved out to catch Lady Mary's eye, I did not at all lose sight of the fact that if the pugnacious mother of my innamorata took one glimpse of me there might result a scene which could end in nothing but my ignominious flight. I edged toward the group, advancing on the Countess's port quarter as she was talking animately over her starboard bow at the entranced little Doctor. At times Lady Mary looked about her, still smiling her smile, which no doubt was born of the ridiculous performances of Chord. Once I thought she looked squarely at me, and my heart beat like a drum so loudly that I thought people must hear. But her glance wandered on casually over the throng, and then I felt truly insignificant, like a man who could hide behind the nail of his own thumb.

Perceiving that I was so insignificant, I judged it prudent as well as advantageous to advance much closer. Suddenly Lady Mary's clear virgin eye met mine,—met it fully.

Now, I don't know what was in this glance we exchanged. I have stopped myself just on the verge of a full explanation of the thrills, quivers, hopes, fears, and dreams which assailed me as I looked back into the beautiful face of Lady Mary. I was also going to explain how the whole scene appeared. But I can see soon enough that my language would not be appropriate to the occasion. But any how we looked each other point-blank in the eye. It was a moment in which that very circling of the earth halted, and all the suns of the universe poised, ready to tumble or to rise. Then Lady Mary lowered her glance, and a pink blush suffused her neck and cheek.

The Countess, Lady Mary, and Doctor Chord moved slowly on through the throng, and I followed. The great question now was whether Lady Mary would look back. If she looked back, I would feel that I was making grand way with her. If she did not look back, I would know myself as a lost man. One can imagine how eagerly I watched her. For a long time it was plain that she had no intention whatever of looking back. I lugubriously arranged my complete downfall. Then, at the very moment of my despair, she gazed studiously off to her extreme left for a certain time, and then suddenly cast one short glance behind her. Only heaven knows what value I placed upon this brief look. It appeared for the moment to me that I had won her, won everything. I bravely forged ahead until I was quite insistently under the eye of Lady Mary, and then she again looked toward me, but it was a look so repelling and frigid that it went through me as if I had been a paper ring in the circus. I slunk away through the crowd, my thoughts busy with trying to find out what had happened to me.

For three minutes I was a miserable human being. At the end of that time I took heart again. I decided that Lady Mary had frowned at me because she was afraid that she had been too good to me with her look and smile. You know what I mean. I have seen a young girl give a young man a flower, and at the very next moment be seemingly willing to give her heart's blood to get that flower back, overcome with panic terror that she had passed—in his opinion, mind you—beyond the lines of best behaviour. Well I said to myself that Lady Mary had given me the hard look for similar reasons. It was rational to make this judgment, for certainly she had no cause for an active dislike. I had never been even so much as a nuisance to her.

Fortified with these philosophic decisions, I again followed the trio, and I was just in time to find Chord handing them into a splendid chariot. I stood out boldly, for I knew if I could not get one more look from Lady Mary I would die.

Seated beside her mother, her eye wandered eagerly over the crowd. I was right, by the saints! She was looking for me.

And now here come the stupid laws of convention. Could I yell? Could I even throw my hat in the air to guide her eye aright? No! I was doomed to stand there as still as a bottle on a shelf.

But she saw me! It was at the very last moment. There was no time for coquetry. She allowed her glance to linger, and God knows what we said to each other in this subtle communication through all the noise and hubbub of the entrance place. Then suddenly the coachman's reins tightened; there were some last bows; the chariot whirled away.

CHAPTER XXII

Chord ambled back, very proud indeed, and still wearing his fatuous smile. He was bursting with a sense of social value, and to everybody he seemed to be saying, "Did you see me?" He was overjoyed to find me waiting for him. He needed a good listener at once. Otherwise he would surely fly to pieces.

"I have been talking to the Countess of Westport and her daughter, Lady Mary Strepp," he said pompously. "The Countess tells that the Earl has been extremely indisposed during their late journey in the West."

He spoke of the Earl's illness with an air of great concern, as if the news had much upset him. He pretended that the day was quite over-gloomed for him. Dear, dear! I doubted if he would be able to eat any supper.

"Have a drop of something, old friend," said I sympathetically. "You can't really go on this way. 'Twill ruin your nerves. I am surprised that the Countess did not break the news to you more gently. She was very inconsiderate, I am sure."

"No, no, don't blame the poor lady," cried Chord. "She herself was quite distracted. The moment she saw me she ran to me—did you see her run to me?"

"I did that," said I with emphasis.

"Aye, she ran to me," said the little fool, "and says she, 'Oh, my dear Doctor, I must tell you at once the condition of the Earl.' And when I heard everything I was naturally cut up, as you remarked, being an old friend of the family, ahem!—yes, an old friend of the family."

He rattled on with his nonsensical lies, and in the mean time I made up my mind to speak plainly to him, as I intended to make him of great service to me.

"Stop a moment," said I good-naturedly. "I will hear no more of this rubbish from you, you impudent little impostor. You care no more for the Earl of Westport's illness than you do for telling the truth, and I know how much you care for that. Listen to me, and I'll see if I can't knock some sense into your little addled head. In the first place the Earl of Westport and my father were old friends and companions-in-arms in the service of the French king, and I came over from Ireland especially to take a dying message and a token from my father to the Earl. That is all you need know about that; but I would have you leave off your prate of your friend the Earl of Westport, for I understand full well you couldn't distinguish between him and a church door, although 'tis scandalously little you know of church doors. So we will stop there on that point. Then I will go on to the next point. The next point is that I am going to marry Lady Mary Strepp."

The little Doctor had been choking and stuttering in a great spasm, but my last point bid fair to flatten him out on the floor. I took the overpowered philosopher and led or carried him to another drink.

"Stap me!" he cried again and again. "The man is mad!"

I surveyed him with a bland smile.

"Let it sink into you," said I soothingly. "Don't snarl and wrangle at it. It is all heaven's truth, and in time you will come to your senses and see what I am telling you."

Well, as soon as he had fully recovered his wind, he fell upon me with thousands of questions; for one may see that he would have plenty of interest in the matter as soon as he was assured that there was much veracity involved in one way or another in my early statement. His questions I answered as it pleased me, but I made clear enough to him that, although Lady Mary was well disposed toward me, neither her father nor her mother would even so much as look at me if I applied for a position as under-footman, I was that low in their estimate.

"However," said I, "I can rearrange all that very easily. And now, my bucko, here is where your fortune meets mine. You are fitted by nature more to attend other people's affairs than to take a strict interest in your own. All kinds of meddling and interference come easily to you. Well, then, here is a chance to exercise your gifts inoffensively, and yet in a way which may make two people happy for life. I will tell you now that I don't even know where is the Earl's town house. There is where your importance appears at once. You must show me the house. That is the first thing. After that we will arrange all the details about ladders and garden walls, and, mayhap, carrier doves. As for your reward, it will appear finally in the shape of a bowing recognition by people of fashion, which is what you most desire in the world, you funny little man."

Again I had stunned him. For a time I could see his brain swimming in a perfect sea of bewilderment. But, as before, sense gradually came to him, and he again volleyed questions at me. But what stuck in his crop was the thought that Lady Mary could prefer me. He tried his best to believe it, but he would always end up by saying: "Well, if Lady Mary cares for you, the affair is not too difficult." Or, "Well, if you are sure Lady Mary loves you—" I could have broken his head a thousand times.

"Bad luck to you, Doctor," I cried. "Don't you know such croaking would spoil the peace of any true lover? Is ever any worthy man able not to be anxious in such matters? 'Tis only foppery coxcombs who have great confidence, and they are usually misled, thank the Lord! Be quiet, now, and try to take everything for granted."

Then the spirit of the adventure came upon him, and he was all for it, heels over head. As I told him, this sort of meddling was his proper vocation. He who as a recreation revelled in the mere shadows of the intrigues of people of quality was now really part of one, an actor in it, the repository of its deep secret. I had to curb his enthusiasm. He had such a sense of the importance of my news, and of his distinction in having heard it, that I think he wanted to tell the secret to the entire world.

As soon as the afternoon grew late I suggested a walk to that part of London in which was situated the Earl's town house. I did not see why we should not be moving at once on the campaign. The Doctor assented, and we went forth to look for Paddy and Jem Bottles. We found them at an ale-house which was the resort of the chairmen, footmen, and coachmen of the grand people. The two rogues had evidently passed a pleasant afternoon. Jem Bottles was still making love to a very pretty girl, some part of whose easy affection or interest he had won; and Paddy, it seems, had had a rip-roaring fight with two lackeys, worsted them with despatch, and even pursued them some distance. To my stern interrogation in regard to the pretty girl, Jem Bottles stoutly rejoined that she was his second cousin whom he had not seen for many years. To this I made no reply, for it does no good to disturb the balance of a good liar. If at times he is led to tell the truth, he becomes very puzzling. In all the years Jem Bottles has been in my service I have never reprimanded him for lying. I would confuse matters to no purpose, inasmuch as I understand him perfectly.

"And how," said I to Paddy, "did you come to engage in this disgraceful brawl of a Sunday?"

"Your honour," answered Paddy, "there was two of these men with fat legs came here, and says one, looking hard at me, 'Here's a furriner,' he says. 'Furriner yourself, you fish-faced ditch-lurker,' says I, and with that he takes up his fists and hits me a knock. There was a little shindy, and afterward they ran away bawling, and I was pursuing them, only I feared to lose my way in these strange parts."

The walk to Lord Westport's house was a long one. It seemed that he had built a great new mansion at a place outside of the old city gates, where other nobles and great brewers had built fine houses, surrounding them all with splendid gardens.

One must not suppose that I had any idea of taking the mansion by storm. My first idea was to dream a lover's dream as I gazed upon the abode of my treasure. This, I believe, is a legitimate proceeding in all careers. Every lover worthy of the name is certain to pilgrimage, muffled in his cloak, to moon over the home of his adored one. Otherwise there can be no real attachment.

In the second place I wished to develop certain plans for gaining speech of Lady Mary. I will not deny that I purposed on a near day to scale the garden wall and hold speech of my sweetheart as she walked alone among

204

the flowers. For my success I depended upon the absolute conventionality of the idea. In all history no lover has even been chased out of a garden by an under-gardener with a hoe.

When we arrived at the house I found that it was indeed a gorgeous mansion. It was surrounded on all sides by high brick walls, but through the elaborate tracery of one of the iron-work gates I saw Lady Mary's home standing among sweeping green lawns.

We reconnoitred all sides, and at the back I found a lonely avenue lined with oaks. Here a small door pierced the wall for the use apparently of the gardeners or grooms. I resolved that here I would make my attack.

As we passed the iron gates on our way back to town, we saw window after window light up with a golden radiance. I wondered which part of that vast edifice hid the form of my Mary.

I had asked Doctor Chord to sup with me at the inn, and on the way thither he proved somewhat loquacious.

"I see in you, sir," said he, "a certain instinct of true romance which is infrequently encountered in this humdrum commercial age. Allow me to express to you, sir, my warm admiration. I did not think that a gallant of this humdrum commercial age could prove such a free spirit. In this humdrum commercial age—"

"I am an Irishman," said I, "and in Ireland we are always humdrum, but we are never commercial, for the reason that we have not the tools."

"Aye," said he, "you must be a great people. Strangely enough, you are the first Irishman I have ever seen, although I have seen many blackamoors. However, I am edified to find you a gentleman of great learning and experience. In this humdrum commercial age—"

"Let go," said I. "I can do very well without your opinion as to my learning and experience. In regard to this being a humdrum commercial age you will find that all ages say the same thing of themselves. I am more interested in the winning of Lady Mary."

"'Twas to that subject I was just about to turn the talk," said the Doctor. "I need not express again to you the interest I feel; and if it is true, as you say, that Lady Mary really loves you—"

"May the devil fly away with you," I cried in a great rage. "Are you never to have done? You are an old frog. I asked you to help me, and you do nothing but dispirit me with these doubts. I'll not put up with it."

"I am very sorry to displease you, sir," answered my friend. "If you examine my intentions with a dispassionate eye, sir, I am convinced you will have found nothing in me which should properly cause these outbursts of disapprobation. When I say, 'If Lady Mary really loves you,' I am referring to the strange mishaps and misconstructions which attend human thought at all times, and when I say—"

"Let go again," I cried. "When I misunderstand you, don't enlighten me; for I find these explanations very hard to bear."

To my surprise the little man answered with great spirit: "I am unable to gain any approval for my deep interest in your affairs, sir," he cried. "Perchance, it would be better if I could affect a profound indifference. I am certainly at a loss for words when each sentence of mine is made the subject of wrathful objection."

"You are right," said I. "But you will understand how ten thousand emotions beset and haggle a lover, and I believe he always revenges himself upon his dearest friends. Forgive me!"

"With all my heart!" answered the little Doctor. "I am aware, sir, that at the present time you are in many ways like a highly-tightened fiddle, which any breeze frets into murmurings. Now, being absolutely certain of the devotion of your beloved, you naturally—"

"By the ten lame pipers of Ballydehob," I shouted, "let go of that talk. I can't be having it. I warn ye. 'Tis either a grave for me, or quiet for you, and I am thinking it is quiet for you."

"Inasmuch," said the Doctor, "as my most judicious speeches seem to inflame your passions, sir, I am of the opinion that a perfect silence on my part becomes almost necessary, and, to further this end, I would recommend that you refrain from making interrogations, or otherwise promulgating opportunities, when an expression of candid opinion seems expected and desired."

"You've hit it," said I. "We will have no more interrogations. However, I would much like to know how you became so intimate with Lord Westport's family."

Doctor Chord blushed with something of his earlier manner. "'Tis a matter which I did not expect to have leap at me out of the darkness in this fashion," he said bashfully. "However, I am convinced of how well you know these people, and I will traffic no more with hollow pretence. As you know, I deal much in chemical knowledge, which I am able to spread to almost every branch of human use and need."

"'Tis an ill work," said I slowly. "I doubt if Father Donovan would care to hear you be speaking in this way. He always objected to scientific improvements as things which do harm to the Church."

"In regard to the estimable friend you mention," said the Doctor, "I unhesitatingly state my profound assurances of respect."

"Quite so," I answered. "He will be pleased to hear of it. And now we will return to the other matter."

"I will obediently proceed," said he. "Five years back the Countess of Westport was thrown from her carriage. Physicians rushed to her rescue. I too appeared, being for the time out for a walk. They wished to immediately bleed her, but I waved them aside and, recognizing me as a figure in the street world of science, they fell back abashed. I prescribed a small drink of hot rum. The lady took it. Almost immediately she recovered. She offered me a guinea. I refused curtly. She inquired here and there for my condition. Afterward she apologized to me for not offering me more than a guinea. Since that time we have been warm friends. She knows me as a great scientist who came to her assistance in time of trouble when numerous quacks wished to bleed her, and I overpowered them and gave her a drink of rum. 'Tis true that after she reached her own bed the Earl's physician bled her, but she did not seem to appreciate it although he drew twenty-five ounces, I think. But she has remained always grateful for the hot rum."

CHAPTER XXIII

At supper that evening Doctor Chord amplified some of his views "A few staunch retainers could quickly aid you to scale the walls of the castle," said he. "But I have forgotten," he added blankly. "'Tis not a castle. 'Tis a house."

"If you would take some of these ancient ideas and bury them in the garden," said I, "they might grow in time to be some kind of turnip or other valuable food. But at the present moment they do not seem to me to serve much purpose. Supposing that the house is not a castle? What of that?"

"Castles—" said he. "Castles lend themselves—"

"Castles!" I cried. "Have done with castles! All castles may be Jews, as you say. But this is a house."

"I remarked that it was a house," he answered gently. "It was that point that I was making."

"Very good," said I. "We will now proceed to define matters. Do you know if Lady Mary walks in the garden? It is absolutely necessary that Lady Mary should walk in the garden."

"She does," he replied at once. "At this season of the year Lady Mary walks in the garden on every fine day at ten of the clock."

"Then," I cried, smiting the table, "our course is clear; I feel elate. My only regret is that my father is not here to give me a word now and then, for 'tis a game he would know down to the ground."

"Although I am not your father," said Doctor Chord modestly, "I may be able to suggest some expedient way of gaining entrance to the castle."

"House," said I.

"House," said he.

"However," said I, "we must lower ourselves to extremely practical matters. Can you climb a tree?"

"A tree?" said he. "Climb a tree? Strap me!"

"'Tis all very well to strap yourself in this fashion," said I rather warmly; "but the climbing of trees appears here as an important matter. In my part of Ireland there are few trees, and so climbing trees did not enter into my education. However, I am willing to attempt the climbing of a tree for the sake of my true love, and if I fall—how high is this wall? Do you remember?"

"'Twas at least ten feet," answered the Doctor. "And there is a murderous row of spikes at the top. But," he added, "the more spikes and all that make them the more convinced that the garden is perfectly safe from intrusion."

"That's a world of sense out of you," I cried. "The spikes convince them the garden is safe from intrusion, and so they give over their watchfulness. So now in the morning we will go there, and I will climb one of the oak-trees bordering the wall—may the saints aid me!"

"You were asking if I could climb a tree," remarked the Doctor. "I will point out to you that it is a question of no importance. It is you yourself who must climb the tree; for even if I succeeded in the arduous and painful task I could not pay your vows to Lady Mary, and for such purpose primarily the tree is to be climbed."

"True for you, Doctor," I answered with a sigh. "True for you. I must climb the tree. I can see that. I had some thought of making Paddy climb it, but, as you say, a man must do his own love-making, and by the same token I would break the head of any one who tried to do it for me. I would that! In this world people must climb their own trees. Now that I think of it seriously, it was ridiculous in me to plan that Paddy should climb the tree."

"'Second thoughts are always best,'" said the little Doctor piously. "'Tis a phrase from one of the greatest writers of the day. And at any rate I myself, because of age and debility, would not be able to climb a tree."

"Let us say no more of it," said I. "I see my mistake. But tell me one thing. I know you are a man with a great deal on your mind. Can you spare the time for this adventure?"

But on this point the Doctor was very clear and emphatic. I think if I had said he could not have a place in the plot he would have died immediately of a broken heart.

"'Tis true I have not yet finished my treatise proving that the touchstone is fallible," he cried eagerly; "but it would give me pleasure to delay the work indefinitely if in the meantime I can be of assistance."

"That is a man's talk," I said. "Well, then, in the morning we will go forth to do or die. And now a glass to success."

That night I slept very heartily, for some of my father's soldier training is in my veins, and on the eve of a hard or precarious work I am always able to get sound rest. My father often said that on the night before a battle in which he would stand seventy-seven chances of being killed he always slept like a dog in front of the fire.

At dawn I was up and ready. My first move was to have Paddy and Jem sent to me, and to give them such information as would lead them to an intelligent performance of their duties during the day. "Mind ye now," said I, "here's where the whole thing may be won or lost. There is a lovely lady inside the walls of that garden which I was showing you yesterday. She lives in the big house. She is the lady who made you feel ashamed when you took the old Earl's—well, never mind! I hope we are all properly repentant over it. However, I had better be getting on with the matter in hand. She lives there, and if I can find no way to gain speech of her we all three of us will have to take to the thickets, and that's the truth."

"If I could but lay my fingers on her throttle," said Jem Bottles in a blood-curdling voice, "she soon enough would—"

"Stop!" I cried. "You misunderstood me!"

"Aye, he does," spoke in Paddy. "But I know what your honour is meaning. You are meaning that the young lady—aye, didn't I see her, and didn't she give me a look of her eye? Aye, I know what your honour is meaning."

"You are knowing it precisely," said I. "The young lady is more to me than three Irelands. You understand? Well, then, in the first place I must gain speech of her. To-day we march out and see what I can accomplish by climbing trees. In the meantime you two are to lay in waiting and assist me when necessary."

"I am foreseeing that everything will be easy," cried Paddy jubilantly.

"You are an Irishman," I responded in anger.

"Aye," he replied bitterly, "and another is within reach of my stick if it weren't for my respect for my betters, although such a thing never could happen, please God!"

"No bold talk," said I. "You may do that after." I bade Jem Bottles load his pistols and carry them handy, but to keep them well concealed. Paddy preferred to campaign with only a stout stick. I took one pistol, and of course my sword.

These preparations deeply stirred Jem Bottles and Paddy.

"Your honour," said Paddy, "if I see a man pulling you by the leg when you would be climbing the tree, may I hit him one lick?"

"Aye," growled Jem Bottles, "and if I get a pistol against his head, he'll find out the difference between gunpowder and sand."

"Stop," I cried. "You have the wrong idea entirely. This talk of carnage startles me and alarms me. Remember we are in London. In London even the smallest massacre arouses great excitement. There are to be no killings, and even no sound thrashings. It is all to be done with dainty gloves. Neither one of the pair of you looks fitted for the work, but I am obliged to make you serve by hook or crook. 'Tis too late to scour the country looking for good comrades. I must put up with you, since I can get no better."

They were well pleased at the prospect of spirited adventures, although

Paddy made some complaints because there was no chance of a great ogre whom he could assail. He wished to destroy a few giants in order to prove his loyalty to the cause. However, I soothed him out of this mood, showing him where he was mistaken, and presently we were all prepared and only waited for the coming of Doctor Chord.

When the little philosopher appeared, however, I must truly say that I fell back a-gasping. He had tied some sort of a red turban about his head, and pulled a black cocked hat down over it until his left eye was wickedly shaded. From beneath his sombre cloak a heavy scabbard protruded. "I have come; I am ready," said he in a deep voice.

"Bedad, you have!" cried I, sinking into a chair. "And why didn't a mob hang you on the road, little man? How did you reach here safely? London surely never could stand two glimpses of such a dangerous-looking pirate. You would give a sedan-chair the vapours."

He looked himself over ruefully. "'Tis a garb befitting the dangerous adventure upon which I engaged," said he, somewhat stiff in the lip.

"But let me make known to you," I cried, "that when a man wears a garb befitting his adventure he fails surely. He should wear something extraneous. When you wish to do something evil, you put on the coat of a parson. That is the clever way. But here you are looking like a gallows-bird of the greatest claim for the rope. Stop it; take off the red thing, tilt your hat until you look like a gentleman, and let us go to our adventure respectably."

"I was never more surprised in my life," said he sincerely. "I thought I was doing a right thing in thus arraying myself for an experience which cannot fail to be thrilling and mayhap deadly. However, I see you in your accustomed attire, and in the apparel of your men-servants I see no great change from yesterday. May I again suggest to you that the adventure upon which we proceed may be fraught with much danger?"

"A red rag around your temples marks no improvement in our risks," said I. "We will sally out as if we were off to a tea-party. When my father led the forlorn hope at the storming of Würstenhausenstaffenberg, he wore a lace collar, and he was a man who understood these matters. And I may say that I wish he was here. He would be a great help."

In time the Doctor removed his red turban and gradually and sadly emerged from the more sanguine part of his paraphernalia and appeared as a simple little philosopher. Personally I have no objection to a man looking like a brigand, but my father always contended that clothes serve no purpose in real warfare. Thus I felt I had committed no great injustice in depriving Chord of his red turban.

We set out. I put much faith in the fact that we had no definite plans, but to my great consternation Doctor Chord almost at once began to develop well-laid schemes. As we moved toward the scene of our adventure he remarked them to me.

"First of all," said he, "a strong party should be stationed at the iron gates, not only to prevent a sally of the garrison, but to prevent an intrepid retainer from escaping and alarming the city. Furthermore—"

"My gallant warrior," said I, interrupting him, "we will drop this question to the level of a humdrum commercial age. I will try to compass my purpose by the simple climbing of a tree, and to that end all I could need from you is a stout lift and a good word. Then we proceed in the established way of making signs over a wall. All this I explained to you fully. I would not have you think I am about to bombard my lady-love's house."

With a countenance of great mournfulness he grumbled: "No fascines have been prepared."

"Very good," said I. "I will climb the tree without the aid of fascines."

As luck would have it, there was a little inn not very far from the Earl's house and on the lonely avenue lined with oaks. Here I temporarily left Jem Bottles and Paddy, for I feared their earnestness, which was becoming more terrible every minute. In order to keep them pacified I gave instructions that they should keep a strict watch up the avenue, and if they saw any signs of trouble they were to come a-running and do whatever I told them. These orders suggested serious business to their minds, and so they were quite

214

content. Their great point was that if a shindy was coming they had a moral right to be mixed up in it.

Doctor Chord and I strolled carelessly under the oaks. It was still too early for Lady Mary's walk in the garden, and there was an hour's waiting to be worn out. In the mean time I was moved to express some of my reflections.

"'Tis possible—nay, probable—that this is a bootless quest," said I dejectedly. "What shadow of an assurance have I that Lady Mary will walk in the garden on this particular morning? This whole thing is absolute folly."

"At any rate," said the Doctor, "now that you already have walked this great distance, it will be little additional trouble to climb a tree."

He had encouraged me to my work at exactly the proper moment.

"You are right," said I, taking him warmly by the hand, "I will climb the tree in any case."

As the hour approached we began to cast about for the proper oak. I am sure they were all the same to me, but Doctor Chord was very particular.

"'Tis logical to contend," said he, "that the question of the girth of the tree will enter importantly into our devices. For example, if a tree be so huge that your hands may not meet on the far side of it, a successful ascension will be impossible. On the other hand, a very slim tree is like to bend beneath your weight, and even precipitate you heavily to the ground, which disaster might retard events for an indefinite period."

"Science your science, then," said I. "And tell me what manner of tree best suits the purpose of a true lover."

"A tree," said the Doctor, "is a large vegetable arising with one woody stem to a considerable height. As to the appearance and quality of a tree, there are many diversifications, and this fact in itself constitutes the chief reason for this vegetable being of such great use to the human family. Ships are made of nought but trees, and if it were not for ships we would know but little of the great world of which these English islands form less than a half. Asia itself is slightly larger than all Scotland, and if it were not for the ships we would be like to delude ourselves with the idea that we and our neighbours formed the major part of the world."

With such wise harangues the Doctor entertained my impatience until it was time for me to climb a tree. And when this time came I went at my work without discussion or delay.

"There," said I resolutely, "I will climb this one if it kills me."

I seized the tree; I climbed. I will not say there was no groaning and puffing, but any how I at last found myself astride of a branch and looking over the wall into the Earl of Westport's garden.

But I might have made myself less labour and care by having somebody paint me a large landscape of this garden and surveyed it at my leisure. There I was high in a tree, dangling my legs, and staring at smooth lawns, ornamental copses, and brilliant flower-beds without even so much as a dog to enliven the scene. "O'Ruddy," said I to myself after a long time, "you've hung yourself here in mid-air like a bacon to a rafter, and I'll not say much to you now. But if you ever reach the ground without breaking your neck, I'll have a word with you, for my feelings are sorely stirred."

I do not know how long I sat in the tree engaged in my bitter meditation. But finally I heard a great scudding of feet near the foot of the tree, and I then saw the little Doctor bolting down the road like a madman, his hat gone, his hair flying, while his two coat-tails stuck out behind him straight as boards.

My excitement and interest in my ally's flight was so great that I near fell from my perch. It was incomprehensible that my little friend could dust the road at such speed. He seemed only to touch the ground from time to time. In a moment or two he was literally gone, like an arrow shot from the bow.

But upon casting my bewildered glance downward I found myself staring squarely into the mouth of a blunderbuss. The mouth of this blunderbuss, I may say, was of about the width of a fair-sized water-pitcher; in colour it was bright and steely. Its appearance attracted me to such an extent that I lost all idea of the man behind the gun. But presently I heard a grim, slow voice say,—

216

"Climb down, ye thief."

The reason for little Doctor Chord's hasty self-removal from the vicinity was now quite clear, and my interest in his departure was no longer speculative.

CHAPTER XXIV

Climb down, ye thief," said the grim, slow voice again. I looked once more into the mouth of the blunderbuss. I decided to climb. If I had had my two feet square on the ground, I would have taken a turn with this man, artillery or no artillery, to see if I could get the upper hand of him. But neither I nor any of my ancestors could ever fight well in trees. Foliage incommodes us. We like a clear sweep for the arm, and everything on a level space, and neither man in a tree. However, a sensible man holds no long discussions with a blunderbuss. I slid to the ground, arriving in a somewhat lacerated state. I thereupon found that the man behind the gun was evidently some kind of keeper or gardener. He had a sour face deeply chiselled with mean lines, but his eyes were very bright, the lighter parts of them being steely blue, and he rolled the pair of them from behind his awful weapon.

"And for whom have you mistaken me, rascal?" I cried as soon as I had come ungracefully to the ground and found with whom I had to deal.

"Have mistaken ye for naught," replied the man proudly. "Ye be the thief of the French pears, ye be."

"French pears—French—French what?" I cried.

"Ay, ye know full well," said he, "and now ye'll just march."

Seeing now plainly that I was in the hands of one of Lord Westport's gardeners, who had mistaken me for some garden-thief for whom he had been on the look-out, I began to expostulate very pointedly. But always this man stolidly faced me with the yawning mouth of the blunderbuss.

"And now ye'll march," said he, and despite everything I marched. I marched myself through the little door in the wall, and into the gardens of the Earl of Westport. And the infernal weapon was clamped against the small of my back.

But still my luck came to me even then, like basket falling out of a blue sky. As, in obedience to my captor's orders, I rounded a bit of shrubbery, I came face to face with Lady Mary. I stopped so abruptly that the rim of the on-coming blunderbuss must have printed a fine pink ring on my back. I lost all intelligence. I could not speak. I only knew that I stood before the woman I loved, while a man firmly pressed the muzzle of a deadly firearm between my shoulder-blades. I flushed with shame, as if I really had been guilty of stealing the French pears.

Lady Mary's first look upon me was one of pure astonishment. Then she quickly recognized the quaint threat expressed in the attitude of the blunderbuss.

"Strammers," she cried, rushing forward, "what would you be doing to the gentleman?"

"'Tis no gentleman, your la'ship," answered the man confidently. "He be a low-born thief o' pears, he be."

"Strammers!" she cried again, and wrested the blunderbuss from his hands. I will confess that my back immediately felt easier.

"And now, sir," she said, turning to me haughtily, "you will please grant me an explanation of to what my father is indebted for this visit to his private grounds?"

But she knew; no fool of a gardener and a floundering Irishman could keep pace with the nimble wits of a real woman. I saw the pink steal over her face, and she plainly appeared not to care for an answer to her peremptory question. However, I made a grave reply which did not involve the main situation.

"Madam may have noticed a certain deluded man with a bell-mouthed howitzer," said I. "His persuasions were so pointed and emphatic that I was induced to invade these gardens, wherein I have been so unfortunate as to disturb a lady's privacy,—a thing which only causes me the deepest regret."

"He be a pear-thief," grumbled Strammers from a distance. "Don't ye take no word o' his, your la'ship, after me bringing 'im down from out a tree."

"From out a tree?" said Lady Mary, and she looked at me, and I looked at her.

"The man is right, Lady Mary," said I significantly. "I was in a tree looking over the garden wall."

"Strammers," said she with decision, "wait for me in the rose-garden, and speak no single word to anybody until I see you again. You have made a great mistake."

The man obediently retired, after saluting me with an air of slightly dubious apology. He was not yet convinced that I had not been after his wretched French pears.

But with the withdrawal of this Strammers Lady Mary's manner changed. She became frightened and backed away from me, still holding the gardener's blunderbuss.

"O sir," she cried in a beautiful agitation, "I beg of you to leave at once. Oh, please!"

But here I saw it was necessary to treat the subject in a bold Irish way.

"I'll not leave, Lady Mary," I answered. "I was brought here by force, and only force can make me withdraw."

A glimmer of a smile came to her face, and she raised the blunderbuss, pointing it full at my breast. The mouth was still the width of a water-jug, and in the fair inexperienced hands of Lady Mary it was like to go off at any moment and blow a hole in me as big as a platter.

"Charming mistress," said I, "shoot!"

For answer she suddenly flung the weapon to the grass, and, burying her face in her hands, began to weep. "I'm afraid it's l-l-loaded," she sobbed out.

In an instant I was upon my knees at her side and had taken her hand. Her fingers resisted little, but she turned away her head.

"Lady Mary," said I softly, "I'm a poor devil of an Irish adventurer,

220

but—I love you! I love you so that if I was dead you could bid me rise! I am a worthless fellow; I have no money, and my estate you can hardly see for the mortgages and trouble upon it; I am no fine suitor, but I love you more than them all; I do, upon my life!"

"Here approaches Strammers in quest of his blunderbuss," she answered calmly. "Perhaps we had better give it to him."

I sprang to my feet, and, sure enough, the thick-headed ninepin of a gardener was nearing us.

"Don't ye trust 'im, your la'ship!" he cried. "I caught 'im in a tree, I did, and he be a bad lot!"

Lady Mary quelled him, and he at once went away with his blunderbuss, still muttering his many doubts. But still one cannot drop a love declaration and pick it up again with the facility of a tailor resuming his work on a waistcoat. One can't say: "Where was I? How far had I gone before this miserable interruption came?" In a word I found mysef stammering and stuttering and wasting moments too precious for words.

"Lady Mary—" I began. "Lady Mary—I love you, Lady Mary! Lady Mary—"

It was impossible for me to depart from this rigmarole and express the many things with which my heart was full. It was a maddening tongue-tie. The moments seemed for me the crisis of my existence, and yet I could only say, "Lady Mary, I love you!" I know that in many cases this statement has seemed to be sufficient, but as a matter of fact I was full of things to say, and it was plain to me that I was losing everything through the fact that my silly tongue clung to the roof of my mouth.

I do not know how long the agony endured, but at any rate it was ended by a thunderous hammering upon the little door in the garden-wall. A high Irish voice could be heard:

"And if ye be not leaving him out immediately, we will be coming over the wall if it is ten thousand feet high, ye murdering rogues."

Lady Mary turned deadly pale. "Oh, we are lost," she cried.

I saw at once that the interview was ended. If I remained doughtily I remained stupidly. I could come back some other day. I clutched Lady Mary's hand and kissed it. Then I ran for the door in the garden wall. In a moment I was out, and I heard her frantically bolting the door behind me.

I confronted Paddy and Jem. Jem had in his hands a brace of pistols which he was waving determinedly. Paddy was wetting his palms and resolutely swinging a club. But when they saw me their ferocity gave way to an outburst of affectionate emotion. I had to assert all my mastership to keep Paddy from singing. He would sing. Sure, if they had never heard an Irish song it was time they did.

"Paddy," said I, "my troubles are on me. I wish to be thinking. Remain quiet."

Presently we reached the little inn, and from there the little Doctor Chord flew out like a hawk at a sparrow.

"I thought you were dead," he shouted wildly. "I thought you were dead."

"No," said I, "I am not dead, but I am very thirsty." And, although they were murmuring this thing and that thing, I would have no word with them until I was led to the parlour of the inn and given a glass.

"Now," said I, "I penetrated to the garden and afterwards I came away and I can say no more."

The little Doctor was very happy and proud.

"When I saw the man with the blunderbuss," he recounted, "I said boldly: 'Sirrah, remove that weapon! Exclude it from the scene! Eliminate it from the situation!' But his behaviour was extraordinary. He trained the weapon in such a manner that I myself was in danger of being eliminated from the situation. I instantly concluded that I would be of more benefit to the cause if I temporarily abandoned the vicinity and withdrew to a place where the climatic conditions were more favourable to prolonged terms of human existence."

"I saw you abandoning the vicinity," said I, "and I am free to declare that I never saw a vicinity abandoned with more spirit and finish."

"I thank you for your appreciation," said the Doctor simply. Then he leaned to my ear and whispered, barring his words from Jem and Paddy, who stood respectfully near our chairs. "And the main object of the expedition?" he asked. "Was there heavy firing and the beating down of doors? And I hope you took occasion to slay the hideous monster who flourished the blunderbuss? Imagine my excitement after I had successfully abandoned the vicinity! I was trembling with anxiety for you. Still, I could adopt no steps which would not involve such opportunities for instant destruction that the thought of them brought to mind the most horrible ideas. I pictured myself lying butchered, blown to atoms by a gardener's blunderbuss. Then the spirit of self-sacrifice arose in me, and, as you know, I sent your two servants to your rescue."

The little man was looking through the window at this moment. Suddenly he started back, flinging up his hands.

"My soul, he is again upon us," he cried.

I hastily followed his glance, and saw the man Strammers making peaceful way toward the inn. Apparently he was going to the taproom for an early pint. The Doctor flurried and dove until I checked him in fear that he would stand on his head in the fireplace.

"No," said I, "calm yourself. There will be no blunderbusses. On the other hand, I see here a great chance for a master-stroke. Be quiet now, and try to hold yourself in a chair and see me deal with the situation. When it comes to a thing like this, it is all child's play for me. Paddy," said I. "Jem," said I, "there is a gardener in the taproom. Go and become his warm friends. You know what I mean. A tuppence here and there won't matter. But, of course, always treat him with the profound consideration which is due to so distinguished a gardener."

They understood me at once and grinned. But even then I was struck with their peculiar reasons for understanding at once. Jem Bottles understood at once because he had been a highwayman; Paddy understood at once because he was an Irishman. One had been all his life a rogue; the other had been born on an intelligent island. And so they comprehended me with equal facility.

They departed on their errand, and when I turned I found myself in the clutches of a maddened Doctor Chord.

"Monster," he screamed, "you have ordered him to be killed!"

"Whist," said I, "it would never do to order him to be killed. He is too valuable."

CHAPTER XXV

You appear more at your ease when you are calm," said I to the Doctor as I squashed him into a chair. "Your ideas of murder are juvenile. Gardeners are murdered only by other gardeners, over some question of a magnolia-tree. Gentlemen of position never murder gardeners."

"You are right, sir," he responded frankly. "I see my mistake. But really, I was convinced that something dreadful was about to happen. I am not familiar with the ways of your nationality, sir, and when you gave the resolute directions to your men it was according to my education to believe that something sinister was at hand, although no one could regret more than I that I have made this foolish mistake."

"No," said I, "you are not familiar with the ways of my nationality, and it will require an indefinite number of centuries to make your country-men understand the ways of my nationality; and when they do they will only pretend that after great research they have discovered something very evil indeed. However, in this detail, I am able to instruct you fully. The gardener will not be murdered. His fluency with a blunderbuss was very annoying, but in my opinion it was not so fluent as to merit death."

"I confess," said Doctor Chord, "that all peoples save my own are great rascals and natural seducers. I cannot change this national conviction, for I have studied politics as they are known in the King's Parliament, and it has been thus proved to me."

"However, the gardener is not to be murdered," said I, "and although I am willing to cure you in that particular ignorance I am not willing to take up your general cure as a life work. A glass of wine with you."

After we had adjusted this slight misunderstanding we occupied our seats comfortably before the fire. I wished to give Paddy and Jem plenty of time to conciliate Strammers, but I must say that the wait grew irksome. Finally I arose and went into the corridor and peered into the taproom. There were Paddy and Jem with their victim, the three of them seated affectionately in a row on a bench, drinking from quart pots of ale. Paddy was clapping the gardener on the shoulder.

"Strammers," he cried, "I am thinking more of you than of my cousin Mickey, who was that gay and that gallant it would make you wonder, although I am truthful in saying they killed him for the peace of the parish. But he had the same bold air with him, and devil the girl in the country-side but didn't know who was the lad for her."

Strammers seemed greatly pleased, but Jem Bottles evinced deep disapproval of Paddy's Celtic methods.

"Let Master Strammers be," said he. "He be a-wanting a quiet draught. Let him have his ale with no talking here and there."

"Ay," said Strammers, now convinced that he was a great man and a philosopher, "a quiet draught o' old ale be a good thing."

"True for you, Master Strammers," cried Paddy enthusiastically. "It is in the way of being a good thing. There you are now. Ay, that's it. A good thing! Sure."

"Ay," said Strammers, deeply moved by this appreciation, which he had believed should always have existed. "Ay, I spoke well."

"Well would be no name for it," responded Paddy fervidly. "By gor, and I wish you were knowing Father Corrigan. He would be the only man to near match you. 'A quiet draught o' old ale is a good thing,' says you, and by the piper 'tis hard to say Father Corrigan could have done it that handily. 'Tis you that are a wonderful man."

"I have a small way o' my own," said Strammers, "which even some of the best gardeners has accounted most wise and humorous. The power o' good speech be a great gift." Whereupon the complacent Strammers lifted his arm and buried more than half his face in his quart pot.

"It is," said Paddy earnestly. "And I'm doubting if even the best gardeners would be able to improve it. And says you: 'A quiet draught o' old ale is a good thing,' 'Twould take a grand gardener to beat that word."

"And besides the brisk way of giving a word now and then," continued the deluded Strammers, "I am a great man with flowers. Some of the finest beds in London are there in my master's park."

"Are they so?" said Paddy. "I would be liking to see them."

"And ye shall," cried the gardener with an outburst of generous feeling. "So ye shall. On a Sunday we may stroll quietly and decently in the gardens, and ye shall see."

Seeing that Paddy and Jem were getting on well with the man, I returned to Doctor Chord.

"'Tis all right," said I. "They have him in hand. We have only to sit still, and the whole thing is managed."

Later I saw the three men in the road, Paddy and Jem embracing the almost tearful Strammers. These farewells were touching. Afterward my rogues appeared before me, each with a wide grin.

"We have him," said Paddy, "and 'tis us that has an invitation to come inside the wall next Sunday. 'I have some fine flowers in the gardens,' said he. 'Have you so?' said I. 'Well, then, 'tis myself will be breaking your head if you don't leave us inside to see them.' 'Master Paddy,' said he, 'you are a gentleman, or if not you are very like one, and you and your handsome friend, Master Jem, as well as another friend or two, is welcome to see the gardens whenever I can make certain the master and mistress is out.' And with that I told him he could go home."

"You are doing well," I said, letting the scoundrel see in my face that I believed his pleasant tale, and he was so pleased that he was for going on and making a regular book out of it. But I checked him. "No," said I. "I am fearing that I would become too much interested and excited. I am satisfied with what you've been telling me. 'Twas more to my mind to have beaten that glass-eyed man, but we have taken the right course. And now we will be returning to where we lodge."

During the walk back to the "Pig and Turnip" Doctor Chord took it upon himself to discourse in his usual style upon the recent events. "Of course, sir, I would care to hear of the tragic scenes which must have transpired soon after I—I—"

"Abandoned the vicinity?" said I.

"Precisely," he responded. "Although I was not in the exact neighbourhood during what must have been a most tempestuous part of your adventure, I can assure you I had lost none of my former interest in the affair."

"I am believing you," said I; "but let us talk now more of the future. I am much absorbed in the future. It appears to me that it will move at a rapid pace."

I did not tell him about my meeting with Lady Mary, because I knew, if occasion arose, he would spread the news over half London. No consideration would have been great enough to bridle the tongue of the little gossip from use of the first bit of news which he had ever received warm from the fire. Besides, after his behaviour in front of the enemy, I was quite certain that an imparting of my news could do nothing in the way of impairing his inefficiency. Consequently it was not necessary to trouble him with dramatic details.

"As to the part of the adventure which took place in the garden, you are consistently silent, I observe, sir," said the Doctor.

"I am," said I. "I come of a long line of silent ancestors. My father was particularly notable in this respect."

"And yet, sir," rejoined the Doctor, "I had gained an impression that your father was quite willing to express himself in a lofty and noble manner on such affairs as attracted his especial notice."

"He was that," said I, pleased. "He was indeed. I am only wishing I had his talent for saying all that was in his mind so fast that even the priest could not keep up with him, and goodness knows Father Donovan was no small talker."

228

"You prove to me the limitations of science, sir," said he. "Although I think I may boast of some small education of a scientific nature, I think I will require some time for meditation and study before I will be able to reconcile your last two statements."

"'Tis no matter," I cried amiably. "Let it pass."

For the rest of that week there was conference following conference at the "Pig and Turnip" and elsewhere. My three companions were now as eager as myself for the advent of the critical Sunday when I, with Paddy and Jem, were to attempt our visit to Strammers's flower-gardens. I had no difficulty in persuading the Doctor that his services would be invaluable at another place; for the memory of the blunderbuss seemed to linger with him. I had resolved to disguise myself slightly, for I had no mind to have complications arising from this gardener's eyes. I think a little disguise is plenty unless one stalks mysteriously and stops and peers here and there. A little unostentatious minding of one's own affairs is a good way to remain undiscovered. Then nobody looks at you and demands: "Who is this fellow?" My father always said that when he wished to disguise himself he dressed as a common man, and although this gained him many a hard knock of the fist and blow of the stick from people who were really his inferiors, he found his disguise was perfection. However, my father only disguised when on some secret mission from King Louis, for it does not become a gentleman to accept a box on the ears from anybody unless it is in the service of his sovereign.

I remember my father saying also these tours as a common man taught him he must ever afterward ride carefully through the streets of villages and towns. He was deeply impressed by the way in which men, women, and children had to scud for their lives to keep from under the hoofs of the chargers of these devil-may-care gentlemen who came like whirlwinds through narrow crowded streets. He himself often had to scramble for his life, he said.

However, that was many years back, and I did not fear any such adventures in my prospective expedition. In such a case I would have trembled for what might happen. I have no such philosophy of temper as had my father. I might take the heel of a gay cavalier and throw him out of the saddle, and then there would be a fine uproar. However, I am quite convinced that it is always best to dodge. A good dodger seldom gets into trouble in this world, and lives to a green old age, while the noble patriot and others of his kind die in dungeons. I remember an honest man who set out to reform the parish in the matter of drink. They took him and—but, no matter; I must be getting on with the main tale.

CHAPTER XXVI

On Saturday night I called the lads to my room and gave them their final instructions.

"Now, you rogues," said I to them, "let there be no drinking this night, and no trapesing of the streets, getting your heads broke just at the critical moment; for, as my father used to say, although a broken head is merrily come by, a clear head's worth two of it when business is to be transacted. So go to your beds at once, the two of you, if there's any drinking to be done, troth it's myself that'll attend to it."

With that I drove them out and sat down to an exhilarating bottle, without ever a thought of where the money was to come from to pay for it. It is one of the advantages of a public house frequented by the nobility that if you come to it with a bold front, and one or two servants behind your back, you have at least a clear week ahead before they flutter the show of a bill at you and ask to see the colour of your gold in exchange for their ink and paper.

My father used to say that a gentleman with money in his pocket might economize and no disgrace to him; but when stomach and purse are both empty, go to the best house in the town, where they will feed you, and lodge you, and drink you, before asking questions. Indeed I never shed many salt tears over the losses of a publican, for he shears so closely those sheep that have plenty of wool that he may well take care of an innocent lamb like myself, on which the crop is not yet grown.

I was drinking quietly and thinking deeply on the wisdom of my father, who knew the world better than ever his son will know it, when there was an unexpected knock at the door, and in walked Doctor Chord. I was not too pleased to see the little man, for I had feared he had changed his mind and wanted to come with us in the morning, and his company was something I had no desire for. He was a coward in a pinch, and a distrustful man in peace, ever casting doubt on the affection I was sure sometimes that Lady Mary held for me; and if he wasn't talking about that, sure he went rambling on,—great discourses on science which held little interest for a young man so deeply in love as I was. The proper study of mankind is womankind, said a philosopher that my father used to quote with approval, but whose name I'm forgetting at this moment. Nevertheless I welcomed the little Doctor and said to him:

"Draw you up a chair, and I'll draw out a cork."

The little man sat him down, and I placed an open bottle nice and convenient to his elbow.

Whether it was the prospect of good wine, or the delight of better company, or the thought of what was going to happen on the morrow, I could not tell; but it seemed to me the little Doctor laboured under a great deal of excitement, and I became more and more afraid that he would insist on bearing us company while the Earl and the Countess were away at church. Now it was enough to have on my hands two such models of stupidity as Paddy and Jem without having to look after Doctor Chord as well, and him glancing his eyes this way and that in apprehension of a blunderbuss.

"Have you made all your plans, O'Ruddy?" he inquired, setting down his cup a good deal emptier than when he lifted it.

"I have," said I.

"Are you entirely satisfied with them?" he continued.

"My plans are always perfect plans," I replied to him, "and trouble only comes in the working of them. When you have to work with such raw material as I have to put up with, the best of plans have the unlucky habit of turning round and hitting you in the eye."

"Do you expect to be hit in the eye to-morrow?" asked the Doctor, very excited, which was shown by the rattle of the bottle against the lip of his cup.

"I'm only sure of one thing for to-morrow," said I, "and that is the certainty that if there's blunder to be made one or other of my following will make it. Still, I'm not complaining, for it's good to be certain of something."

"What's to be your mode of procedure?" said the Doctor, giving me a

232

touch of his fine language.

"We wait in the lane till the church bells have stopped ringing, then Paddy and Jem go up to the little door in the wall, and Paddy knocks nice and quietly, in the expectation that the door will be opened as quietly by Strammers, and thereupon Jem and Paddy will be let in."

"But won't ye go in with them?" inquired the little Doctor very hurriedly.

"Doctor Chord," said I, lifting up my cup, "I have the honour to drink wine with you, and to inform you that it's myself that's outlining the plan."

"I beg your pardon for interrupting," said the Doctor; then he nodded to me as he drank.

"My two villains will go in alone with Strammers, and when the door is bolted, and they have passed the time of day with each other, Paddy will look around the garden and exclaim how it excels all the gardens that ever was, including that of Eden; and then Jem will say what a pity it was they couldn't have their young friend outside to see the beauty of it. It is my expectation that Strammers will rise to this, and request the pleasure of their young friend's company; but if he hesitates Paddy will say that the young friend outside is a free-handed Irishman who would no more mind a shilling going from his pocket into that of another man than he would the crooking of an elbow when a good drink is to be had. But be that as it may, they're to work me in through the little door by the united diplomacy of England and Ireland, and, once inside of the walls, it is my hope that I can slip away from them and see something of the inside of the house as well."

"And you have the hope that you'll find Lady Mary in the withdrawing-room," said the Doctor.

"I'll find her," says I, "if she's in the house; for I'm going from room to room on a tour of inspection to see whether I'll buy the mansion or not."

"It's a very good plan," said the Doctor, drawing the back of his hand across his lips. "It's a very good plan," he repeated, nodding his head several times.

"Now, by the Old Head of Kinsale, little man," said I, "what do you mean by that remark and that motion of the head? What's wrong with the plan?"

"The plan's a good one, as I have said," reiterated the Doctor. But I saw there was something on his mind, and told him so, urging him to be out with it.

"Do you think," said I, "that Lady Mary will be in church with her father and mother?"

"I do not," muttered the Doctor, cautiously bringing his voice down to a whisper; "but I want to warn you that there's danger here in this room while you're lurking around my Earl's palace."

"How can danger harm me here when I am somewhere else?" I asked.

A very mysterious manner fell upon the little man, and he glanced, one after the other, at the four corners of the room, as if he heard a mouse moving and wanted to detect it. Then he looked sternly at the door, and I thought he was going to peer up the chimney, but instead he leaned across the table and said huskily,—

"The papers!"

"What papers?" I asked, astonished.

"Your thoughts are so intent on the young lady that you forget everything else. Have you no recollection of the papers the Earl of Westport is so anxious to put himself in possession of?"

I leaned back in my chair and gazed steadily at Chord; but his eyes would not bring themselves to meet mine, and so he made some pother about filling up his cup again, with the neck of the bottle trembling on the edge, as if its teeth were chattering.

Now my father used to say when a man is afraid to meet your eye, be prepared to have him meet your fist. I disremembered saying anything to the Doctor about these same papers, which, truth to tell, I had given but little thought to recently, with other things of more importance to crowd them out of mind.

"How come you to know anything about the papers?" I said at last.

"Oh, your memory is clean leaving you!" cried the little Doctor, as if the cup of wine he drank had brought back his courage to him. "You told me all about the papers when we were in Kensington Gardens."

"If I did," says I, "then I must have further informed you that I gave them as a present to Lady Mary herself. Surely I told you that?"

"You told me that, of course; but I thought you said they had come back into your possession again. If I'm wrong, it's no matter at all, and there's nothing to be said about them. I'm merely speaking to you by way of a friend, and I thought if you had the papers here in your room it was very unsafe to leave them unprotected by yourself or some one you can trust. I was just speaking as your well-wisher, for I don't want to hear you crying you are robbed, and us at our wit's end not getting either the thief or the booty."

He spoke with great candour and good humour, and the only thing that made me suspicious at first was that for the life of me I could not ever remember mentioning the papers to him, yet it was very likely that I did; for, as my father used to say, an Irishman talks more than the recording angel can set down in his busiest day, and therefore it is lucky that everything he says is not held against him. It seemed to me that we talked more of scandal than of papers in the park, but still I might be mistaken.

"Very good, Doctor," I cried, genially. "The papers it is, and, true for you, the Earl would like to get his old claws on them. Have you any suggestions to make?"

"Well, it seems to me, O'Ruddy, that if the Earl got wind of them it would be the easiest thing in the world to have your apartment rifled during your absence."

"That is true enough," I agreed, "so what would you do about the papers if you were in my boots?"

"If I had a friend I could trust," said Doctor Chord slowly, "I would give the papers to him and tell him to take good care of them."

"But why not carry them about in my own pocket?" I asked.

"It seemed to me they were not any too safe last time they were there," said the Doctor, pleasantly enough. "You see, O'Ruddy, you're a marked man if once the Earl gets wind of your being in town. To carry the papers about on your own person would be the unsafest thing you could do, ensuring you a stab in the back, so that little use you'd have for the papers ever after. I have no desire to be mixed further in your affairs than I am at the present moment, but nevertheless I could easily take charge of the packet for you; then you would know where it was."

"But would I be sure to know where you were?" said I, my first suspicion of him returning to me.

The little Doctor laughed.

"I am always very easily found," he said; "but when I offered to take the papers it was merely in case a stranger like yourself should not have a faster friend beside him than I am. If you have any such, then I advise you to give custody of the papers to him."

"I have no real friend in London that I know of," said I, "but Paddy."

"The very thing," cried the Doctor, joyously, at once putting to rest all my doubts concerning him. "The very thing. I would give the papers to Paddy and tell him to protect them with his life. I'm sure he'll do it, and you'll know where to find both them and him when you want them. But to go away from the 'Pig and Turnip' right across to the other end of the town, taking your two servants with you, leaving nobody to guard papers that are of importance to you, strikes me as the height of folly. I'll just fill up another cup, and so bid you good-night, and good luck for the morrow."

And with that the little man drained the bottle, taking his leave with great effusion, and begging my pardon for even so much as mentioning the papers, saying they had been on his mind for the last day or two, and, feeling friendly toward me, he wished to warn me not to leave them carelessly about.

After he left I thought a good deal about what the Doctor had said, and I wondered at myself that I had ever misdoubted him; for, although he was a man given greatly to talk, yet he had been exceedingly friendly with me from the very first night I had met him, and I thought shame of myself that I was losing trust in my fellow man here in this great city of London, because in Ireland we trust each other entirely; and indeed we are under some compulsion in that same matter, for there is so little money about that if you do not take a man's word now and then there's nothing else for you to take.

CHAPTER XXVII

I slept well that night, and it was broad daylight when I awoke. A most beautiful morning it seemed to me, and just the time for a lonely stroll in the beautiful gardens, so long as there was some one with you that you thought a great deal of. I made a good breakfast, and then took out the papers and placed them on the table before me. They were all safe so far. I could not comprehend how the Earl would know anything of my being in London, unless, indeed, he caught sight of me walking in his own gardens with his own daughter, and then, belike, he was so jealous a man that he would maybe come to the conclusion I was in London as well as himself.

After breakfast Paddy and Jem came in, looking as bold as Blarney Castle; and when I eyed them both I saw that neither one nor the other was a fit custodian for papers that might make the proudest Earl in England a poor man or a rich man, depending which way they went. So I put the documents in my own pocket without more ado, and gave up my thoughts to a pleasanter subject. I changed my mind about a disguise, and put on my back the best clothes that I had to wear. I wished I had the new suits I had been measured for, but the spalpeen of a tailor would not let me have them unless I paid him some of the money they cost. When I came to think over it I saw that Strammers would surely never recognize me as a gay spark of fashion when he had merely seen me once before, torn and ragged, coming down from a tree on top of his blunderbuss. So I instructed Paddy to say that he and Jem were servants of the best master in the world, who was a great lover of gardens; that he was of immense generosity, and if Strammers allowed him to come into the gardens by the little door he would be a richer man when the door was opened than he would be if he kept it shut. I had been long enough in London to learn the golden method of persuasion; any how I could not bring myself to the chance of meeting with my lady, and me dressed worse than one of her own servants.

We were all in the lane when the church bells ceased to ring, and if any one had seen us he would simply have met a comely young Irish gentleman taking the air of a Sunday morning with two faithful servants at his heels. I allowed something like ten impatient minutes to crawl past me, and then, as the lane was clear and every one for the church within its walls, I tipped a nod to Paddy, and he, with Jem by his side, tapped lightly at the door, while I stood behind the trunk of the tree up which I had climbed before. There was no sign of Doctor Chord in the vicinity, and for that I was thankful, because up to the last moment I feared the little man could not help intruding himself on what was somebody else's business.

The door was opened with some caution, letting Paddy and Jem enter; then it was closed, and I heard the bolts shot into their places. But I was speedily to hear more than bolts that Sunday morning. There was a sound of thumping sticks, and I heard a yell that might well have penetrated to the "Pig and Turnip" itself, although it was miles away. I knew Paddy's cry, and next there came some good English cursing from Jem Bottles, while a shrill voice called out:—

"Catch the red-haired one; he's the villain we want!"

In the midst of various exclamations, maledictions, and other constructions of speech, mingled, I thought, with laughter, I flung my shoulder against the door, but I might as well have tried to batter down the wall itself. The door was as firm as Macgillicuddy Reeks. I know when I am beat as well as the next man, and, losing no more time there, I ran as fast as I could along the wall, out of the lane, and so to the front of the house. The main entrance was protected by great gates of wrought iron, which were opened on occasion by a man in a little cubby of a cabin that stood for a porter's lodge. The man wasn't there, and the gates were locked; but part of one of the huge wings of wrought iron was a little gate that stood ajar. This I pushed open, and, unmolested, stepped inside.

The trees and shrubbery hid from me the scene that was taking place inside the little wooden door. I dashed through the underbrush and came to the edge of a broad lawn, and there was going on as fine a scrimmage as any man could wish to see. Jem Bottles had his back against the wooden door, and was laying about him with a stout stick; half a dozen tall fellows in livery making a great show of attack, but keeping well out of range of his weapon. Poor Paddy had the broad of his back on the turf, and it looked like they were trying to tear the clothes off him, for another half-dozen were on top of him; but I can say this in his favour, Paddy was using his big feet and doing great execution with them. Every now and then he planted a boot in the well-fed front of a footman or under-gardener, and sent him flying. The whole household seemed to be present, and one could hardly believe there was such a mob in a single mansion. The Earl of Westport was there, and who stood beside him but that little villain, Doctor Chord.

But it was the Countess herself that was directing operations. She had an ebony stick in her hands, and when Paddy kicked one of her underlings the vigorous old lady smote the overturned servant to make him to the fray again. It was an exciting scene, and Donnybrook was nothing to it. Their backs were all toward me, and I was just bubbling with joy to think what a surprise I was about to give them,—for I drew my sword and had a yell of defiance on my lips,—when a cry that nobody paid the least attention to turned my mind in another direction entirely.

One of the first-floor windows was open, and over the sill leaned Lady Mary herself, her face aflush with anger.

"Father! Mother!" she cried. "Are not you ashamed of yourselves, making this commotion on a Sunday morning? Call the servants away from there! Let the two poor men go! Oh, shame, shame upon you."

She wrung her hands, but, as I was saying, nobody paid the slightest heed to her, and I doubt if any of them heard her, for Paddy was not keeping silence by any manner of means. He was taking the worst of all the blows that fell on him in a vigorous outcry.

"Murther! murther!" he shouted. "Let me on me feet, an' I'll knock yez all into the middle of county Clare."

No one, however, took advantage of this generous offer, but they kept as clear as they could of his miscellaneous feet, and the Countess poked him in the ribs with the point of her ebony stick whenever she wasn't laying it over

240

the backs of her servants.

Now, no man can ever say that I was a laggard when a good old-fashioned contest was going on, and the less indolence was observable on my own part when friends of mine were engaged in the fray. Sure I was always eager enough, even when it was a stranger's debate, and I wonder what my father would think of me now, to see me veer from the straight course of battle and thrust my unstruck sword once more into its scabbard. It was the face in the window that made me forget friend and foe alike. Lady Mary was the only member of the household that was not on the lawn, and was protesting unheard against the violence to two poor men who were there because they had been invited to come by the under-gardener.

I saw in the twinkling of an eye that the house had been deserted on the first outcry. Doors were left wide open for the whole world to enter. I dodged behind the trees, scuttled up the gravelled driveway, leaped the stone steps three at a time, and before you could say "Ballymuggins" I was in the most superb hall in which I ever set my foot. It was a square house with the stairway in the middle. I kept in my mind's eye the direction of the window in which Lady Mary had appeared. Quick as a bog-trotter responds to an invitation to drink, I mounted that grand stairway, turned to my right, and came to a door opposite which I surmised was the window through which Lady Mary was leaning. Against this door I rapped my knuckles, and speedily I heard the sweet voice of the most charming girl in all the world demand with something like consternation in its tones,—

"Who is there?"

"It's me, Lady Mary!" said I. "The O'Ruddy, who begs the privilege of a word with you."

I heard the slam of a window being shut, then the sound of a light step across the floor, and after that she said with a catch in her voice,—

"I'll be pleased you should come in, Mr. O'Ruddy."

I tried the door, but found it locked.

"How can I come in, Lady Mary," says I, "if you've got bolts held against me?"

"There are no bolts," said Lady Mary; "the key should be on the outside. I am locked in. Look for the key and open the door."

Was ever a more delightful sentence spoken to a man? My heart was in my throat with joy. I glanced down, and there, sure enough, stuck the key. I turned it at once, then pulled it out of the lock and opened the door.

"Lady Mary," says I, "with your permission, it seems to me a door should be locked from the inside."

With that I thrust the key through the far side of the door, closed it, and locked it. Then I turned round to face her.

The room, it was plain to be seen, was the parlour of a lady,—a boudoir, as they call it in France, a word that my father was very fond of using, having caught it when he was on the campaign in that delightful country. The boudoir was full of confections and charming little dainties in the way of lace, and easy chairs, and bookcases, and little writing-desks, and a work-basket here and there; but the finest ornament it possessed was the girl who now stood in the middle of the floor with a frown on her brow that was most becoming. Yes, there was a frown on her brow, although I expected a smile on her lips because of the cordial invitation she had given me to come in.

It would seem to either you or me that if a lady suffered the indignity of being locked in her room, just as if she was a child of six years old, she would welcome with joy the person who came and released her. Now, my father, who was the wisest man since Solomon,—and indeed, as I listened to him, I've often thought that Solomon was overpraised,—my father used to say there was no mystery at all about women. "You just think," he would say, "of what a sensible man would do on a certain occasion; then configure out in your mind the very opposite, and that's what a woman will do." A man who had been imprisoned would have held out his hand and have said, "God bless you, O'Ruddy; but I'm glad to see you." And here stood this fine lady in the middle of her room, looking at me as if I were the dirt beneath her feet, and had forced my way into her presence, instead of being invited like a man of honour to enter.

"Well, Mr. O'Ruddy," she said, throwing back her head, haughty-like, "Why do you stand dallying in a lady's bower when your followers are being beaten on the lawn outside?"

I cannot give you Lady Mary's exact words, for I was so astonished at their utterance; but I give you a very good purport of them.

"Is it the beating of my men?" I said. "Troth, that's what I pay them for. And whoever gives them a good drubbing saves me the trouble. I saw they had Paddy down on the turf, but he's a son of the ould sod, and little he'll mind being thrown on his mother. But if it's Jem Bottles you're anxious about, truth to tell I'm more sorry for those that come within range of his stick than for Jem with his back to the wall. Bottles can take care of himself in any company, for he's a highwayman in an excellent way of business."

I always like to mention anything that's in favour of a man, and so I told her what profession Bottles followed. She gave a toss of her head, and gave me a look that had something like contempt in it, which was far from being pleasant to endure. Then she began walking up and down the room, and it was plain to see that my Lady was far from being pleased with me.

"Poor fellows! Poor faithful fellows! That's what comes of having a fool for a master."

"Indeed, your ladyship," said I, drawing myself up to my full height, which wasn't so very much short of the door itself, "there are worse things than blows from a good honest cudgel. You might better say, 'This is what comes to a master with two fools for servants.'"

"And what comes to a master?" she demanded. "Sure no one asks you to be here."

"That shows how short your ladyship's memory is," said I with some irritation. "Father Donovan used to tell me that the shortest thing in the world was the interval between an insult and a blow in Ireland, but I think a lady's memory is shorter still. 'Turn the key and come in,' says you. What is that, I would like to know, but an invitation."

It appeared to me that she softened a bit, but she continued her walk up and down the room and was seemingly in great agitation. The cries outside had stopped, but whether they had murdered both Jem Bottles and Paddy I had no means at that moment of knowing, and I hope the two will forgive me when I say that my thoughts were far from them.

"You will understand," said Lady Mary, speaking still with resentment in her voice, "that the papers you held are the key to the situation. Have you no more sense than to trust them to the care of a red-headed clown from whom they can be taken as easy as if they were picked up off the street?"

"Indeed, believe me, Lady Mary, that no red-headed clown has any papers of mine."

"Indeed, and I think you speak the true word there. The papers are now in my father's possession, and he will know how to take care of them."

"Well, he didn't know that the last time he had them," I cried, feeling angry at these unjust accusations, and not being able to bear the compliment to the old man, even if he was an Earl. "The papers," said I, "are as easily picked from me as from the street, like you were saying just now; but it isn't a pack of overfed flunkeys that will lift them from me. Lady Mary, on a previous occasion I placed the papers in your hands; now, with your kind permission, I lay them at your feet,"—and, saying this with the most courteous obeisance, I knelt with one knee on the floor and placed the packet of papers where I said I would place them.

Now, ever since that, the Lady Mary denies that she kicked them to the other end of the room. She says that as she was walking to and fro the toe of her foot touched the packet and sent it spinning; and, as no real Irishman ever yet contradicted a lady, all I will say is that the precious bundle went hurtling to the other end of the room, and it is very likely that Lady Mary thought the gesture of her foot a trifle too much resembled an action of her mother, the Countess, for her manner changed in the twinkling of an eye, and she laughed like her old self again.

"Mr. O'Ruddy," she said, "you put me out of all patience. You're as simple as if you came out of Ireland yesterday."

"It's tolerably well known," said I, "by some of your expert swordsmen, that I came out the day before."

Again Lady Mary laughed.

"You're not very wise in the choice of your friends," she said.

"I am, if I can count you as one of them," I returned.

She made no direct reply to this, but continued:

"Can't you see that that little Doctor Chord is a traitor? He has been telling my father all you have been doing and all you have been planning, and he says you are almost simple enough to have given the papers into his own keeping no longer ago than last night."

"Now, look you, Lady Mary, how much you misjudged me. The little villain asked for the papers, but he didn't get them; then he advised me to give them to a man I could trust, and when I said the only man I could trust was red-headed Paddy out yonder, he was delighted to think I was to leave them in his custody. But you can see for yourself I did nothing of the kind, and if your people thought they could get anything out of Paddy by bad language and heroic kicks they were mistaken."

At that moment we had an interruption that brought our conversation to a standstill and Lady Mary to the door, outside which her mother was crying,—

"Mary, Mary! where's the key?"

"Where should it be?" said Lady Mary, "but in the door."

"It is not in the door," said the Countess wrathfully, shaking it as if she would tear it down.

"It is in the door," said Lady Mary positively; and quite right she was, for both of us were looking at it.

"It is not in the door," shouted her mother. "Some of the servants have taken it away."

Then we heard her calling over the banisters to find out who had taken away the key of Lady Mary's room. There was a twinkle in Mary's eye, and a quiver in the corners of her pretty mouth that made me feel she would burst out laughing, and indeed I had some ado to keep silence myself.

"What have you done with those two poor wretches you were maltreating out in the garden?" asked Lady Mary.

"Oh, don't speak of them," cried the Countess, evidently in no good humour. "It was all a scandal for nothing. The red-headed beast did not have the papers. That little fool, Chord, has misled both your father and me. I could wring his neck for him, and now he is palavering your father in the library and saying he will get the papers himself or die in the attempt. It serves us right for paying attention to a babbling idiot like him. I said in the first place that that Irish baboon of an O'Ruddy was not likely to give them to the ape that follows him."

"Tare-an-ounds!" I cried, clenching my fists and making for the door; but Lady Mary rattled it so I could not be heard, and the next instant she placed her snow-flake hand across my mouth, which was as pleasant a way of stopping an injudicious utterance as ever I had been acquainted with.

"Mary," said the Countess, "your father is very much agitated and disappointed, so I'm taking him out for a drive. I have told the butler to look out for the key, and when he finds it he will let you out. You've only yourself to blame for being locked in, because we expected the baboon himself and couldn't trust you in his presence."

It was now Lady Mary's turn to show confusion at the old termagant's talk, and she coloured as red as a sunset on the coast of Kerry. I forgave the old hag her discourteous appellation of "baboon" because of the joyful intimation she gave me through the door that Lady Mary was not to be trusted when I was near by. My father used to say that if you are present when an embarrassment comes to a lady it is well not to notice it, else the

246

embarrassment will be transferred to yourself. Remembering this, I pretended not to see Lady Mary's flaming cheeks, and, begging her pardon, walked up the room and picked from the corner the bundle of papers which had, somehow or other come there, whether kicked or not. I came back to where she was standing and offered them to her most respectfully, as if they, and not herself, were the subject of discussion.

"Hush," said Lady Mary in a whisper; "sit down yonder and see how long you can keep quiet."

She pointed to a chair that stood beside a beautifully polished table of foreign wood, the like of which I had never seen before, and I, wishing very much to please her, sat down where she told me and placed the bundle of papers on the table. Lady Mary tiptoed over, as light-footed as a canary-bird, and sat down on the opposite side of the table, resting her elbows on the polished wood, and, with her chin in her hands, gazed across at me, and a most bewildering scrutiny I found it, rendering it difficult for me to keep quiet and seated, as she had requested. In a minute or two we heard the crunch of wheels on the gravel in front, then the carriage drove off, and the big gates clanked together.

Still Lady Mary poured the sunshine of her eyes upon me, and I hope and trust she found me a presentable young man, for under the warmth of her look my heart began to bubble up like a pot of potatoes on a strong fire.

"You make me a present of the papers, then?" said Lady Mary at last.

"Indeed and I do, and of myself as well, if you'll have me. And this latter is a thing I've been trying to say to you every time I met you, Mary acushla, and no sooner do the words come to my lips than some doddering fool interrupts us; but now, my darling, we are alone together, in that lover's paradise which is always typified by a locked door, and at last I can say the things—"

Just here, as I mentioned the word "door," there came a rap at it, and Lady Mary started as if some one had fired a gun.

"Your ladyship," said the butler, "I cannot find the key. Shall I send for a locksmith?"

"Oh, no," said Lady Mary, "do not take the trouble. I have letters to write, and do not wish to be disturbed until my mother returns."

"Very good, your ladyship," returned the butler, and he walked away.

"A locksmith!" said Lady Mary, looking across the table at me.

"Love laughs at them," said I.

Lady Mary smiled very sweetly, but shook her head.

"This is not a time for laughter," she said, "but for seriousness. Now, I cannot risk your staying here longer, so will tell you what I have to say as quickly as possible. Your repeatedly interrupted declaration I take for truth, because the course of true love never did run smooth. Therefore, if you want me, you must keep the papers."

At this I hastily took the bundle from the table and thrust it in my pocket, which action made Lady Mary smile again.

"Have you read them?" she asked.

"I have not."

"Do you mean to say you have carried these papers about for so long and have not read them?"

"I had no curiosity concerning them," I replied. "I have something better to look at," I went on, gazing across at her; "and when that is not with me the memory of it is, and it's little I care for a pack of musty papers and what's in them."

"Then I will tell you what they are," said Lady Mary. "There are in that packet the title-deeds to great estates, the fairest length of land that lies under the sun in Sussex. There is also a letter written by my father's own hand, giving the property to your father."

"But he did not mean my father to keep it," said I.

"No, he did not. He feared capture, and knew the ransom would be heavy if they found evidence of property upon him. Now all these years he has been saying nothing, but collecting the revenues of this estate and using them, while another man had the legal right to it."

"Still he has but taken what was his own," said I, "and my father never disputed that, always intending to come over to England and return the papers to the Earl; but he got lazy-like, by sitting at his own fireside, and seldom went farther abroad than to the house of the priest; but his last injunctions to me were to see that the Earl got his papers, and indeed he would have had them long since if he had but treated me like the son of an old friend."

"Did your father mention that the Earl would give you any reward for returning his property to him?"

"He did not," I replied with indignation. "In Ireland, when a friend does a friend's part, he doesn't expect to be paid for it."

"But don't you expect a reward for returning them?"

"Lady Mary," said I, "do you mean to be after insulting me? These papers are not mine, but the Earl of Westport's, and he can have them without saying as much as 'Thank you kindly' for them."

Lady Mary leaned back in her chair and looked at me with half-closed eyes, then she stretched forth her hand and said:

"Give me the papers."

"But it's only a minute since," I cried, perplexed, "that you held them to be the key of the situation, and said if I didn't keep them I would never get you."

"Did I say that?" asked Lady Mary with the innocence of a three-year-old child. "I had no idea we had come to such a conclusion. Now do you want a little advice about those same papers?"

"As long as the advice comes from you, Mary darling, I want it on any subject."

"You have come into England brawling, sword-playing, cudgel-flinging,

249

and never till this moment have you given a thought to what the papers are for. These papers represent the law."

"Bad cess to it," said I. "My father used to say, have as little to do with the law as possible, for what's the use of bringing your man into the courts when a good shillelah is speedier and more satisfactory to all concerned."

"That may be true in Ireland, but it is not true in England. Now, here is my advice. You know my father and mother, and if you'll just quit staring your eyes out at me, and think for a minute, you may be able to tell when you will get their consent to pay your addresses to me without interruption." Here she blushed and looked down.

"Indeed," said I, "I don't need to take my eyes from you to answer that question. It'll be the afternoon following the Day of Judgment."

"Very well. You must then stand on your rights. I will give you a letter to a man in the Temple, learned in the law. He was legal adviser to my aunt, who left me all her property, and she told me that if I ever was in trouble I was to go to him; but instead of that I'll send my trouble to him with a letter of introduction. I advise you to take possession of the estate at Brede, and think no more of giving up the papers to my father until he is willing to give you something in return. You may then ask what you like of him; money, goods, or a farm,"—and again a bright red colour flooded her cheeks. With that she drew toward her pen and paper and dashed off a letter which she gave to me.

"I think," she said, "it would be well if you left the papers with the man in the Temple; he will keep them safely, and no one will suspect where they are; while, if you need money, which is likely, he will be able to advance you what you want on the security of the documents you leave with him."

"Is it money?" said I, "sure I couldn't think of drawing money on property that belongs to your good father, the Earl."

"As I read the papers," replied Lady Mary, very demurely, casting down her eyes once more, "the property does not belong to my good father, the Earl, but to the good-for-nothing young man named O'Ruddy. I think that my father, the Earl, will find that he needs your signature before he can call

250

the estate his own once more. It may be I am wrong, and that your father, by leaving possession so long in the hands of the Earl, may have forfeited his claim. Mr. Josiah Brooks will tell you all about that when you meet him in the Temple. You may depend upon it that if he advances you money your claim is good, and, your claim being good, you may make terms with even so obstreperous a man as my father."

"And if I make terms with the father," I cried, "do you think his comely daughter will ratify the bargain?"

Lady Mary smiled very sweetly, and gave me the swiftest and shyest of glances across the table from her speaking eyes, which next instant were hidden from me.

"May be," she said, "the lawyer could answer that question."

"Troth," I said, springing to my feet, "I know a better one to ask it of than any old curmudgeon poring over dry law-books, and the answer I'm going to have from your own lips."

Then, with a boldness that has ever characterized the O'Ruddys, I swung out my arms and had her inside o' them before you could say Ballymoyle. She made a bit of a struggle and cried breathlessly:

"I'll answer, if you'll sit in that chair again."

"It's not words," says I, "I want from your lips, but this,"—and I smothered a little shriek with one of the heartiest kisses that ever took place out of Ireland itself, and it seemed to me that her struggle ceased, or, as one might say, faded away, as my lips came in contact with hers; for she suddenly weakened in my arms so that I had to hold her close to me, for I thought she would sink to the floor if I did but leave go, and in the excitement of the moment my own head was swimming in a way that the richest of wine had never made it swim before. Then Lady Mary buried her face in my shoulder with a little sigh of content, and I knew she was mine in spite of all the Earls and Countesses in the kingdom, or estates either, so far as that went. At last she straightened up and made as though she would push me from her, but held me thus at arms' length, while her limpid eyes looked like twin lakes of

Killarney on a dreamy misty morning when there's no wind blowing.

"O'Ruddy," she said, solemnly, with a little catch in her voice, "you're a bold man, and I think you've no doubt of your answer; but what has happened makes me the more anxious for your success in dealing with those who will oppose both your wishes and mine. My dear lover, is what I call you now; you have come over in tempestuous fashion, with a sword in your hand, striving against every one who would stand up before you. After this morning, all that should be changed, for life seems to have become serious and momentous. O'Ruddy, I want your actions to be guided, not by a drawn sword, but by religion and by law."

"Troth, Mary acushla, an Irishman takes to religion of his own nature, but I much misdoubt me if it comes natural to take to the law."

"How often have you been to mass since you came to England, O'Ruddy?"

"How often?" says I, wrinkling my brow, "indeed you mean, how many times?"

"Yes; how many times?"

"Now, Mary, how could you expect me to be keeping count of them?"

"Has your attendance, then, been so regular?"

"Ah, Mary, darling; it's not me that has the face to tell you a lie, and yet I'm ashamed to say that I've never set foot in a church since I crossed the channel, and the best of luck it is for me that good old Father Donovan doesn't hear these same words."

"Then you will go to church this very day and pray for heaven's blessing on both of us."

"It's too late for the mass this Sunday, Mary, but the churches are open, and the first one I come to will have me inside of it."

With that she drew me gently to her, and herself kissed me, meeting none of that resistance which I had encountered but a short time before; and then, as bitter ill luck would have it, at this delicious moment we were startled by the sound of carriage-wheels on the gravel outside.

"Oh!" cried Lady Mary in a panic; "how time has flown!"

"Indeed," said I, "I never knew it so fast before."

And she, without wasting further time in talking, unlocked the door, whipped out the key, and placed it where I had found it in the beginning. She seemed to think of everything in a moment, and I would have left her letter and the papers on the table if it hadn't been for that cleverest of all girls, who, besides her lips of honey, had an alert mind, which is one of the things appreciated in Ireland. I then followed her quickly down a narrow back stairway and out into a glass house, where a little door at the end led us into a deliciously shaded walk, free from all observation, with a thick screen of trees on the right hand and the old stone wall on the left.

Here I sprang quickly to overtake her, but she danced away like a fairy in the moonlight, throwing a glance of mischief over her shoulder at me, with her finger on her lips. It seemed to me a pity that so sylvan a dell should merely be used for the purposes of speed, but in a jiffy Mary was at the little door in the wall and had the bolts drawn back, and I was outside before I understood what had happened, listening to bolts being thrust back again, and my only consolation was the remembrance of a little dab at my lips as I passed through, as brief and unsatisfactory as the peck of a sparrow.

CHAPTER XXVIII

It was a beautiful day, as lovely as any an indulgent Providence had ever bestowed upon an unthankful generation.

Although I wished I had had an hour or two to spend with Mary wandering up and down that green alley through which we had rushed with such indecent haste, all because two aged and angry members of the nobility might have come upon us, yet I walked through the streets of London as if I trod on the air, and not on the rough cobble-stones of the causeway. It seemed as if I had suddenly become a boy again, and yet with all the strength and vigour of a man, and I was hard put to it not to shout aloud in the sunlight, or to slap on the back the slow and solemn Englishmen I met, who looked as if they had never laughed in their lives. Sure it's a very serious country, this same land of England, where their dignity is so oppressive that it bows down head and shoulders with thinking how grand they are; and yet I'll say nothing against them, for it was an Englishwoman that made me feel like a balloon. Pondering over the sobriety of the nation, I found myself in the shadow of a great church, and, remembering what my dear Mary had said, I turned and went in through the open door, with my hat in my hand. It was a great contrast to the bright sunlight I had left, and to the busy streets with their holiday-making people. There were only a few scattered here and there in the dim silence of the church, some on their knees, some walking slowly about on tiptoe, and some seated meditating in chairs. No service was going forward, so I knelt down in the chapel of Saint Patrick himself; I bowed my head and thanked God for the day and for the blessing that had come with it. As I said, I was like a boy again, and to my lips, too long held from them, came the prayers that had been taught me. I was glad I had not forgotten them, and I said them over and over with joy in my heart. As I raised my head, I saw standing and looking at me a priest, and, rising to my feet, I made my bow to him, and he came forward, recognizing me before I recognized him.

"O'Ruddy," he said, "if you knew the joy it gives to my old heart to meet you in this sacred place and in that devout attitude, it would bring some corresponding happiness to yourself."

"Now by the piper that played before Moses, Father Donovan, and is this yourself? Sure I disrecognized you, coming into the darkness, and me just out of the glare beyond,"—and I took his hand in both of mine and shook it with a heartiness he had not met since he left the old turf. "Sure and there's no one I'd rather meet this day than yourself,"—and with that I dropped on one knee and asked for his blessing on me and mine.

As we walked out of the church together, his hand resting on my shoulder, I asked how such a marvel came to pass as Father Donovan, who never thought to leave Ireland, being here in London. The old man said nothing till we were down the steps, and then he told me what had happened.

"You remember Patsy O'Gorman," he said.

"I do that," I replied, "and an old thief of the world and a tight-fisted miser he is."

"Whist," said Father Donovan, quietly crossing himself. "O'Gorman is dead and buried."

"Do you tell me that!" said I, "then rest his soul. He would be a warm man and leave more money than my father did, I'm thinking."

"Yes, he left some money, and to me he left three hundred pounds, with the request that I should accomplish the desire of my life and take the pilgrimage to Rome."

"The crafty old chap, that same bit of bequestration will help him over many a rough mile in purgatory."

"Ah, O'Ruddy, it's not our place to judge. They gave a harder name to O'Gorman than he deserved. Just look at your own case. The stories that have come back to Ireland, O'Ruddy, just made me shiver. I heard that you were fighting and brawling through England, ready to run through any man that looked cross-eyed at you. They said that you had taken up with a highwayman; that you spent your nights in drink and breathing out smoke; and here I find you, a proper young man, doing credit to your country, meeting you, not in a tavern, but on your knees with bowed head in the chapel of Saint Patrick, giving the lie to the slanderer's tongue."

The good old man stopped in our walk, and with tears in his eyes shook hands with me again, and I had not the heart to tell him the truth.

"Ah well," I said, "Father Donovan, I suppose nobody, except yourself, is quite as good as he thinks, and nobody, including myself, is as bad as he appears to be. And now, Father Donovan, where are you stopping, and how long will you be in London?"

"I am stopping with an old college friend, who is a priest in the church where I found you. I expect to leave in a few days' time and journey down to the seaport of Rye, where I am to take ship that will land me either in Dunkirk or in Calais. From there I am to make my way to Rome as best I can."

"And are you travelling alone?"

"I am that, although, by the blessing of God, I have made many friends on the journey, and every one I met has been good to me."

"Ah, Father Donovan, you couldn't meet a bad man if you travelled the world over. Sure there's some that carry such an air of blessedness with them that every one they meet must, for very shame, show the best of his character. With me it's different, for it seems that where there's contention I am in the middle of it, though, God knows, I'm a man of peace, as my father was before me."

"Well," said Father Donovan slowly, but with a sweet smile on his lip, "I suppose the O'Ruddys were always men of peace, for I've known them before now to fight hard enough to get it."

The good father spoke a little doubtfully, as if he were not quite approving of our family methods, but he was a kindly man who always took the most lenient view of things. He walked far with me, and then I turned and escorted him to the place where he resided, and, bidding good-bye, got a promise from him that he would come to the "Pig and Turnip" a day later and have a bite and sup with me, for I thought with the assistance of the landlord I could put a very creditable meal before him, and Father Donovan was always one that relished his meals, and he enjoyed his drink too, although he was set against too much of it. He used to say, "It's a wise drinker that knows when geniality ends and hostility begins, and it's just as well to stop before you come to the line."

With this walking to and fro the day was near done with when I got back to the "Pig and Turnip" and remembered that neither a bit of pig nor a bit of turnip had I had all that long day, and now I was ravenous. I never knew anything make me forget my appetite before; but here had I missed my noonday meal, and not in all my life could I overtake it again. Sure there was many an experience crowded together in that beautiful Sunday, so, as I passed through the entrance to the inn I said to the obsequious landlord:

"For the love of Heaven, get placed on my table all you have in the house that's fit to eat, and a trifle of a bottle or two, to wash it down with."

So saying, I passed up the creaking old oaken stair and came to my room, where I instantly remembered there was something else I had forgotten. As I opened the door there came a dismal groan from Paddy, and something that sounded like a wicked oath from Jem Bottles. Poor lads! that had taken such a beating that day, such a cudgelling for my sake; and here I stood at my own door in a wonder of amazement, and something of fright, thinking I had heard a banshee wail. The two misused lads had slipped out of my memory as completely as the devil slipped off Macgillicuddy Reeks into the pond beneath when Saint Patrick had sent the holy words after him.

"Paddy," said I, "are you hurted? Where is it you're sore?"

"Is it sore?" he groaned. "Except the soles of my feet, which they couldn't hit with me kickin' them, there isn't an inch of me that doesn't think it's worse hurted than the rest."

"It's sorry I am to hear that," I replied, quite truthfully, "and you, Jem, how did you come off?"

"Well, I gave a better account of myself than Paddy here, for I made most of them keep their distance from me; but him they got on the turf before you could say Watch me eye, and the whole boiling of them was on top of him in the twinkling of the same."

"The whole boiling of them?" said I, as if I knew nothing of the occurrence, "then there was more than Strammers to receive you?"

"More!" shouted Jem Bottles, "there was forty if there was one."

Paddy groaned again at the remembrance, and moaned out:

"The whole population of London was there, and half of it on top of me before I could wink. I thought they would strip the clothes off me, and they nearly did it."

"And have you been here alone ever since? Have you had nothing to eat or drink since you got back?"

"Oh," said Jem, "we had too much attention in the morning, and too little as the day went on. We were expecting you home, and so took the liberty of coming up here and waiting for you, thinking you might be good enough to send out for some one who would dress our wounds; but luckily that's not needed now."

"Why is it not needed?" I asked. "I'll send at once."

"Oh, no," moaned Paddy, "there was one good friend that did not forget us."

"Well," said Jem, "he seemed mighty afeerd of coming in. I suppose he thought it was on his advice that we went where we did, and he was afeerd we thought badly of him for it; but of course we had no blame to put on the poor little man."

"In Heaven's name, who are you talking of?" said I.

"Doctor Chord," answered Jem. "He put his head inside the door and inquired for us, and inquired specially where you were; but that, of course, we couldn't tell him. He was very much put out to find us mis-handled, and he sent us some tankards of beer, which are now empty, and we're waiting for him because he promised to come back and attend to our injuries."

"Then you didn't see Doctor Chord in the gardens?"

"In what gardens?" asked Bottles.

"You didn't see him among that mob that set on you?"

"No fear," said Jem, "wherever there is a scrimmage Doctor Chord will keep away from it."

"Indeed and in that you're wrong," said I. "Doctor Chord has been the instigator of everything that has happened, and he stood in the background and helped to set them on."

Paddy sat up with wild alarm in his eyes.

"Sure, master," says he, "how could you see through so thick a wall as that?"

"I did not see through the wall at all; I was in the house. When you went through the back door, I went through the front gate, and what I am telling you is true. Doctor Chord is the cause of the whole commotion. That's why he was afraid to come in the room. He thought perhaps you had seen him, and, finding you had not, he'll be back here again when everything is over. Doctor Chord is a traitor, and you may take my word for that."

Paddy rose slowly to his feet, every red hair in his head bristling with scorn and indignation; but as he stood erect he put his hand to his side and gave a howl as he limped a step or two over the floor.

"The black-hearted villain," he muttered through his teeth. "I'll have his life."

"You'll have nothing of the sort," said I, "and we'll get some good attendance out of him, for he's a skillful man. When he has done his duty in repairing what he has inflicted upon you, then you can give him a piece of your mind."

"I'll give him a piece of my boot; all that's left of it," growled Jem Bottles, scowling.

"You may take your will of him after he has put some embrocation on your bruises," said I; and as I was speaking there came a timorous little knock at the door.

"Come in," I cried, and after some hesitation the door opened, and there stood little Doctor Chord with a big bottle under his arm. I was glad there was no supper yet on the table, for if there had been I must have asked the little man to sit down with me, and that he would do without a second's hesitation, so I could not rightly see him maltreated who had broken a crust with me.

He paid no attention to Jem or Paddy at first, but kept his cunning little eye on me.

"And where have you been to-day, O'Ruddy?" he asked.

"Oh," said I, "I accompanied these two to the door in the wall, and when they got through I heard yells fit to make a hero out of a nigger; but you know how stout the bolts are and I couldn't get to them, so I had just to go out of hearing of their bellowings. On the way back I happened to meet an old friend of mine, Father Donovan, and—"

Here Paddy, forgetting his good manners, shouted out:

"Thank God there's a holy father in this hole of perdition; for I know I'm goin' t' die to-morrow at the latest."

"Stop your nonsense," said I. "You'll have to hold on to life at least a day longer; for the good father is not coming here until two days are past. You're more frightened than hurt, and the Doctor here has a lotion that will make you meet the priest as a friend and not as a last counsellor."

"As I was saying, Doctor Chord, I met Father Donovan, and we strolled about the town, so that I have only now just come in. The father is a stranger in London, on a pilgrimage to Rome. And sure I had to show him the sights."

"It was a kindly action of you," said Doctor Chord, pulling the cork of the medicine-bottle. "Get those rags off," he called to Paddy, "and I'll rub you down as if you were the finest horse that ever followed the hounds."

There was a great smell of medicine in the air as he lubricated Paddy over the bruised places; then Jem Bottles came under his hands, and either he was not so much hurt as Paddy was, or he made less fuss about it, for he glared at the Doctor all the time he was attending him, and said nothing.

It seemed an inhospitable thing to misuse a man who had acted the good Samaritan so arduously as the little Doctor with three quarters of his bottle gone, but as he slapped the cork in it again I stepped to the door and turned the key. Paddy was scowling now and then, and groaning now and again, when the cheerful Doctor said to him, as is the way with physicians when they wish to encourage a patient:

"Oh, you're not hurt nearly as bad as you think you are. You'll be a little sore and stiff in the morning, that's all, and I'll leave the bottle with you."

"You've never rubbed me at all on the worst place," said Paddy angrily.

"Where was that?" asked Doctor Chord,—and the words were hardly out of his mouth when Paddy hit him one in the right eye that sent him staggering across the room.

"There's where I got the blow that knocked me down," cried Paddy.

Doctor Chord threw a wild glance at the door, when Jem Bottles, with a little run and a lift of his foot, gave him one behind that caused the Doctor to turn a somersault.

"Take that, you thief," said Jem; "and now you've something that neither of us got, because we kept our faces to the villains that set on us."

Paddy made a rush, but I cried:

"Don't touch the man when he's down."

"Sure," says Paddy, "that's when they all fell on me."

"Never strike a man when he's down," I cried.

"Do ye mean to say we shouldn't hit a man when he's down?" asked Jem Bottles.

"You knew very well you shouldn't," I told him. "Sure you've been in the ring before now."

"That I have," shouted Bottles, pouncing on the unfortunate Doctor. He grabbed him by the scruff of the neck and flung him to his feet, then gave him a bat on the side of the head that sent him reeling up toward the ceiling again.

"That's enough, Jem," I cautioned him.

"I'm not only following the Doctor," said Jem, "but I'm following the Doctor's advice. He told us to take a little gentle exercise and it would allay the soreness."

"The exercise you're taking will not allay the soreness on the Doctor's part. Stop it, Jem! Now leave him alone, Paddy; he's had enough to remember you by, and to learn that the way of the traitor is the rocky road to Dublin. Come now, Doctor, the door is open; get out into the passage as quick as you can, and I hope you have another bottle of that excellent lotion at home."

The threatening attitude of both Jem and Paddy seemed to paralyse the little man with fear, and he lay on the boards glaring up at them with terror in his eyes.

"I'm holding the door open for you," said I, "and remember I may not be able to hold Paddy and Jem as easily as I hold the door; so make your escape before they get into action again."

Doctor Chord rolled himself over quickly, but, not daring to get on his feet, trotted out into the passage like a big dog on his hands and knees; and just then a waiter, coming up with a tray and not counting on this sudden apparition in the hallway, fell over him; and if it were not for my customary agility and presence of mind in grasping the broad metal server, a good part of my supper would have been on the floor. The waiter luckily leaned forward when he found himself falling, holding the tray high over his head, and so, seizing it, I saved the situation and the supper.

"What are ye grovelling down there for, ye drunken beast?" shouted the angry waiter, as he came down with a thud. "Why don't you walk on your two feet like a Christian?"

Doctor Chord took the hint and his departure, running along the passage and stumbling down the stairway like a man demented. When he got down into the courtyard he shook his fist at my window and swore he would have the law of us; but I never saw the little man again, although Paddy and Jem were destined to meet him once more, as I shall tell later on.

The supper being now laid, I fell at it and I dis-remember having ever enjoyed a meal more in my life. I sent Paddy and Jem to their quarters with food and a bottle of good wine to keep them company, and I think they deserved it, for they said the lotion the Doctor had put on the outside of them was stinging, so they thought there should be something in the inside to counteract the inconvenience.

I went to sleep the moment I touched the pillow, and dreamed I was in the most umbrageous lover's walk that ever was, overhung with green branches through which the sunlight flickered, and closed in with shrubbery. There I chased a flying nymph that always just eluded me, laughing at me over her shoulder and putting her finger to her lips, and at last, when I caught her, it turned out to be Doctor Chord, whereupon I threw him indignantly into the bushes, and then saw to my dismay it was the Countess. She began giving her opinion of me so vigorously that I awoke and found it broad daylight.

CHAPTER XXIX

After a comforting and sustaining breakfast I sent for Paddy and Jem, both of whom came in limping.

"Are you no better this morning?" I asked them.

"Troth, we're worse," said Paddy with a most dismal look on his face.

"I'm sorry to hear it," said I; "but I think the trouble will wear off today if you lie snug and quiet in the inn. Here's this bottle of embrocation, or what is left of it, so you may take it with you and divide it fairly between you, remembering that one good rub deserves another, and that our chief duty on this earth is to help our fellow man; and as there's nothing like easy employment for making a man forget his tribulations, Jem will rub Paddy, and Paddy will rub Jem, and thus, God blessing you both, you will pass the time to your mutual benefit."

"Yer honour," sniffed Jem Bottles, "I like your own prescriptions better than Doctor Chord's. I have but small faith in the liniment; the bottle of wine you gave us last night—and I wish it had been as double as it made us see—was far better for our trouble than this stuff."

"I doubt it, Jem," said I, "for you're worse this morning than you were last night; so I'll change the treatment and go back to Doctor Chord's remedy, for sure the Doctor is a physician held in high esteem by the nobility of London. But you're welcome to a double mug of beer at my expense, only see that you don't take too much of that."

"Yer honour," said Jem, "it's only when we're sober that we fall upon affliction. We had not a drop to drink yesterday morning, and see what happened us."

"It would have made no differ," I said, "if you had been as tipsy as the Earl himself is when dinner's over. Trust in Providence, Jem, and rub hard with the liniment, and you'll be a new man by the morrow morn."

With this I took my papers and the letter of introduction, and set out as brave as you please to find the Temple, which I thought would be a sort of a church, but which I found to be a most sober and respectable place very difficult for a stranger to find his way about in. But at last I came to the place where Mr. Josiah Brooks dispensed the law for a consideration to ignorant spalpeens like myself, that was less familiar with the head that had a gray wig on than with cracking heads by help of a good shillelah that didn't know what a wig was. As it was earlier in the morning than Mr. Brooks's usual hour I had to sit kicking my heels in a dismal panelled anteroom till the great lawyer came in. He was a smooth-faced serious-looking man, rather elderly, and he passed through the anteroom without so much as casting a look at me, and was followed by a melancholy man in rusty black who had told me to take a chair, holding in his hand the letter Lady Mary had written. After a short time the man came out again, and, treating me with more deference than when he bade me be seated, asked me kindly if I would step this way and Mr. Brooks would see me.

"You are Mr. O'Ruddy, I take it," he said in a tone which I think he thought was affable.

"I am."

"Have you brought with you the papers referred to in this letter?"

"I have."

And with that I slammed them down on the table before him. He untied the bundle and sorted out the different documents, apparently placing them in their right order. After this he adjusted his glasses more to his liking and glanced over the papers rapidly until he came to one that was smaller than the rest, and this he read through twice very carefully. Then he piled them up together at his right hand very neatly, for he seemed to have a habit of old maid's precision about him. He removed his glasses and looked across the table at me.

"Are you the son of the O'Ruddy here mentioned?"

"I am."

"His eldest son?"

"His only son."

"You can prove that, I suppose?"

"Troth, it was never disputed."

"I mean there would be no difficulty in getting legal and documentary proof."

"I think not, for my father said after my first fight, that it might be questioned whether I was my mother's son or no,—there was no doubt that I was his."

The legal man drew down his brows at this, but made no comment as, in tones that betrayed little interest in the affair, he demanded:

"Why did your father not claim this property during his lifetime?"

"Well, you see, Mr. Brooks, my father was an honest man, and he never pretended the property was his. From what I remember of his conversation on the subject the Earl and him was in a tight place after a battle in France, and it was thought they would both be made prisoners. The Earl had his deeds with him, and if he were caught the enemy would demand a large ransom for him, for these would show him to be a man of property. So he made the estate over to my father, and my father ran the risk of being captured and taken for the Earl of Westport. Now that I have been made happy by the acquaintance of his lordship, I'm thinking that if my father had fallen into the hands of the enemy he might have remained there till this day without the Earl raising a hand to help him. Nobody in England would have disputed the Earl's ownership of his own place, which I understand has been in his family for hundreds of years, so they might very well have got on without the deeds, as in fact they have done. That's all I know about it."

"Then, sir," said Mr. Brooks, "do you intend to contest the ownership of the property on the strength of these documents?"

"I do," said I firmly.

"Very well. You must leave them with me for a few days until I get opinion upon them. I may say I have grave doubts of your succeeding in such litigation unless you can prove that your father gave reasonable consideration for the property made over to him."

"Troth, he'd no consideration to give except his own freedom and the loan of a pair of breeches, and it seems that the Earl never troubled his head whether he gave the first-named or not. He might have given his life for all the thanks his son got from my Lord of Westport."

"From a rapid glance at these instruments I can see that they may be of great value to his lordship, but I doubt their being of any value at all to you; in fact you might find the tables turned upon you, and be put in the position of a fraudulent claimant or a levier of blackmail."

"It's not blackmail I'm going to levy at all," cried I, "but the whitest of white mail. I have not the slightest intention of going into the courts of law; but, to tell you the plain truth about it, Lady Mary and me are going to get married in spite of all the Earls that ever drank, or all the Countesses that ever scolded. Now this dear girl has a great confidence in you, and she has sent me to you to find what's best to be done. I want nothing of this property at all. Sure I've estates enough of my own in Ireland, and a good castle forby, save that the roof leaks a little in places; but a bundle of straw will soon set that to rights, only old Patsy is so lazy through not getting his money regular. Now it struck me that if I went boldly to Brede Castle, or whatever it is, and took possession of it, there would first be the finest scrimmage any man ever saw outside of Ireland, and after that his lordship the Earl would say to me,—

"'O'Ruddy, my boy, my limbs are sore; can't we crack a bottle instead of our heads over this, and make a compromise?'

"'Earl of Westport,' I'll say to him, 'a bottle will be but the beginning of it. We'll sit down at a table and settle this debate in ten minutes if you're reasonable.'

"He'll not be reasonable, of course, but you see what I have in my mind."

"Brede Place," said the lawyer slowly, "is not exactly a castle, but it's a very strong house and might be held by a dozen determined men against an army."

"Then once let me get legally inside, and I'll hold it till the Earl gets more sense in his head than is there at the present moment."

"Possession," said Mr. Brooks, "is nine points of the law."

"It is with a woman," said I, thinking of something else.

"It is with an estate," answered Josiah severely.

"True for you," I admitted, coming back to the point at issue, for it was curious, in spite of the importance of the interview, how my mind kept wandering away to a locked room in the Earl of Westport's house, and to a shady path that ran around the edge of his garden.

"I intend to get possession of the Brede estate if I have to crack the crown of every man at present upon it. But I am an Irishman, and therefore a person of peace, and I wish to crack the crowns in accordance with the law of England, so I come to you for directions how it should be done."

"It is not my place," said Brooks, looking very sour, "to counsel a man to break either heads or the law. In fact it is altogether illegal to assault another unless you are in danger of your own life."

"The blessing of all the Saints be upon you," said I, "yet, ever since I set foot in this land, coming across the boiling seas, entirely to do a kindness to the Earl of Westport, I have gone about in fear of my life."

"You have surely not been assaulted?" demanded Mr. Brooks, raising his eyebrows in surprise.

"Assaulted, is it? I have been set upon in every manner that is possible for a peace-lover to be interfered with. To tell you the truth, no longer ago than yesterday morning, as quiet and decent a Sunday as ever came down on London, my two innocent servants, garrulous creatures that wouldn't hurt a fly, were lured into the high walled garden of the Earl of Westport to see the flowers which both of them love, and there they were pounced upon by the whole body-guard of my lord the Earl, while himself and his quiet-mannered Countess were there to urge them on. Doctor Chord, a little snobbish creature, basking in the smiles of their noble countenances, stood by and gave medical advice showing where best to hit the poor innocent unfortunates that had fallen into their hands."

"Tut, tut!" said Josiah Brooks, his face frowning like a storm-cloud over the hills of Donegal. "If such is indeed the case, an action would lie—"

"Oh, well and as far as that goes, so would Doctor Chord, and all the rest that was there. My poor lads lie now, bruised and sore, in the upper rooms of the stable at the 'Pig and Turnip.' They want no more action, I can tell you, nor lying either."

"You can prove, then," said the lawyer, "that you have suffered violence from the outset."

"Indeed and I could."

"Well, well, we must look into the matter. You recite a most curious accumulation of offences, each of which bears a serious penalty according to the law of England. But there is another matter mentioned in Lady Mary's letter which is even more grave than any yet alluded to."

"And what is that?" I asked in surprise.

"She says that she wishes to have advanced to you, upon the security of these papers, five hundred golden guineas."

"Do you tell me that now?" I cried with delight. "Sure I have always said that Mary was the most sensible girl within the boundaries of this realm."

"That may all be; but women, you see, know little of money or the methods of obtaining it."

"You're right in that," I admitted. "It's the other end of the stick they hold; they know a good deal of the way of spending it."

"You will understand," went on Mr. Brooks, "that if money is to be raised on the security of these documents, your rights in possessing them must be severely scrutinized, while—you will pardon my saying so—the security of your estates in Ireland might be looked at askance by the money-lenders of London."

"Oh, don't let the estates in Ireland trouble you, for the money-lenders of Dublin have already mortgaged them a foot deep. You can raise little on my estates in Ireland but the best turf you ever burned, and that's raised with a spade."

"Very well," said Josiah Brooks, gathering up the papers and tying them together with a bit of red ribbon which he took out of his drawer, ignoring the Irish cord that had held them through all their emergencies. "Very well, I shall seek advice and let you know the result."

"Seek advice," I cried. "Sure a man of your attainments doesn't need to seek advice of any one. Aren't you learned in the law yourself?"

"I must have counsel's opinion," said Josiah solemnly, as if he were speaking of the decisions of Providence.

"Well, you astonish me, Mr. Brooks, for I thought you knew it all, and that's why I came to you; but perhaps it's only your own modesty that makes you reluctant to speak of your attainments, though I suppose what you really mean is that you want to take a pipe in your mouth and a glass of good liquor at your elbow and read the papers at your leisure."

Mr. Josiah Brooks was a solemn man, and he did not appear to relish the picture I so graphically drew of him, when in truth I was thinking only of his own comfort; so I changed the subject with an alertness of mind which perhaps he was incapable of appreciating.

"How far from London is this estate of Brede?" I asked, "and how do you get to it?"

"It is fifty or sixty miles away," he said, "and lies in the county of Sussex, close to the sea, but not on it. If you wish to visit Brede estate," he went on, as if I had not been telling him I was going to do that very thing in force, "if you wish to visit Brede estate, the best plan is to go to Rye and there engage a guide who will lead you to it."

"Rye," said I in astonishment, wondering where I had heard the name before; then, suddenly remembering, I said:

"Rye is a seaport town, is it not?"

"It is," agreed Mr. Brooks.

"Rye is the spot," rejoined I, "where Father Donovan will embark on his pilgrimage to Rome. Sure, and I'm glad to hear that, for the good old man and I will travel there together, and the blessing of Providence will surround me, which I hope will be helpful if the Earl's cut-throats bar the way, as is more than likely."

"Very well, Mr. O'Ruddy, as you are doubtless impatient to know the result, you may call upon me to-morrow afternoon at four o'clock, and I may be in a position to give you more information than I can offer at present."

I took that as a dismissal, and, getting up, shook him warmly by the hand, although his arm was as stiff as a pump handle, and he seemed to take little pleasure in the farewell. And so I left the Temple, that was as lonely as the road between Innishannon and the sea, and trudged out into Fleet Street, which was as lively as Skibbereen Fair. I was so overjoyed to find that my journey lay in the same direction as Father Donovan's that I tramped on westward till after some trouble I found the priest's house in which he was stopping, to tell the good father that I would go part of the way to Rome with him. He was indeed delighted to see me, and introduced me to his host, Father Kilnane, nearly as fine a man and as good a priest as Father Donovan himself.

We had dinner there all together at mid-day, and I invited Father Donovan to come out and see the town with me, which he did. The peaceful father clung to my arm in a kind of terror at what he was witnessing, for he was as innocent of the ways of a big town as if he had been a gossoon from a hedge-school in Ireland. Yet he was mightily interested in all he saw, and asked me many thousand questions that day, and if I did not know the correct answer to them, it made no differ to Father Donovan, for he did not know the answer himself and took any explanation as if it was as true as the gospels he studied and preached.

Daylight was gone before we got back to the house he lodged in, and nothing would do but I must come in and have a bit of supper, although I told him that supper would be waiting for me at the "Pig and Turnip." It had been agreed between us that we would travel together as far as Rye, and that there I should see him off on his tempestuous voyage to Dunkirk or Calais, as the case might be. The old man was mightily delighted to find that our ways lay together through the south of England. He was pleased to hear that I had determined on my rights through the courts of law, with no more sword-playing and violence, which, to tell the truth, until it reached its height, the old man was always against; although, when a quarrel came to its utmost interesting point, I have seen Father Donovan fidget in his cassock, and his eyes sparkle with the glow of battle, although up till then he had done his best to prevent the conflict.

It was getting late when I neared the "Pig and Turnip," and there was a good deal of turmoil in the streets. I saw one or two pretty debates, but, remembering my new resolution to abide by law and order, I came safely past them and turned up the less-frequented street that held my inn, when at the corner, under the big lamp, a young man with something of a swagger about him, in spite of the meanness of his dress, came out from the shadow of the wall and looked me hard in the face.

"Could you direct me, sir, to a hostelry they call the 'Pig and Turnip'?" he asked with great civility.

"If you will come with me," said I, "I'll bring you to the place itself, for that's where I'm stopping."

"Is it possible," he said, "that I have the honour of addressing The O'Ruddy?"

"That great privilege is yours," said I, coming to a standstill in the middle of the street, as I saw the young man had his sword drawn and pressed close against his side to allay suspicion. I forgot all about law and order, and had

272

my own blade free of the scabbard on the instant; but the young man spoke smoothly and made no motion of attack, which was very wise of him.

"Mr. O'Ruddy," he says, "we are both men of the world and sensible men and men of peace. Where two gentlemen, one down on his luck and the other in prosperity, have a private matter to discuss between them, I think this discussion should take place quietly and in even tones of voice."

"Sir," said I, giving my sword-hand a little shake, so that the weapon settled down into its place, "Sir, you express my sentiments exactly, and as you are a stranger to me perhaps you will be good enough to announce the subject that concerns us."

"I may say at the outset," he remarked almost in a whisper, so polite he was, "that I have eight good swordsmen at my back, who are not visible until I give the signal; therefore you see, sir, that your chances are of the slightest if I should be compelled to call upon them. I know the fame of The O'Ruddy as a swordsman, and you may take it as a compliment, sir, that I should hesitate to meet you alone. So much for saving my own skin, but I am a kindly man and would like to save your skin as well. Therefore if you will be kind enough to hand to me the papers which you carry in your pocket, you will put me under strong obligations, and at the same time sleep peaceably to-night at the 'Pig and Turnip' instead of here in the gutter, to be picked up by the watch, for I can assure you, sir, as a man that knows the town, the watch will not be here to save you whatever outcry you may make."

"I am obliged to you, sir, for your discourse and your warning, to both of which I have paid strict attention; and in the interests of that peace which we are each of us so loath to break I may announce to you that the papers you speak of are not in my possession."

"Pardon me, sir, but they must be; for we have searched your room thoroughly, and we have also searched your servants."

"A thief of the night," cried I with mighty indignation, "may easily search an honest man's room; and his poor servants, beaten and bruised by your master's orders, would fall easy victims to the strength and numbers of your ruffians; but you will find it a difficult matter to search me."

"Sir," he replied, bowing as polite as Palermo, "I grieve to state that you are in error. The searching of both your servants and your rooms was accomplished, not through the employment of force, but by the power of money. Your servants insisted they had nothing on their persons but liniment, and they accepted one gold piece each to allow me to verify their statements. Another gold piece gave me, for a time, the freedom of your room. If you have not the papers upon you, then there is no harm in allowing me to run my hand over your clothes, because the package is a bulky one and I will speedily corroborate your statement."

"Sir," said I, not to be outdone in courtesy by this gentleman of the gutter, "I will tell you truthfully that I have nothing on me but my sword, and to that you are quite welcome if you leave to me the choice of which end I hold and which I present to you,"—and with that I sprang with my back to the wall, under the lamp, leaving myself partially in shadow, but having spread in front of me a semicircle of light which any assailant attacking must cross, or indeed remain in its effulgence if he would keep free of the point of my blade.

"It grieves me to find that you are a man of violence," replied the scoundrel in the mildest of tones, "and you will bear witness afterward that I did my best to keep you from harm."

"I freely acknowledge it now," said I. "Bring on your men."

To tell the truth, I had no belief at all in the existence of his force, and thought he was playing a game on me, hoping to take me unawares; for if the man knew anything at all he must have known what a swordsman I was, and it was no charge of cowardice against him that he was loath to come to close quarters with me. I speedily discovered, however, that all he said was true; for he gave a low whistle, and out of the darkness instantly sprang seven or eight as malicious-looking villains as a man would care to see, each one with a sword in his hand.

As many erroneous and exaggerated accounts of this encounter have been given in the coffee-houses, and even in the public prints, it is well that I should now tell the truth about it. No man that has the hang of his blade need fear the onset of a mob except in one case, and that is this,—if the whole eight set upon me at once with every sword extended, there was a chance that though I might, by great expertness, disable half of them, the other half would run me through. But it should never be forgotten that these men were fighting for money, and I was fighting for my life, and that makes all the difference in the world. Each man makes a show of attack, but he holds off, hoping that one of the others will dare to thrust. This is fatal to success, but not necessarily fatal to their intended victim. An active man with a wall at his back can generally account for all that comes in front of him if he is deeply in earnest and has not too much liquor in him. It astonished London that I was able to defeat eight men, each one of whom was armed as efficiently as myself; but, as my father used to say, if you are not wholly taken up with the determination to have a man's life, you may pink him in what spot you choose if you give a little thought to the matter. The great object is the disarming of the enemy. Now, if you give a man a jab in the knuckles, or if you run your blade delicately up his arm from the wrist to the elbow, this is what happens. The man involuntarily yells out, and as involuntarily drops his sword on the flags. If you prick a man on the knuckle-bone, he will leave go his sword before he has time to think, it being an action entirely unconscious on his part, just like winking your eye or drawing your breath; yet I have seen men run through the body who kept sword in hand and made a beautiful lunge with it even as they staggered across the threshold of death's door.

Now I had no desire for any of these men's lives, but I determined to have their swords. I glittered my own shining blade before their eyes, flourishing a semicircle with it, and making it dart here and there like the tongue of an angry snake; and instantly every man in front of me felt uncomfortable, not knowing where the snake was going to sting, and then, as I said before, they were fighting for money and not for honour. When I had dazzled their eyes for a moment with this sword-play and bewildered their dull brains, I suddenly changed my tactics and thrust forward quicker than you can count one, two, three, four, five, six, seven, eight,—and each man was holding a bleeding fist to his mouth, while the swords clattered on the cobbles like hail on the copper roof of a cathedral. It was the most beautiful and complete thing I ever saw. I then swept the unarmed men back a pace or two with a flirt of my weapon, and walked up the pavement, kicking the swords together till they lay in a heap at my feet. The chief ruffian stood there dazed, with his sword still in his hand, for he had stepped outside the circle, he acting as captain, and depending on the men to do the work.

"Drop that," I shouted, turning on him, and he flung his sword in the street as if it was red hot.

"Sir," said I to him, "a sword in your hand is merely an inconvenience to you; see if you don't look better with an armful of them. Pick up these nine blades in a bundle and walk on before me to the 'Pig and Turnip.' When we come into the courtyard of that tavern, you are to turn round and make me the lowest bow you can without rubbing your nose against the pavement. Then you will say, as gracefully as the words can be uttered:

"'Mr. O'Ruddy,' you say, 'these swords are yours by right of conquest. You have defeated nine armed men to-night in less than as many minutes, so I present you with the spoil.' Then you will bow to the people assembled in the courtyard,—for there is aways a mob of them there, late and early,—and you will make another low obeisance to me. If you do all this acceptably to my sense of politeness, I will let you go unmolested; but if you do otherwise, I will split your gullet for you."

"Sir," said the captain, "I accept your terms."

With that he stooped and picked up the bundle of weapons, marching on stolidly before me till he came to the "Pig and Turnip." All the rest had disappeared in the darkness, and had gone to their dens, very likely to nurse sore knuckles and regret the loss of good stout blades.

Our coming to the tavern caused a commotion, as you may well imagine; and although I don't make too much of the encounter, yet it is my belief that such an incident never happened in London before. The captain carried out his part of the presentation with an air of deference and a choice of good language that charmed me; then he backed out under the archway to the street, bowing six or seven times as he went. I had never any fault to find with the man's manner. Paddy and Jem, now seemingly quite recovered from their misusage of Sunday, stood back of the group with eyes and mouths open, gazing upon me with an admiration I could not but appreciate.

"Come out of that," said I, "and take this cutlery up to my room," and they did.

I sat down at the table and wrote a letter to Mr. Brooks.

"Sir," said I in it, "I don't know whether I am plaintiff or defendant in the suit that's coming on, but whichever it is here's a bundle of legal evidence for your use. You mentioned the word 'violence' to me when I had the pleasure of calling on you. This night I was set upon by nine ruffians, who demanded from me the papers now in your possession. I took their knives from them, so they would not hurt themselves or other people, and I send you these knives to be filed for reference."

I tied up the swords in two bundles, and in the morning sent Paddy and Jem off with them and the letter to the Temple, which caused great commotion in that peaceable quarter of the city, and sent forth the rumour that all the lawyers were to be at each other's throats next day.

CHAPTER XXX

In the afternoon I went slowly to the Temple, thinking a good deal on the way. It's truth I tell, that in spite of the victory of the night before I walked to the Temple rather downhearted. Whether Josiah Brooks was an attorney, or a barrister, or a solicitor, or a plain lawyer, I don't know to this day, and I never could get my mind to grasp the distinction that lies between those names in that trade; but whichever it was it seemed to me he was a cold, unenthusiastic man, and that he thought very little indeed of my game. There is small pleasure in litigation in England as compared with the delight of the law in the old Ark. If I had gone to see a lawyer in Dublin or Cork he would have been wild with excitement before I had got half through my story. He would have slapped me on the back and shook me by the hand, and cried "Whurroo" at the prospect of a contest. My quarrel would have been his before I had been ten minutes in his presence, and he would have entered into the spirit of the fight as if he were the principal in it instead of merely acting for him; but in this gloomy country of England, where they engage upon a lawsuit, not with delight, but as if they were preparing for a funeral; there is no enjoyment in the courts at all at all. I wished I could transfer the case to the old turf, where there is more joy in being defeated than there is in winning in England; for I have seen the opposing lawyers rise from the most gentlemanly and elegant language you ever heard to a heated debate; then fling books at each other, and finally clench, while the judge stood up and saw fair play. But this man Brooks was so calm and collected and uninterested that he fairly discouraged me, and I saw that I was going to get neither the money I needed nor the support I expected from him.

As I went up his dark stairway in the Temple and came to the passage that led to the outer room, I saw standing in a corner the two bundles of swords I had sent him, as if he had cast them out, which indeed he had done. After some delay in the outer room, the melancholy man in rusty black asked me, would I go in, and there sat Josiah Brooks at his table as if he had never left it since I took my departure the day before. He looked across at me with a scrutiny which seemed to be mingled with dislike and disapproval.

"Mr. O'Ruddy," he said, quiet-like, "it is not customary to send to a law office a number of swords, which are entirely out of place in such rooms. They have been counted and are found to number nine. I shall be obliged if you sign this receipt for them, accept delivery of the same, and remove them from the premises at your earliest convenience."

So I signed the receipt without a word and handed it back to him. Then I said,—

"I will send my servant for the swords as soon as I return to the inn."

He inclined his head the merest trifle, drew some papers toward him, and adjusted his glasses.

"It is my duty to tell you, Mr. O'Ruddy, that if you go into the courts with this case you will assuredly be defeated, and the costs will follow. There is also a possibility that when the civil proceedings are determined a criminal action against yourself may ensue."

"I told you, sir," said I, with my heart sinking, "I had no intention of troubling the courts at all at all. In the land I come from we are more inclined to settle a case with a good stout blackthorn than with the aid of a lawyer's wig. These papers say in black and white that I am the owner of Brede estate, and I intend to take possession of it."

"It is only right to add," continued Brooks, with that great air of calm I found so exasperating, "it is only right to add that you are in a position to cause great annoyance to the Earl of Westport. You can at least cast doubt on his title to the estate; and he stands this jeopardy, that if contrary to opinion your cause should prove successful,—and we must never forget that the law is very uncertain,—the Earl would have to account for the moneys he has drawn from the estate, which would run into many thousands of pounds, and, together with the loss of the property, would confront his lordship with a most serious situation. Your case, therefore, though weak from a strictly legal point of view, is exceptionally strong as a basis for compromise."

These words cheered me more than I can say, and it is an extraordinary fact that his frozen, even tone, and his lack of all interest in the proceedings had an elevating effect upon my spirits which I could not have believed possible.

"As it is a compromise that I'm after," said I, "what better case can we want?"

"Quite so," he resumed; "but as there is no encouragement in the strictly legal aspect of the plea, you will understand that no money-lender in London will advance a farthing on such unstable security. Even though I am acting in your interests, I could not take the responsibility of advising any capitalist to advance money on such uncertain tenure."

This threw me into the depths again; for, although I never care to meet trouble half way, I could not conceal from myself the fact that my bill at the "Pig and Turnip" had already reached proportions which left me no alternative but to slip quietly away in liquidation of the account. This was a thing I never liked to do; and when I am compelled to make that settlement I always take note of the amount, so that I may pay it if I am ever that way again and have more money than I need at the moment. Even if I succeeded in getting away from the inn, what could I do at Brede with no money at all?—for in that part of the country they would certainly look upon the Earl of Westport as the real owner of the property, and on me as a mere interloper; and if I could not get money on the documents in London, there was little chance of getting credit even for food at Brede.

"It is rather a blue look-out then," said I as cheerfully as I could.

"From a legal standpoint it is," concurred Mr. Brooks, as unconcerned as if his own payment did not depend on my raising the wind with these papers. "However, I have been instructed by a person who need not be named, who has indeed stipulated that no name shall be mentioned, to advance you the sum of five hundred guineas, which I have here in my drawer, and which I will now proceed to count out to you if you, in the mean time, will sign this receipt, which acquits me of all responsibility and certifies that I have handed the money over to you without rebate or reduction."

And with that the man pulled open a drawer and began to count out the glittering gold.

I sprang to my feet and brought my fist down on the table with a thump. "Now, by the Great Book of Kells, what do you mean by chopping and changing like a rudderless lugger in a ten-knot breeze? If the expedition is possible, and you had the money in your drawer all the time, why couldn't you have spoken it out like a man, without raising me to the roof and dropping me into the cellar in the way you've done?"

The man looked unruffled across the table at me. He pushed a paper a little farther from him, and said without any trace of emotion:

"Will you sign that receipt at the bottom, if you please?"

I sat down and signed it, but I would rather have jabbed a pen between his close-set lips to give him a taste of his own ink. Then I sat quiet and watched him count the gold, placing it all in neat little pillars before him. When it was finished, he said:

"Will you check the amount?"

"Is that gold mine?" I asked him.

"It is," he replied.

So I rose up without more ado and shovelled it into my pockets, and he put the receipt into the drawer after reading it over carefully, and arched his eyebrows without saying anything when he saw me pocket the coins uncounted.

"I wish you good afternoon," said I.

"I have to detain you one moment longer," he replied. "I have it on the most trustworthy information that the Earl of Westport is already aware of your intention to proceed to the country estate alleged to be owned by him. Your outgoings and incomings are watched, and I have to inform you that unless you proceed to Rye with extreme caution there is likelihood that you may be waylaid, and perchance violence offered to you."

"In that case I will reap a few more swords; but you need not fear, I shall not trouble you with them."

"They are out of place in a solicitor's chamber," he murmured gently. "Is there anything further I can do for you?"

"Yes," I said, "there is one thing more. I would be obliged if you could make me a bundle of legal-looking papers that are of no further use to you: a sheet of that parchment, and some of the blue stuff like what I carried. The Earl seems determined to have a packet of papers from me, and I would like to oblige him, as he's going to be my father-in-law, although he doesn't know it. I'd like some writing on these papers,—Latin for preference."

Josiah Brooks thought steadily for a few moments, then he called out and the melancholy rusty man came in. He took a few instructions and went out again. After a long time he entered once more and placed on the table a packet I would have sworn was my own. This the lawyer handed to me without a word, and the rusty man held open the door for me. So, with the bogus papers in my pocket, not to mention the genuine gold, I took my leave of Josiah and the Temple.

As soon as I was outside I saw at once that there was no time to be lost. If the Earl had guessed my intention, as was hinted, what would he do? Whenever I wish to answer a question like that to myself, I think what would I do if I were in the position of the other man. Now what I would have done, was this, if I were the Earl of Westport. I would send down to Brede all the ruffians at my disposal and garrison the house with them; and if the Earl did this, I would be on the outside, and he on the inside with advantage over me accordingly. Most men fight better behind stone walls than out in the open; and, besides, a few men can garrison a barracks that five hundred cannot take by assault. However, as it turned out, I was crediting the Earl with brains equal to my own, which in truth neither he nor any of his followers had below their bonnets. He trusted to intercepting me on the highway, just as if he hadn't already failed in that trick. But it takes a score of failures to convince an Englishman that he is on the wrong track altogether, while an Irishman has so many plans in his head that there's never time to try one of them twice in succession. But if I was wrong about the Earl, I was right about his daughter, when I suspected that she gave the lawyer the information about the Earl's knowledge of my plans, and I was also right when I credited the dear girl with drawing on her own funds to give me the golden guineas,—"and may each one of them," said I to myself, "prove a golden blessing on her head."

At any rate, there was no time to be lost, so I made straight to Father Donovan and asked him would he be ready to begin the journey to Rye after an early breakfast with me at the "Pig and Turnip."

You never saw a man in your life so delighted at the prospect of leaving London as was Father Donovan, and indeed I was glad to get away from the place myself. The good father said the big town confused him; and, although he was glad to have seen it, he was more happy still to get out of it and breathe a breath of fresh country air once more. So it was arranged that he would come to the "Pig and Turnip" next morning between six and seven o'clock. I then turned back to the shop of a tailor who for a long time had had two suits of clothing waiting for me that were entirely elegant in their design. The tailor, however, would not take the word of a gentleman that payment would follow the delivery of the costumes; for a little later would be more convenient for me to give him the money, and this made me doubt, in spite of the buttons and gold lace, if the garments were quite the fashionable cut, because a tailor who demands money on the spot shows he is entirely unaccustomed to deal with the upper classes; but I needed these clothes, as the two suits I possessed were getting a little the worse for wear.

When I went into his shop he was inclined to be haughty, thinking I had come to ask credit again; but when he saw the glitter of the money the man became obsequious to a degree that I never had witnessed before. I was affable to him, but distant; and when he offered me everything that was in his shop, I told him I would take time and consider it. He sent a servant following behind me with the goods, and so I came once more to the "Pig and Turnip," where I ordered Paddy and Jem to go to the Temple and fetch away the swords.

There seemed to be a pleased surprise on the face of the landlord when I called for my bill and paid it without question, chiding him for his delay in not sending it before. I engaged a horse for Father Donovan to ride on the following morning, and ordered breakfast ready at six o'clock, although I gave my commands that I was to be wakened an hour before daylight.

I spent the rest of the day in my room with Paddy and Jem, trying to knock into their heads some little notion of geography, wishing to make certain that they would sooner or later arrive in Rye without stumbling in on Belfast while on the way. My own knowledge of the face of the country was but meagre, so the landlord brought in a rough map of the south of England, and I cautioned the lads to get across London Bridge and make for the town of Maidstone, from where they could go due south, and if they happened on the coast they were to inquire for Rye and stay there until further orders. Jem Bottles, who thought he had brains in his head, said he would not be so open in telling every one we were going to Rye if he was me, because he was sure the Earl had people on the look-out, and money was plenty with his lordship. If every one knew when we were taking our departure, there would be no difficulty in following us and overcoming us on some lonely part of the road.

"Jem," said I, "that's all very true; but when they attacked us before they got very little change for their trouble; and if you are afraid of some slight commotion on the road, then you can stay back here in London."

"I am not afraid at all," said Jem, "but if there's anything particular you would like to see in Rye, there's no use in blocking the road to it."

"Sure, Jem, then be quiet about it."

Turning to the landlord, who was standing by, I said to him:

"My men fear we are going to be intercepted, so I think if I began the journey some time before daylight, and they followed me soon after, I might slip away unnoticed."

The landlord scratched his head and crinkled up his brow, for to think was unusual with him.

"I don't see," he said at last, "what you have to gain by going separately. It seems to me it would be better to go in a body, and then, if you are set on,

284

Stephen Crane

there are three instead of one."

"Very well," said I, "I'll take your caution into consideration, and act upon it or not as seems best when the time comes."

I told Paddy and Jem to sleep that night on the floor of my own room, and cautioned them to wake me an hour before daylight at the latest. Jem slept through until I had to kick him into consciousness; but poor Paddy, on the other hand, wakened me four times during the night,—the first time two hours after I had gone to sleep, and I could have cudgelled him for his pains, only I knew the lad's intentions were good. The last time I could stand it no longer, although it was still earlier than the hour I had said, so I got up and dressed myself in one of my new suits.

"And here, Paddy," said I, "you will wear the costume I had on yesterday."

"I couldn't think of it," said Paddy, drawing back from the grandeur.

"You are not to think, you impudent gossoon, but to do as I tell you. Put them on, and be as quick as you can."

"Troth, yer honour," said Paddy, still shrinking from them, "they're too grand for the likes o' me, an' few will be able to tell the differ atween us."

"You conceited spalpeen, do ye think there's no difference between us but what the clothes make? Get into them. I intend certain other people to take you for me in the dark, and I can warrant you these clothes, grand as you think them, will be very soundly beaten before this day is done with."

"Ochone, ochone," moaned Paddy, "am I to get another beating already, and some of the bruises not yet off my flesh?"

"Put on the coat now, and don't do so much talking. Sure it's all in the day's work, and I promise you before long you'll have your revenge on them."

"It's not revenge I'm after," wailed Paddy, "but a whole skin."

"Now you're transformed into a gentleman," said I, "and many a lad would take a beating for the privilege of wearing such gorgeous raiment. Here is a packet of paper that you're to keep in your pocket till it's taken away from you. And now I'll help you to saddle the horse, and once you're across London Bridge you'll likely come upon Maidstone and Rye some time in your life, for you can't get back over the river again except by the same bridge, so you'll know it when you come to it."

And so I mounted Paddy in the courtyard; the sleepy watchman undid the bolts in the big gate in the archway; and my man rode out into the darkness in no very cheerful humour over his journey. I came back and took forty winks more in the arm-chair, then, with much difficulty, I roused Jem Bottles. He also, without a murmur, but with much pride in his dressing, put on the second of my discarded suits, and seemed to fancy himself mightily in his new gear. With plenty of cord I tied and retied the two bundles of swords and placed them across the horse in front of his saddle, and it was not yet daylight when Jem jingled out into the street like a moving armoury. Two huge pistols were in his holsters, loaded and ready to his hand.

"By the Saints," said Jem proudly, "the man that meddles with me shall get hot lead or cold steel for his breakfast," and with that he went off at a canter, waking the echoes with the clash of his horse's shoes on the cobble-stones.

I went up stairs again and threw myself down on the bed and slept peacefully with no Paddy to rouse me until half-past-six, when a drawer knocked at the door and said that a priest that was downstairs would be glad to see me. I had him up in a jiffy, and a hot breakfast following fast on his heels, which we both laid in in quantities, for neither of us knew where our next meal was to be. However, the good father paid little thought to the future as long as the present meal was well served and satisfactory. He had no more idea than a spring lamb how we were to get to Rye, but thought perhaps a coach set out at that hour in the morning. When I told him I had a horse saddled and waiting for him, he was pleased, for Father Donovan could scamper across the country in Ireland with the best of them. So far as I could judge, the coast was clear, for every one we met between the "Pig and Turnip" and the bridge seemed honest folk intent on getting early to their work. It was ten minutes past seven when we clattered across the bridge and set our faces toward Rye.

CHAPTER XXXI

Looking back over my long life I scarcely remember any day more pleasant than that I spent riding side by side with Father Donovan from London to Rye. The fine old man had a fund of entertaining stories, and although I had heard them over and over again there was always something fresh in his way of telling them, and now and then I recognized a narrative that had once made two separate stories, but which had now become welded into one in the old man's mind. There was never anything gloomy in these anecdotes, for they always showed the cheerful side of life and gave courage to the man that wanted to do right; for in all of Father Donovan's stories the virtuous were always made happy. We talked of our friends and acquaintances, and if he ever knew anything bad about a man he never told it; while if I mentioned it he could always say something good of him to balance it, or at least to mitigate the opinion that might be formed of it. He was always doing some man a good turn or speaking a comforting word for him.

"O'Ruddy," he said, "I spent most of the day yesterday writing letters to those that could read them in our part of Ireland, setting right the rumours that had come back to us, which said you were fighting duels and engaged in brawls, but the strangest story of all was the one about your forming a friendship with a highwayman, who, they said, committed robberies on the road and divided the spoil with you, and here I find you without a servant at all at all, leading a quiet, respectable life at a quiet, respectable inn. It's not even in a tavern that I first come across you, but kneeling devoutly, saying a prayer in your mother church. I see you leaving your inn having paid your bill like a gentleman, when they said you took night-leave of most of the hostelries in England. Dear me, and there was the landlord bowing to you as if you were a prince, and all his servants in a row with the utmost respect for you. Ah, O'Ruddy, it's men like you that gives the good name to Ireland, and causes her to be looked up to by all the people of the world."

I gave Father Donovan heartfelt thanks for his kindness, and prayed to myself that we would not come upon Jem Bottles on the road, and that we would be left unmolested on our journey until we saw the sea-coast. Of course, if we were set upon, it would not be my fault, and it's not likely he would blame me; but if we came on Bottles, he was inclined to be very easy in conversation, and, in spite of my warnings, would let slip words that would shock the old priest. But when a day begins too auspiciously, its luck is apt to change before the sun sets, as it was with me.

It was nearing mid-day, and we were beginning to feel a trifle hungry, yet were in a part of the country that gave little promise of an inn, for it was a lonely place with heath on each side of the road, and, further on, a bit of forest. About half-way through this wooded plain an astonishing sight met my eyes. Two saddled horses were tied to a tree, and by the side of the road appeared to be a heap of nine or ten saddles, on one of which a man was sitting, comfortably eating a bit of bread, while on another a second man, whose head was tied up in a white cloth, lay back in a recumbent position, held upright by the saddlery. Coming closer, I was disturbed to see that the man eating was Jem Bottles, while the other was undoubtedly poor Paddy, although his clothes were so badly torn that I had difficulty in recognizing them as my own. As we drew up Jem stood and saluted with his mouth full, while Paddy groaned deeply. I was off my horse at once and ran to Paddy.

"Where are ye hurted?" said I.

"I'm killed," said Paddy.

"I've done the best I could for him," put in Jem Bottles. "He'll be all right in a day or two."

"I'll not," said Paddy, with more strength than one would suspect; "I'll not be all right in a day or two, nor in a week or two, nor in a month or two, nor in a year or two; I'm killed entirely."

"You're not," said Bottles. "When I was on the highway I never minded a little clip like that."

"Hush, Bottles," said I, "you talk altogether too much. Paddy," cried I, "get on your feet, and show yer manners here to Father Donovan."

288

Paddy got on his feet with a celerity which his former attitude would not have allowed one to believe possible.

"My poor boy!" said the kindly priest; "who has misused you?" and he put his two hands on the sore head.

"About two miles from here," said Paddy, "I was set on by a score of men—"

"There was only nine of them," interrupted Jem, "count the saddles."

"They came on me so sudden and unexpected that I was off my horse before I knew there was a man within reach. They had me down before I could say my prayers, and cudgelled me sorely, tearing my clothes, and they took away the packet of papers you gave me, sir. Sure I tried to guard it with my life, an' they nearly took both."

"I am certain you did your best, Paddy," said I; "and it's sorry I am to see you injured."

"Then they rode away, leaving me, sore wounded, sitting on the side of the road," continued Paddy. "After a while I come to myself, for I seemed dazed; and, my horse peacefully grazing beside me, I managed to get on its back, and turned toward London in the hope of meeting you; but instead of meeting you, sir, I came upon Jem with his pile of saddles, and he bound up my head and did what he could to save me, although I've a great thirst on me at this moment that's difficult to deal with."

"There's a ditch by the side of the road," said the priest.

"Yes," said Paddy sadly; "I tried some of that."

I went to my pack on the horse and took out a bottle and a leather cup. Paddy drank and smacked his lips with an ecstasy that gave us hope for his ultimate recovery. Jem Bottles laughed, and to close his mouth I gave him also some of the wine.

"I hope," said Father Donovan with indignation, "that the miscreant who misused you will be caught and punished."

"I punished them," said Jem, drawing the back of his hand across his mouth.

"We'll hear about it another time," said I, having my suspicions.

"Let the good man go on," begged Father Donovan, who is not without human curiosity.

Jem needed no second bidding.

"Your Reverence," he said, "I was jogging quietly on as a decent man should, when, coming to the edge of this forest, I saw approach me a party of horsemen, who were very hilarious and laughed loudly. If you look up and down the road and see how lonely it is, and then look at the wood, with no hedge between it and the highway, you'll notice the place was designed by Providence for such a meeting."

"Sure the public road is designed as a place for travellers to meet," said the father, somewhat bewildered by the harangue.

"Your Reverence is right, but this place could not afford better accommodation if I had made it myself. I struck into the wood before they saw me, tore the black lining from my hat, punched two holes in it for the eyes, and tied it around my forehead, letting it hang down over my face; then I primed my two pistols and waited for the gentlemen. When they were nearly opposite, a touch of the heels to my horse's flank was enough, and out he sprang into the middle of the road.

"'Stand and deliver!' I cried, pointing the pistols at them, the words coming as glibly to my lips as if I had said them no later ago than yesterday. 'Stand and deliver, ye—'" and here Jem glibly rattled out a stream of profane appellatives which was disgraceful to listen to.

"Tut, tut, Jem," I said, "you shouldn't speak like that. Any way we'll hear the rest another time."

"That's what I called them, sir," said Jem, turning to me with surprise, "you surely would not have me tell an untruth."

"I wouldn't have you tell anything. Keep quiet. Father Donovan is not interested in your recital."

"I beg your pardon, O'Ruddy," said Father Donovan, looking at me reproachfully; "but I am very much interested in this man's narrative."

"As any good man should be," continued Jem, "for these were arrant scoundrels; one of them I knew, and his name is Doctor Chord. He fell off his horse on the roadway at once and pleaded for mercy. I ordered the others instantly to hold their hands above their heads, and they did so, except one man who began fumbling in his holster, and then, to show him what I could do with a pistol, I broke his wrist. At the sound of the shot the horses began to plunge, nearly trampling Doctor Chord into the dust.

"'Clasp your hands above your heads, ye—'"

Here went on another stream of terrible language again, and in despair I sat down on the pile of saddles, allowing things to take their course. Jem continued:

"The lesson of the pistol was not misread by my gentlemen, when they noticed I had a second loaded one; so, going to them one after the other I took their weapons from them and flung them to the foot of that tree, where, if you look, you may see them now. Then I took a contribution from each one, just as you do in church, your Reverence. I'm sure you have a collection for the poor, and that was the one I was taking up this day. I have not counted them yet," said the villain turning to me, "but I think I have between sixty and seventy guineas, which are all freely at your disposal, excepting a trifle for myself and Paddy there. There's no plaster like gold for a sore head, your Reverence. I made each one of them dismount and take off his saddle and throw it in the pile; then I had them mount again and drove them with curses toward London, and very glad they were to escape."

"He did not get the papers again," wailed Paddy, who was not taking as jubilant a view of the world as was Jem at that moment.

"I knew nothing of the papers," protested Bottles. "If you had told me about the papers, I would have had them, and if I had been carrying the papers these fellows would not have made away with them."

"Then," said the horrified priest, "you did not commit this action in punishment for the injury done to your friend? You knew nothing of that at the time. You set on these men thinking they were simple travellers."

"O, I knew nothing of what happened to Paddy till later, but you see, your Reverence, these men themselves were thieves and robbers. In their case it was nine men against one poor half-witted Irish lad—"

"Half-witted yourself," cried Paddy angrily.

"But you, sir," continued his Reverence, "were simply carrying out the action of a highwayman. Sir, you are a highwayman."

"I was, your Reverence, but I have reformed."

"And this pile of saddles attests your reformation!" said the old man, shaking his head.

"But you see, your Reverence, this is the way to look at it—"

"Keep quiet, Jem!" cried I in disgust.

"How can I keep quiet," urged Bottles, "when I am unjustly accused? I do not deny that I was once a highwayman, but Mr. O'Ruddy converted me to better ways—"

"Highways," said Paddy, adding, with a sniff, "Half-witted!"

"Your Reverence, I had no more intention of robbing those men than you have at this moment. I didn't know they were thieves themselves. Then what put it into my head to jump into the wood and on with a mask before you could say, Bristol town? It's the mysterious ways of Providence, your Reverence. Even I didn't understand it at the time, but the moment I heard Paddy's tale I knew at once I was but an instrument in the hand of Providence, for I had not said, 'Stand and deliver!' this many a day, nor thought of it."

"It may be so; it may be so," murmured the priest, more to himself than to us; but I saw that he was much troubled, so, getting up, I said to Paddy:

"Are you able to ride farther on to-day?"

"If I'd another sup from the cup, sir, I think I could," whereat Jem Bottles laughed again, and I gave them both a drink of wine.

"What are you going to do with all this saddlery?" said I to Bottles.

"I don't know anything better than to leave it here; but I think, your honour, the pistols will come handy, for they're all very good ones, and Paddy and me can carry them between us, or I can make two bags from these leather packs, and Paddy could carry the lot in them, as I do the swords."

"Very well," I said. "Make your preparations as quickly as you can and let us be off, for this latest incident, in spite of you, Jem, may lead to pursuit and get us into trouble before we are ready for it."

"No fear, sir," said Jem confidently. "One thief does not lay information against another. If they had been peaceable travellers, that would be another thing; but, as I said, Providence is protecting us, no doubt because of the presence of his Reverence here, and not for our own merits."

"Be thankful it is the reward of some one else's merits you, reap, Bottles, instead of your own. No more talk now, but to horse and away."

For some miles Father Donovan rode very silently. I told him something of my meeting with Jem Bottles and explained how I tried to make an honest man of him, while this was the first lapse I had known since his conversion. I even pretended that I had some belief in his own theory of the interposition of Providence, and Father Donovan was evidently struggling to acquire a similar feeling, although he seemed to find some difficulty in the contest. He admitted that this robbery appeared but even justice; still he ventured to hope that Jem Bottles would not take the coincidence as a precedent, and that he would never mistake the dictates of Providence for the desires of his own nature.

"I will speak with the man later," he said, "and hope that my words will make some impression upon him. There was a trace of exaltation in his recital that showed no sign of a contrite spirit."

On account of the delay at the roadside it was well past twelve o'clock before we reached Maidstone, and there we indulged in a good dinner that put heart into all of us, while the horses had time to rest and feed. The road to Rye presented no difficulties whatever, but under ordinary conditions I would have rested a night before travelling to the coast. There would be a little delay before the Earl discovered the useless nature of the papers which he had been at such expense to acquire, but after the discovery there was no doubt in my mind that he would move upon Brede as quickly as horses could carry his men, so I insisted upon pressing on to Rye that night, and we reached the town late with horses that were very tired. It was a long distance for a man of the age of Father Donovan to travel in a day, but he stood the journey well, and enjoyed his supper and his wine with the best of us.

We learned that there was no boat leaving for France for several days, and this disquieted me, for I would have liked to see Father Donovan off early next morning, for I did not wish to disclose my project to the peace-loving man. I must march on Brede next day if I was to get there in time, and so there was no longer any possibility of concealing my designs. However, there was no help for it, and I resolved to be up bright and early in the morning and engage a dozen men whom I could trust to stand by me. I also intended to purchase several cartloads of provisions, so that if a siege was attempted we could not be starved out. All this I would accomplish at as early an hour as possible, get the carts on their way to Brede, and march at the head of the men myself; so I went to bed with a somewhat troubled mind, but fell speedily into a dreamless sleep nevertheless, and slept till broad daylight.

CHAPTER XXXII

I found Rye a snug little town, and so entirely peaceable-looking that when I went out in the morning I was afraid there would be nobody there who would join me in the hazardous task of taking possession of the place of so well-known a man as the Earl of Westport. But I did not know Rye then as well as I do now: it proved to be a great resort for smugglers when they were off duty and wished to enjoy the innocent relaxation of a town after the comparative loneliness of the sea-coast, although, if all the tales they tell me are true, the authorities sometimes made the sea-shore a little too lively for their comfort. Then there were a number of seafaring men looking for a job, and some of them had the appearance of being pirates in more prosperous days.

As I wandered about I saw a most gigantic ruffian, taking his ease with his back against the wall, looking down on the shipping.

"If that man's as bold as he's strong," said I to myself, "and I had half a dozen more like him, we'd hold Brede House till the day there's liberty in Ireland;" so I accosted him.

"The top o' the morning to you," said I genially.

He eyed me up and down, especially glancing at the sword by my side, and then said civilly:

"The same to you, sir. You seem to be looking for some one?"

"I am," said I, "I'm looking for nine men."

"If you'll tell me their names I'll tell you where to find them, for I know everybody in Rye."

"If that's the case you'll know their names, which is more than I do myself."

"Then you're not acquainted with them?"

"I am not; but if you'll tell me your name I think then I'll know one of them."

There was a twinkle in his eye as he said:

"They call me Tom Peel."

"Then Tom," said I, "are there eight like you in the town of Rye?"

"Not quite as big perhaps," said Tom, "but there's plenty of good men here, as the French have found out before now,—yes, and the constables as well. What do you want nine men for?"

"Because I have nine swords and nine pistols that will fit that number of courageous subjects."

"Then it's not for the occupation of agriculture you require them?" said Peel with the hint of a laugh. "There's a chance of a cut in the ribs, I suppose, for swords generally meet other swords."

"You're right in that; but I don't think the chance is very strong."

"And perhaps a term in prison when the scrimmage is ended?"

"No fear of that at all at all; for if any one was to go to prison it would be me, who will be your leader, and not you, who will be my dupes, do you see?"

Peel shrugged his shoulders.

"My experience of the world is that the man with gold lace on his coat goes free, while they punish the poor devil in the leather jacket. But, turn the scheme out bad or ill, how much money is at the end of it?"

"There'll be ten guineas at the end of it for each man, win or lose."

"And when will the money be paid?"

"Half before you leave Rye, the other half in a week's time, and perhaps before,—a week's time at the latest; but I want men who will not turn white if a blunderbuss happens to go off."

The rascallion smiled and spat contemptuously in the dust before him.

"If you show me the guineas," said he, "I'll show you the men."

"Here's five of them, to begin with, that won't be counted against you. There'll be five more in your pocket when we leave Rye, and a third five when the job's ended."

His big hand closed over the coins.

"I like your way of speaking," he said. "Now where are we to go?"

"To the strong house of Brede, some seven or eight miles from here. I do not know how far exactly, nor in what direction."

"I am well acquainted with it," said Peel. "It was a famous smuggler's place in its time."

"I don't mean a smuggler's place," said I. "I am talking of the country house of the Earl of Westport."

"Yes, curse him, that's the spot I mean. Many a nobleman's house is put to purposes he learns little of, although the Earl is such a scoundrel he may well have been in with the smugglers and sold them to the government."

"Did he sell them?"

"Somebody sold them."

There was a scowl on Peel's face that somehow encouraged me, although I liked the look of the ruffian from the first.

"You're an old friend of his lordship's, then?" said I.

"He has few friends in Rye or about Rye. If you're going to do anything against Westport, I'll get you a hundred men for nothing if there's a chance of escape after the fight."

"Nine men will do me, if they're the right stuff. You will have good cover to sleep under, plenty to eat and drink, and then I expect you to hold Brede House against all the men the Earl of Westport can bring forward."

"That's an easy thing," said Peel, his eye lighting up. "And if worse comes to the worst I know a way out of the house that's neither through door or window nor up a chimney. Where will I collect your men?"

"Assemble them on the road to Brede, quietly, about half a mile from Rye. Which direction is Brede from here?"

"It lies to the west, between six and seven miles away as the crow flies."

"Very well, collect your men as quickly as you can, and send word to me at the 'Anchor.' Tell your messenger to ask for The O'Ruddy."

Now I turned back to the tavern sorely troubled what I would do with Father Donovan. He was such a kindly man that he would be loath to shake hands with me at the door of the inn, as he had still two or three days to stop, so I felt sure he would insist on accompanying me part of the way. I wished I could stop and see him off on his ship; but if we were to get inside of Brede's House unopposed, we had to act at once. I found Paddy almost recovered from the assault of the day before. He had a bandage around his forehead, which, with his red hair, gave him a hideous appearance, as if the whole top of his head had been smashed. Poor Paddy was getting so used to a beating each day that I wondered wouldn't he be lonesome when the beatings ceased and there was no enemy to follow him.

Father Donovan had not yet appeared, and the fire was just lit in the kitchen to prepare breakfast, so I took Jem and Paddy with me to the eating shop of the town, and there a sleepy-looking shop-keeper let us in, mightily resenting this early intrusion, but changed his demeanour when he understood the size of the order I was giving him, and the fact that I was going to pay good gold; for it would be a fine joke on The O'Ruddy if the Earl surrounded the house with his men and starved him out. So it was no less than three cartloads of provisions I ordered, though one of them was a cartload of drink, for I thought the company I had hired would have a continuous thirst on them, being seafaring men and smugglers, and I knew that strong, sound ale was brewed in Rye.

The business being finished, we three went back to the "Anchor," and found an excellent breakfast and an excellent man waiting for me, the latter

298

being Father Donovan, although slightly impatient for closer acquaintance with the former.

When breakfast was done with, I ordered the three horses saddled, and presently out in the courtyard Paddy was seated on his nag with the two sacks of pistols before him, and Jem in like manner with his two bundles of swords. The stableman held my horse, so I turned to Father Donovan and grasped him warmly by the hand.

"A safe journey across the Channel to you, Father Donovan, and a peaceful voyage from there to Rome, whichever road you take. If you write to me in the care of the landlord of this inn I'll be sending and sending till I get your letter, and when you return I'll be standing and watching the sea, at whatever point you land in England, if you'll but let me know in time. And so good-bye to you, Father Donovan, and God bless you, and I humbly beseech your own blessing in return."

The old man's eyes grew wider and wider as I went on talking and talking and shaking him by the hand.

"What's come over you, O'Ruddy?" he said, "and where are you going?"

"I am taking a long journey to the west and must have an early start."

"Nonsense," cried Father Donovan, "it's two or three days before I can leave this shore, so I'll accompany you a bit of the way."

"You mustn't think of it, Father, because you had a long day's ride yesterday, and I want you to take care of yourself and take thought on your health."

"Tush, I'm as fresh as a boy this morning. Landlord, see that the saddle is put on that horse I came into Rye with."

The landlord at once rushed off and gave the order, while I stood there at my wit's end.

"Father Donovan," said I, "I'm in great need of haste at this moment, and we must ride fast, so I'll just bid good-bye to you here at this comfortable spot, and you'll sit down at your ease in that big arm-chair."

"I'll do nothing of the kind, O'Ruddy. What's troubling you, man? and why are you in such a hurry this morning, when you said nothing of it yesterday?"

"Father, I said nothing of it yesterday, but sure I acted it. See how we rode on and on in spite of everything, and did the whole journey from London to Rye between breakfast and supper. Didn't that give you a hint that I was in a hurry?"

"Well, it should have done, it should have done, O'Ruddy; still, I'll go a bit of the way with you and not delay you."

"But we intend to ride very fast, Father."

"Ah, it's an old man you're thinking I'm getting to be. Troth, I can ride as fast as any one of the three of you, and a good deal faster than Paddy."

At this moment the landlord came bustling in.

"Your Reverence's horse is ready," he said.

And so there was nothing for it but to knock the old man down, which I hadn't the heart to do. It is curious how stubborn some people are; but Father Donovan was always set in his ways, and so, as we rode out of Rye to the west, with Paddy and Jem following us, I had simply to tell his Reverence all about it, and you should have seen the consternation on his countenance.

"Do you mean to tell me you propose to take possession of another man's house and fight him if he comes to claim his own?"

"I intend that same thing, your Reverence;" for now I was as stubborn as the old gentleman himself, and it was not likely I was going to be put off my course when I remembered the happiness that was ahead of me; but there's little use in trying to explain to an aged priest what a young man is willing to do for the love of the sweetest girl in all the land.

"O'Ruddy," he said, "you'll be put in prison. It's the inside of a gaol, and not the inside of a castle, you'll see. It's not down the aisle of a church you'll

300

march with your bride on your arm, but its hobbling over the cobbles of a Newgate passage you'll go with manacles on your legs. Take warning from me, my poor boy, who would be heart-broken to see harm come to you, and don't run your neck into the hangman's noose, thinking it the matrimonial halter. Turn back while there's yet time, O'Ruddy."

"Believe me, Father Donovan, it grieves me to refuse you anything, but I cannot turn back."

"You'll be breaking the law of the land."

"But the law of the land is broken every day in our district of Ireland, and not too many words said about it."

"Oh, O'Ruddy, that's a different thing. The law of the land in Ireland is the law of the alien."

"Father, you're not logical. It's the alien I'm going to fight here,"—but before the father could reply we saw ahead of us the bulky form of Tom Peel, and ranged alongside of the road, trying to look very stiff and military-like, was the most awkward squad of men I had ever clapped eyes on; but determined fellows they were, as I could see at a glance when I came fornenst them, and each man pulled a lock of his hair by way of a salute.

"Do you men understand the use of a sword and a pistol?" said I.

The men smiled at each other as though I was trying some kind of a joke on them.

"They do, your honour," answered Tom Peel on their behalf. "Each one of them can sling a cutlass to the king's taste, and fire a pistol without winking, and there are now concealed in the hedge half a dozen blunderbusses in case they should be needed. They make a loud report and have a good effect on the enemy, even when they do no harm."

"Yes, we'll have the blunderbusses," said I, and with that the men broke rank, burst through the hedge, and came back with those formidable weapons. "I have ammunition in the carts," I said, "did you see anything of them?"

"The carts have gone on to the west, your honour; but we'll soon overtake

301

them," and the men smacked their lips when they thought of the one that had the barrels in it. Now Paddy came forward with the pistols, and Bottles followed and gave each man a blade, while I gave each his money.

"O dear! O dear!" groaned Father Donovan.

"There's just a chance we may be attacked before we get to Brede, and, Father, though I am loath to say good-bye, still it must be said. It's rare glad I'll be when I grip your hand again."

"All in good time; all in good time," said Father Donovan; "I'll go a bit farther along the road with you and see how your men march. They would fight better and better behind a hedge than in the open, I'm thinking."

"They'll not have to fight in the open, Father," said I, "but they'll be comfortably housed if we get there in time. Now, Peel, I make you captain of the men, as you've got them together, and so, Forward, my lads."

They struck out along the road, walking a dozen different kinds of steps, although there were only nine of them; some with the swords over their shoulders, some using them like walking-sticks, till I told them to be more careful of the points; but they walked rapidly and got over the ground, for the clank of the five guineas that was in each man's pocket played the right kind of march for them.

"Listen to reason, O'Ruddy, and even now turn back," said Father Donovan.

"I'll not turn back now," said I, "and, sure, you can't expect it of me. You're an obstinate man yourself, if I must say so, Father."

"It's a foolhardy exploit," he continued, frowning. "There's prison at the end of it for some one," he murmured.

"No, it's the House of Brede, Father, that's at the end of it."

"Supposing the Earl of Westport brings a thousand men against you,—what are you going to do?"

"Give them the finest fight they have ever seen in this part of England."

302

In spite of himself I saw a sparkle in Father Donovan's eye. The nationality of him was getting the better of his profession.

"If it were legitimate and lawful," at last he said, "it would be a fine sight to see."

"It will be legitimate and lawful enough when the Earl and myself come to terms. You need have no fear that we're going to get into the courts, Father."

"Do you think he'll fight?" demanded the father suddenly, with a glint in his eyes that I have seen in my own father's when he was telling us of his battles in France.

"Fight? Why of course he'll fight, for he's as full of malice as an egg's full of meat; but nevertheless he's a sensible old curmudgeon, when the last word's said, and before he'll have it noised over England that his title to the land is disputed he'll give me what I want, although at first he'll try to master me."

"Can you depend on these men?"

"I think I can. They're old smugglers and pirates, most of them."

"I wonder who the Earl will bring against you?" said Father Donovan, speaking more to himself than to me. "Will it be farmers or regular soldiers?"

"I expect they will be from among his own tenantry; there's plenty of them, and they'll all have to do his bidding."

"But that doesn't give a man courage in battle?"

"No, but he'll have good men to lead them, even if he brings them from London."

"I wouldn't like to see you attacked by real soldiers; but I think these men of yours will give a good account of themselves if there's only peasantry brought up against them. Sure, the peasantry in this country is not so warlike as in our own,"—and there was a touch of pride in the father's remark that went to my very heart.

After riding in silence for a while, meditating with head bowed, he looked suddenly across at me, his whole face lighted up with delicious remembrance.

"Wouldn't you like to have Mike Sullivan with you this day," he cried, naming the most famous fighter in all the land, noted from Belfast to our own Old Head of Kinsale.

"I'd give many a guinea," I said, "to have Mike by my side when the Earl comes on."

The old father suddenly brought down his open hand with a slap on his thigh.

"I'm going to stand by you, O'Ruddy," he said.

"I'm glad to have your blessing on the job at last, Father," said I; "for it was sore against me to go into this business when you were in a contrary frame of mind."

"You'll not only have my blessing, O'Ruddy, but myself as well. How could I sail across the ocean and never know which way the fight came out? and then, if it is to happen in spite of me, the Lord pity the frailness of mankind, but I'd like to see it. I've not seen a debate since the Black Fair of Bandon."

By this time we had overtaken the hirelings with their carts, and the men were swinging past them at a good pace.

"Whip up your horses," said I to the drivers, "and get over the ground a little faster. It's not gunpowder that's in those barrels, and when we reach the house there will be a drink for every one of you."

There was a cheer at this, and we all pushed on with good hearts. At last we came to a lane turning out from the main road, and then to the private way through fields that led to Brede House. So far there had been no one to oppose us, and now, setting spurs to our horses, we galloped over the private way, which ran along the side of a gentle hill until one end of the mansion came into view. It seemed likely there was no suspicion who we were, for a man digging in the garden, stood up and took off his cap to us. The front door looked like the Gothic entrance of a church, and I sprang from my horse and knocked loudly against the studded oak. An old man opened the door without any measure of caution, and I stepped inside. I asked him who he was, and he said he was the caretaker.

"How many beside yourself are in this house?"

He said there was only himself, his wife, and a kitchen wench, and two of the gardeners, while the family was in London.

"Well," said I, "I'd have you know that I'm the family now, and that I'm at home. I am the owner of Brede estate."

"You're not the Earl of Westport!" said the old man, his eyes opening wide.

"No, thank God, I'm not!"

He now got frightened and would have shut the door, but I gently pushed him aside. I heard the tramp of the men, and, what was more, the singing of a sea song, for they were nearing the end of their walk and thinking that something else would soon pass their lips besides the tune. The old man was somewhat reassured when he saw the priest come in; but dismay and terror took hold of him when the nine men with their blunderbusses and their swords came singing around a corner of the house and drew up in front of it. By and by the carts came creaking along, and then every man turned to and brought the provisions inside of the house and piled them up in the kitchen in an orderly way, while the old man, his wife, the wench, and the two gardeners stood looking on with growing signs of panic upon them.

"Now, my ancient caretaker," said I to the old man, in the kindest tones I could bring to my lips, so as not to frighten him more than was already the case, "what is the name of that little village over yonder?" and I pointed toward the west, where, on the top of a hill, appeared a church and a few houses.

"That, sir," he said, with his lips trembling, "is the village of Brede."

"Is there any decent place there where you five people can get lodging; for you see that this house is now filled with men of war, and so men of peace should be elsewhere? Would they take you in over at the village?"

"Yes, sir, it is like they would."

"Very well. Here is three guineas to divide among you, and in a week or thereabouts you will be back in your own place, so don't think disaster has fallen on you."

The old man took the money, but seemed in a strange state of hesitancy about leaving.

"You will be unhappy here," I said, "for there will be gun-firing and sword-playing. Although I may not look it, I am the most bloodthirsty swordsman in England, with a mighty uncertain temper on me at times. So be off, the five of you!"

"But who is to be here to receive the family?" he asked.

"What family?"

"Sir, we had word last night that the Earl of Westport and his following would come to this house to-day at two of the clock, and we have much ado preparing for them; for the messenger said that he was bringing many men with him. I thought at first that you were the men, or I would not have let you in."

"Now the Saints preserve us," cried I, "they'll be on us before we get the windows barricaded. Tom Peel," I shouted, "set your men to prepare the defence at once, and you'll have only a few hours to do it in. Come, old man, take your wife and your gardeners, and get away."

"But the family, sir, the family," cried the old man, unable to understand that they should not be treated with the utmost respect.

"I will receive the family. What is that big house over there in the village?"

"The Manor House, sir."

"Very well, get you gone, and tell them to prepare the Manor House for the Earl of Westport and his following; for he cannot lodge here to-night,"—

and with that I was compelled to drag them forth, the old woman crying and the wench snivelling in company. I patted the ancient wife on the shoulder and told her there was nothing to be feared of; but I saw my attempt at consolation had little effect.

Tom Peel understood his business; he had every door barred and stanchioned, and the windows protected, as well as the means to his hand would allow. Up stairs he knocked out some of the diamond panes so that the muzzle of a blunderbuss would go through. He seemed to know the house as if it was his own; and in truth the timbers and materials for defence which he conjured up from the ample cellars or pulled down from the garret seemed to show that he had prepared the place for defence long since.

"Your honour," he said, "two dangers threaten this house which you may not be aware of."

"And what are those, Tom?" I asked.

"Well, the least serious one is the tunnel. There is a secret passage from this house down under the valley and out and up near the church. If it was not guarded they could fill this house unknown to you. I will stop this end of it with timber if your honour gives the word. There's not many knows of it, but the Earl of Westport is certain to have the knowledge, and some of his servants as well."

"Lead me to this tunnel, Tom," said I, astonished at his information.

We came to a door in one of the lower rooms that opened on a little circular stone stairway, something like a well, and, going down to the bottom, we found a tunnel in which a short man could stand upright.

"Thunder and turf, Tom!" said I, "what did they want this for?"

"Well, some thought it was to reach the church, but no one ever lived in this house that was so anxious to get to church that he would go underground to it. Faith, they've been a godless lot in Brede Place until your honour came, and we were glad to see you bring a priest with you. It put new heart in the men; they think he'll keep off Sir Goddard Oxenbridge."

"Does he live near here? What has he to do with the place?"

"He is dead long since, sir, and was owner of this house. Bullet wouldn't harm him, nor steel cut him, so they sawed him in two with a wooden saw down by the bridge in front. He was a witch of the very worst kind, your honour. You hear him groaning at the bridge every night, and sometimes he walks through the house himself in two halves, and then every body leaves the place. And that is our most serious danger, your honour. When Sir Goddard takes to groaning through these rooms at night, you'll not get a man to stay with you, sir; but as he comes up from the pit by the will of the Devil we expect his Reverence to ward him off."

Now this was most momentous news, for I would not stop in the place myself if a ghost was in the habit of walking through it; but I cheered up Tom Peel by telling him that no imp of Satan could appear in the same county as Father Donovan, and he passed on the word to the men, to their mighty easement.

We had a splendid dinner in the grand hall, and each of us was well prepared for it; Father Donovan himself, standing up at the head of the table, said the holy words in good Latin, and I was so hungry that I was glad the Latins were in the habit of making short prayers.

Father Donovan and I sat at table with a bottle for company, and now that he knew all about the situation, I was overjoyed to find him an inhabitant of the same house; for there was no gentleman in all the company, except himself, for me to talk with.

Suddenly there was a blast of a bugle, and a great fluttering outside. The lower windows being barricaded, it was not possible to see out of them, and I was up the stair as quick as legs could carry me; and there in front were four horses harnessed to a great carriage, and in it sat the old Earl and the Countess, and opposite them who but Lady Mary herself, and her brother, Lord Strepp. Postilions rode two of the horses, and the carriage was surrounded by a dozen mounted men.

Everybody was looking at the house and wondering why nobody was there to welcome them, and very forbidding this stronghold must have seemed to those who expected to find the doors wide open when they drove up. I undid the bolts of one of the diamond-paned windows, and, throwing it open, leaned with my arms on the sill, my head and shoulders outside.

"Good day to your ladyship and your lordship," I cried,—and then all eyes were turned on me,—"I have just this day come into my inheritance, and I fear the house is not in a state to receive visitors. The rooms are all occupied by desperate men and armed; but I have given orders to your servants to prepare the Manor House in the village for your accommodation; so, if you will be so good as to drive across the valley, you will doubtless meet with a better reception than I can give you at this moment. When you come again, if there are no ladies of the party, I can guarantee you will have no complaint to make of the warmth of your reception."

His lordship sat dumb in his carriage, and for once her ladyship appeared to find difficulty in choosing words that would do justice to her anger. I could not catch a glimpse of Lady Mary's face at all at all, for she kept it turned toward the village; but young Lord Strepp rose in the carriage, and, shaking his fist at me, said:

"By God, O'Ruddy, you shall pay for this;" but the effect of the words was somewhat weakened by reason that his sister, Lady Mary, reached out and pulled him by the coat-tails, which caused him to be seated more suddenly than he expected; then she gave me one rapid glance of her eye and turned away her face again.

Now his lordship, the great Earl of Westport, spoke, but not to me.

"Drive to the village," he said to the postilions; then horsemen and carriage clattered down the hill.

We kept watch all that night, but were not molested. In the southern part of the house Father Donovan found a well-furnished chapel, and next morning held mass there, which had a very quieting effect on the men, especially as Oxenbridge had not walked during the night. The only one of them who did not attend mass was Jem Bottles, who said he was not well enough and therefore would remain on watch. Just as mass was finished Jem appeared in the gallery of the chapel and shouted excitedly:

"They're coming, sir; they're coming!"

I never before saw a congregation dismiss themselves so speedily. They were at their posts even before Tom Peel could give the order. The opposing party was leaving the village and coming down the hill when I first caught sight of them from an upper window. There seemed somewhere between half a dozen and a dozen horsemen, and behind them a great mob of people on foot that fairly covered the hillside. As they crossed the brook and began to come up, I saw that their leader was young Lord Strepp himself, and Jem whispered that the horsemen behind him were the very men he had encountered on the road between London and Maidstone. The cavalry were well in advance, and it seemed that the amateur infantry took less and less pleasure in their excursion the nearer they drew to the gloomy old house, so much so that Lord Strepp turned back among them and appeared to be urging them to make haste. However, their slow progress may be explained by the fact that a certain number of them were carrying a huge piece of timber, so heavy that they had to stagger along cautiously.

"That," said Tom Peel, who stood at my elbow, "is to batter in the front door and take us by storm. If you give the word, your honour, we can massacre the lot o' them before they get three blows struck."

"Give command to the men, Peel," said I, "not to shoot any one if they can help it. Let them hold their fire till they are within fifty yards or so of the front, then pass the word to fire into the gravel of the terrace; and when you shoot let every man yell as if he were a dozen, and keep dead silence till that moment. I'll hold up my hand when I want you to fire."

There was a deep stillness over all the beautiful landscape. The bushes and the wood, however, were an exception to this, although the songs of the birds among the trees and singing of the larks high in the air seemed not to disturb the silence; but the whole air of the country-side was a suggestion of restful peace, at great variance with the designs of the inhabitants, who were preparing to attack each other.

310

Father Donovan stood beside me, and I saw his lips moving in prayer; but his eyes were dancing with irredeemable delight, while his breath came quick and expectant.

"I'm afraid those chaps will run at the first volley," he said, smiling at me. "They come on very slowly and must be a great trial to the young lord that's leading them."

It was indeed a trial to the patience of all of us, for the time seemed incredibly long till they arrived at the spot where I had determined they should at least hear the report of the blunderbusses, although I hoped none of them would feel the effects of the firing. Indeed, the horsemen themselves, with the exception of Lord Strepp, appeared to take little comfort in their position, and were now more anxious to fall behind and urge on the others on foot than to lead the band with his lordship.

I let them all get very close, then held up my hand, and you would think pandemonium was let loose. I doubt if all the cannon in Cork would have made such a noise, and the heathen Indians we read of in America could not have given so terrifying a yell as came from my nine men. The blunderbusses were more dangerous than I supposed, and they tore up the gravel into a shower of small stones that scattered far and wide, and made many a man fall down, thinking he was shot. Then the mob ran away with a speed which made up for all lost time coming the other direction. Cries of anguish were heard on every side, which made us all laugh, for we knew none of them were hurted. The horses themselves seemed seized with panic; they plunged and kicked like mad, two riders being thrown on the ground, while others galloped across the valley as if they were running away; but I suspect that their owners were slyly spurring them on while pretending they had lost control of them. Lord Strepp and one or two others, however, stood their ground, and indeed his lordship spurred his horse up opposite the front door. One of my men drew a pistol, but I shouted at him:

"Don't shoot at that man, whatever he does," and the weapon was lowered.

I opened the window and leaned out.

"Well, Lord Strepp," cried I, "'tis a valiant crowd you have behind you."

"You cursed highwayman," he cried, "what do you expect to make by this?"

"I expect to see some good foot-racing; but you are under an error in your appellation. I am not a highwayman; it is Jem Bottles here who stopped nine of your men on the Maidstone road and piled their saddles by the side of it. Is it new saddlery you have, or did you make a roadside collection?"

"I'll have you out of that, if I have to burn the house over your head."

"I'll wager you'll not get any man, unless it's yourself, to come near enough to carry a torch to it. You can easily have me out of this without burning the house. Tell your father I am ready to compromise with him."

"Sir, you have no right in my father's house; and, to tell you the truth, I did not expect such outlawry from a man who had shown himself to be a gentleman."

"Thank you for that, Lord Strepp; but, nevertheless, tell your father to try to cultivate a conciliatory frame of mind, and let us talk the matter over as sensible men should."

"We cannot compromise with you, O'Ruddy," said Lord Strepp in a very determined tone, which for the first time made me doubt the wisdom of my proceedings; for of course it was a compromise I had in mind all the time, for I knew as well as Father Donovan that if he refused to settle with me my position was entirely untenable.

"We cannot compromise with you," went on the young man. "You have no right, legal or moral, to this place, and you know it. I have advised my father to make no terms with you. Good day to you, sir."

And with that he galloped off, while I drew a very long face as I turned away.

"Father Donovan," I said, when I had closed the window, "I am not sure but your advice to me on the way here was nearer right than I thought at the

312

time."

"Oh, not a bit of it," cried Father Donovan cheerfully. "You heard what the young man said, that he had advised his father not to make any terms with you. Very well, that means terms have been proposed already; and this youth rejects the wisdom of age, which I have known to be done before."

"You think, then, they will accept a conference?"

"I am sure of it. These men will not stand fire, and small blame to them. What chance have they? As your captain says, he could annihilate the lot of them before they crushed in the front door. The men who ran away have far more sense than that brainless spalpeen who led them on, although I can see he is brave enough. One or two more useless attacks will lead him to a more conciliatory frame of mind, unless he appeals to the law, which is what I thought he would do; for I felt sure a sheriff would be in the van of attack. Just now you are opposed only to the Earl of Westport; but, when the sheriff comes on, you're fornenst the might of England."

This cheered me greatly, and after a while we had our dinner in peace. The long afternoon passed slowly away, and there was no rally in the village, and no sign of a further advance; so night came on and nothing had been done. After supper I said good-night to Father Donovan, threw myself, dressed as I was, on the bed, and fell into a doze. It was toward midnight when Tom Peel woke me up; that man seemed to sleep neither night nor day; and there he stood by my bed, looking like a giant in the flicker of the candle-light.

"Your honour," he said, "I think there's something going on at the mouth of the tunnel. Twice I've caught the glimpse of a light there, although they're evidently trying to conceal it."

I sat up in bed and said:

"What do you propose to do?"

"Well, there's a man inside here that knows the tunnel just as well as I do,—every inch of it,—and he's up near the other end now. If a company begins coming in, my man will run back without being seen and let us know. Now, sir, shall I timber this end, or shall we deal with them at the top of the stair one by one as they come up. One good swordsman at the top of the stair will prevent a thousand getting into the house."

"Peel," said I, "are there any stones outside, at the other end of the tunnel?"

"Plenty. There's a dyke of loose stones fronting it."

"Very well; if your man reports that any have entered the tunnel, they'll have left one or two at the other end on guard; take you five of your most trusted men, and go you cautiously a roundabout way until you are within striking distance of the men on guard. Watch the front upper windows of this house; and if you see two lights displayed, you will know they are in the tunnel. If you waited here till your man comes back, you would be too late; so go now, and, if you see the two lights, overpower the men at the mouth of the tunnel unless they are too many for you. If they are, then there's nothing to do but retreat. When you have captured the guard, make them go down into the tunnel; then you and your men tear down the dyke and fill the hole full of stones; I will guard this end of the passage."

Tom Peel pulled his forelock and was gone at once, delighted with his task. I knew that if I got them once in the tunnel there would no longer be any question of a compromise, even if Lord Strepp himself was leading them. I took two lighted candles with me and sat patiently at the head of the stone stairway that led, in circular fashion, down into the depths. Half an hour passed, but nothing happened, and I began to wonder whether or not they had captured our man, when suddenly his face appeared.

"They are coming, sir," he cried, "by the dozen. Lord Strepp is leading them."

"Will they be here soon, do you think?"

"I cannot tell. First I saw torches appear, then Lord Strepp came down and began giving instructions, and, after counting nearly a score of his followers, I came back as quick as I could."

314

"You've done nobly," said I. "Now stand here with this sword and prevent any man from coming up."

I took one of the candles, leaving him another, and lighted a third. I went up the stair and set them in the front window; then I opened another window and listened. The night was exceedingly still,—not even the sound of a cricket to be heard. After a few minutes, however, there came a cry, instantly smothered, from the other side of the valley; another moment and I heard the stones a rolling, as if the side of a wall had tumbled over, which indeed was the case; then two lights were shown on the hill and were waved up and down; and although Peel and I had arranged no signal, yet this being the counterpart of my own, I took to signify that they had been successful, so, leaving the candles burning there, in case there might have been some mistake, I started down the stair to the man who was guarding the secret passage.

"Has anything happened?"

"Nothing, sir."

I think the best part of an hour must have passed before there was sign or sound. Of course I knew if the guards were flung down the hole, they would at once run after their comrades and warn them that both ends of the tunnel were in our possession. I was well aware that the imprisoned men might drag away the stones and ultimately win a passage out for themselves; but I trusted that they would be panic-stricken when they found themselves caught like rats in a trap. In any case it would be very difficult to remove stones from below in the tunnel, because the space was narrow and few could labour at a time; then there was every chance that the stones might jam, when nothing could be done. However, I told the man beside me to go across the valley and ask Peel and his men to pile on rocks till he had a great heap above the entrance, and, if not disturbed, to work till nearly daylight, so I sat on the top of the circular stair step with my rapier across my knees, waiting so long that I began to fear they all might be smothered, for I didn't know whether the stopping of air at one end would prevent it coming in at the other, for I never heard my father say what took place in a case like that. Father Donovan was in bed and asleep, and I was afraid to leave the guarding of the stair to any

315

one else. It seemed that hours and hours passed, and I began to wonder was daylight never going to come, when the most welcome sound I ever heard was the well-known tones of a voice which came up from the bottom of the well.

"Are you there, Mr. O'Ruddy?"

There was a subdued and chastened cadence in the inquiry that pleased me.

"I am, and waiting for you."

"May I come up?"

"Yes, and very welcome; but you'll remember, Lord Strepp, that you come up as a prisoner."

"I quite understand that, Mr. O'Ruddy."

So, as I held the candle, I saw the top of his head coming round and round and round, and finally he stood before me stretching out his sword, hilt forward.

"Stick it in its scabbard," said I, "and I'll do the same with mine." Then I put out my hand, "Good morning to your lordship," I said. "It seems to me I've been waiting here forty days and forty nights. Will you have a sup of wine?"

"I would be very much obliged to you for it, Mr. O'Ruddy."

With that I called the nearest guard and bade him let nobody up the stair without my knowing it.

"I suppose, my lord, you are better acquainted with this house than I am; but I know a spot where there's a drop of good drink."

"You have discovered the old gentleman's cellar, then?"

"Indeed, Lord Strepp, I have not. I possess a cellar of my own. It's you that's my guest, and not me that's yours on this occasion."

I poured him out a flagon, and then one for myself, and as we stood by the table I lifted it high and said:

"Here's to our better acquaintance."

His lordship drank, and said with a wry face, as he put down the mug:

"Our acquaintance seems to be a somewhat tempestuous one; but I confess, Mr. O'Ruddy, that I have as great a respect for your generalship as I have for your swordsmanship. The wine is good and revivifying. I've been in that accursed pit all night, and I came to this end of it with greater reluctance than I expected to when I entered the other. We tried to clear away the stones; but they must have piled all the rocks in Sussex on top of us. Are your men toiling there yet?"

"Yes, they're there, and I gave them instructions to work till daylight."

"Well, Mr. O'Ruddy, my poor fellows are all half dead with fright, and they fancy themselves choking; but although the place was foul enough when we entered it, I didn't see much difference at the end. However, I did see one thing, and that was that I had to come and make terms. I want you to let the poor devils go, Mr. O'Ruddy, and I'll be parole that they won't attack you again."

"And who will give his parole that Lord Strepp will not attack me again?"

"Well, O'Ruddy,"—I took great comfort from the fact that he dropped the Mr.,—"Well, O'Ruddy, you see we cannot possibly give up this estate. You are not legally entitled to it. It is ours and always has been."

"I'm not fighting for any estate, Lord Strepp."

"Then, in Heaven's name, what are you fighting for?"

"For the consent of the Earl and Countess of Westport to my marriage with Lady Mary, your sister."

Lord Strepp gave a long whistle; then he laughed and sat down in the nearest chair.

"But what does Mary say about it?" he asked at last.

"The conceit of an Irishman, my lord, leads me to suspect that I can ultimately overcome any objections she may put forward."

"Oho! that is how the land lies, is it? I'm a thick-headed clod, or I would have suspected something of that sort when Mary pulled me down so sharply as I was cursing you at the front door." Then, with a slight touch of patronage in his tone, he said:

"There is some difference in the relative positions of our families, Mr. O'Ruddy."

"Oh, I'm quite willing to waive that," said I. "Of course it isn't usual for the descendant of kings, like myself, to marry a daughter of the mere nobility; but Lady Mary is so very charming that she more than makes up for any discrepancy, whatever may be said for the rest of the family."

At this Lord Strepp threw back his head and laughed again joyously, crying,—

"King O'Ruddy, fill me another cup of your wine, and I'll drink to your marriage."

We drank, and then he said:

"I'm a selfish beast, guzzling here when those poor devils think they're smothering down below. Well, O'Ruddy, will you let my unlucky fellows go?"

"I'll do that instantly," said I, and so we went to the head of the circular stair and sent the guard down to shout to them to come on, and by this time the daylight was beginning to turn the upper windows grey. A very bedraggled stream of badly frightened men began crawling up and up and up the stairway, and as Tom Peel had now returned I asked him to open the front door and let the yeomen out. Once on the terrace in front, the men seemed not to be able to move away, but stood there drawing in deep breaths of air as if they had never tasted it before. Lord Strepp, in the daylight, counted the mob, asking them if they were sure every one had come up, but they all seemed to be there, though I sent Tom Peel down along the tunnel to find if any had been left behind.

Lord Strepp shook hands most cordially with me at the front door.

"Thank you for your hospitality, O'Ruddy," he said, "although I came in by the lower entrance. I will send over a flag of truce when I've seen my father; then I hope you will trust yourself to come to the Manor House and have a talk with him."

"I'll do it with pleasure," said I.

"Good morning to you," said Lord Strepp.

"And the top o' the morning to you, which is exactly what we are getting at this moment, though in ten minutes I hope to be asleep."

"So do I," said Lord Strepp, setting off at a run down the slope.

CHAPTER XXXIII

Once more I went to my bed, but this time with my clothes off, for if there was to be a conference with the Earl and the Countess at the Manor House, not to speak of the chance of seeing Lady Mary herself, I wished to put on the new and gorgeous suit I had bought in London for that occasion, and which had not yet been on my back. I was so excited and so delighted with the thought of seeing Lady Mary that I knew I could not sleep a wink, especially as daylight was upon me, but I had scarcely put my head on the pillow when I was as sound asleep as any of my ancestors, the old Kings of Kinsale. The first thing I knew Paddy was shaking me by the shoulder just a little rougher than a well-trained servant should.

"Beggin' your pardon," says he, "his lordship, the great Earl of Westport, sends word by a messenger that he'll be pleased to have account with ye, at your early convenience, over at the Manor House beyond."

"Very well, Paddy," said I, "ask the messenger to take my compliments to the Earl and say to him I will do myself the honour of calling on him in an hour's time. Deliver that message to him; then come back and help me on with my new duds."

When Paddy returned I was still yawning, but in the shake of a shillelah he had me inside the new costume, and he stood back against the wall with his hand raised in amazement and admiration at the glory he beheld. He said after that kings would be nothing to him, and indeed the tailor had done his best and had won his guineas with more honesty than you'd expect from a London tradesman. I was quietly pleased with the result myself.

I noticed with astonishment that it was long after mid-day, so it occurred to me that Lord Strepp must have had a good sleep himself, and sure the poor boy needed it, for it's no pleasure to spend life underground till after you're dead, and his evening in the tunnel must have been very trying to him, as indeed he admitted to me afterward that it was.

I called on Father Donovan, and he looked me over from head to foot with wonder and joy in his eye.

"My dear lad, you're a credit to the O'Ruddys," he said, "and to Ireland," he said, "and to the Old Head of Kinsale," he said.

"And to that little tailor in London as well," I replied, turning around so that he might see me the better.

In spite of my chiding him Paddy could not contain his delight, and danced about the room like an overgrown monkey.

"Paddy," said I, "you're making a fool of yourself."

Then I addressed his Reverence.

"Father Donovan," I began, "this cruel war is over and done with, and no one hurt and no blood shed, so the Earl—"

At this moment there was a crash and an unearthly scream, then a thud that sounded as if it had happened in the middle of the earth. Father Donovan and I looked around in alarm, but Paddy was nowhere to be seen. Toward the wall there was a square black hole, and, rushing up to it, we knew at once what had happened. Paddy had danced a bit too heavy on an old trap-door, and the rusty bolts had broken. It had let him down into a dungeon that had no other entrance; and indeed this was a queer house entirely, with many odd nooks and corners about it, besides the disadvantage of Sir Goddard Oxenbridge tramping through the rooms in two sections.

"For the love of Heaven and all the Saints," I cried down this trap-door, "Paddy, what has happened to you?"

"Sure, sir, the house has fallen on me."

"Nothing of the kind, Paddy. The house is where it always was. Are you hurted?"

"I'm dead and done for completely this time, sir. Sure I feel I'm with the angels at last."

"Tut, tut, Paddy, my lad; you've gone in the wrong direction altogether for them."

"Oh, I'm dying, and I feel the flutter of their wings," and as he spoke two or three ugly blind bats fluttered up and butted their stupid heads against the wall.

"You've gone in the right direction for the wrong kind of angels, Paddy; but don't be feared, they're only bats, like them in my own tower at home, except they're larger."

I called for Tom Peel, as he knew the place well.

"Many a good cask of brandy has gone down that trap-door," said he, "and the people opposite have searched this house from cellar to garret and never made the discovery Paddy did a moment since."

He got a stout rope and sent a man down, who found Paddy much more frightened than hurt. We hoisted both of them up, and Paddy was a sight to behold.

"Bad luck to ye," says I; "just at the moment I want a presentable lad behind me when I'm paying my respects to the Earl of Westport, you must go diving into the refuse heap of a house that doesn't belong to you, and spoiling the clothes that does. Paddy, if you were in a seven years' war, you would be the first man wounded and the last man killed, with all the trouble for nothing in between. Is there anything broken about ye?"

"Every leg and arm I've got is broken," he whimpered, but Father Donovan, who was nearly as much of a surgeon as a priest, passed his hand over the trembling lad, then smote him on the back, and said the exercise of falling had done him good.

"Get on with you," said I, "and get off with those clothes. Wash yourself, and put on the suit I was wearing yesterday, and see that you don't fall in the water-jug and drown yourself."

I gave the order for Tom Peel to saddle the four horses and get six of his men with swords and pistols and blunderbusses to act as an escort for me.

"Are you going back to Rye, your honour?" asked Peel.

"I am not. I am going to the Manor House."

"That's but a step," he cried in surprise.

"It's a step," said I, "that will be taken with dignity and consequence."

So, with the afternoon sun shining in our faces, we set out from the house of Brede, leaving but few men to guard it. Of course I ran the risk that it might be taken in our absence; but I trusted the word of Lord Strepp as much as I distrusted the designs of his father and mother, and Strepp had been the captain of the expedition against us; but if I had been sure the mansion was lost to me, I would have evaded none of the pomp of my march to the Manor House in the face of such pride as these upstarts of Westports exhibited toward a representative of a really ancient family like the O'Ruddy. So his Reverence and I rode slowly side by side, with Jem and Paddy, also on horseback, a decent interval behind us, and tramping in their wake that giant, Tom Peel, with six men nearly as stalwart as himself, their blunderbusses over their shoulders, following him. It struck panic in the village when they saw this terrible array marching up the hill toward them, with the sun glittering on us as if we were walking jewellery. The villagers, expecting to be torn limb from limb, scuttled away into the forest, leaving the place as empty as a bottle of beer after a wake. Even the guards around the Manor House fled as we approached it, for the fame of our turbulence had spread abroad in the land. Lord Strepp tried to persuade them that nothing would happen to them, for when he saw the style in which we were coming he was anxious to make a show from the Westport side and had drawn up his men in line to receive us. But we rode through a silent village that might have been just sacked by the French. I thought afterward that this desertion had a subduing effect on the old Earl's pride, and made him more easy to deal with. In any case his manner was somewhat abated when he received me. Lord Strepp himself was there at the door, making excuses for the servants, who he said had gone to the fields to pick berries for their supper. So, leaving Paddy to hold one horse and Jem the other, with the seven men drawn up fiercely in front of the Manor House, Father Donovan and myself followed Lord Strepp into a large room, and there, buried in an arm-chair, reclined the aged Earl of Westport, looking none too pleased to meet his visitors. In cases like this it's as well to be genial at the first, so that you may remove the tension in the beginning.

"The top of the morning—I beg your pardon—the tail of the afternoon to you, sir, and I hope I see you well."

"I am very well," said his lordship, more gruffly than politely.

"Permit me to introduce to your lordship, his Reverence, Father Donovan, who has kindly consented to accompany me that he may yield testimony to the long-standing respectability of the House of O'Ruddy."

"I am pleased to meet your Reverence," said the Earl, although his appearance belied his words. He wasn't pleased to meet either of us, if one might judge by his lowering countenance, in spite of my cordiality and my wish to make his surrender as easy for him as possible.

I was disappointed not to see the Countess and Lady Mary in the room, for it seemed a pity that such a costume as mine should be wasted on an old curmudgeon, sitting with his chin in his breast in the depths of an easy-chair, looking daggers though he spoke dumplings.

I was just going to express my regret to Lord Strepp that no ladies were to be present in our assemblage, when the door opened, and who should sail in, like a full-rigged man-o'-war, but the Countess herself, and Lady Mary, like an elegant yacht floating in tow of her. I swept my bonnet to the boards of the floor with a gesture that would have done honour to the Court of France; but her Ladyship tossed her nose higher in the air, as if the man-o'-war had encountered a huge wave. She seated herself with emphasis on a chair, and says I to myself, "It's lucky for you, you haven't Paddy's trap-door under you, or we'd see your heels disappear, coming down like that."

Lady Mary very modestly took up her position standing behind her mother's chair, and, after one timid glance at me, dropped her eyes on the floor, and then there were some moments of silence, as if every one was afraid to begin. I saw I was going to have trouble with the Countess, and although I think it will be admitted by my enemies that I'm as brave a man as ever faced a foe, I was reluctant to throw down the gage of battle to the old lady.

It was young Lord Strepp that began, and he spoke most politely, as was

324

his custom.

"I took the liberty of sending for you, Mr. O'Ruddy, and I thank you for responding so quickly to my invitation. The occurrences of the past day or two, it would be wiser perhaps to ignore—"

At this there was an indignant sniff from the Countess, and I feared she was going to open her batteries, but to my amazement she kept silent, although the effort made her red in the face.

"I have told my father and mother," went on Lord Strepp, "that I had some conversation with you this morning, and that conditions might be arrived at satisfactory to all parties concerned. I have said nothing to my parents regarding the nature of these conditions, but I gained their consent to give consideration to anything you might say, and to any proposal you are good enough to make."

The old gentleman mumbled something incomprehensible in his chair, but the old lady could keep silence no longer.

"This is an outrage," she cried, "the man's action has been scandalous and unlawful. If, instead of bringing those filthy scoundrels against our own house, those cowards that ran away as soon as they heard the sound of a blunderbuss, we had all stayed in London, and you had had the law of him, he would have been in gaol by this time and not standing brazenly there in the Manor House of Brede."

And after saying this she sniffed again, having no appreciation of good manners.

"Your ladyship has been misinformed," I said with extreme deference. "The case is already in the hands of dignified men of law, who are mightily pleased with it."

"Pleased with it, you idiot," she cried. "They are pleased with it simply because they know somebody will pay them for their work, even it's a beggar from Ireland, who has nothing on him but rags."

"Your ladyship," said I, not loath to call attention to my costume, "I assure you these rags cost golden guineas in London."

"Well, you will not get golden guineas from Brede estate," snapped her ladyship.

"Again your ladyship is misinformed. The papers are so perfect, and so well do they confirm my title to this beautiful domain, that the money-lenders of London simply bothered the life out of me trying to shovel gold on me, and both his lordship and your ladyship know that if a title is defective there is no money to be lent on it."

"You're a liar," said the Countess genially, although the Earl looked up in alarm when I mentioned that I could draw money on the papers. Again I bowed deeply to her ladyship, and, putting my hands in my pockets, I drew out two handfuls of gold, which I strewed up and down the floor as if I were sowing corn, and each guinea was no more than a grain of it.

"There is the answer to your ladyship's complimentary remark," said I with a flourish of my empty hands; and, seeing Lady Mary's eyes anxiously fixed on me, I dropped her a wink with the side of my face farthest from the Countess, at which Lady Mary's eyelids drooped again. But I might have winked with both eyes for all the Countess, who was staring like one in a dream at the glittering pieces that lay here and there and gleamed all over the place like the little yellow devils they were. She seemed struck dumb, and if anyone thinks gold cannot perform a miracle, there is the proof of it.

"Is it gold?" cried I in a burst of eloquence that charmed even myself, "sure I could sow you acres with it by the crooking of my little finger from the revenues of my estate at the Old Head of Kinsale."

"O'Ruddy, O'Ruddy," said Father Donovan very softly and reprovingly, for no one knew better than him what my ancestral revenues were.

"Ah well, Father," said I, "your reproof is well-timed. A man should not boast, and I'll say no more of my castles and my acres, though the ships on the sea pay tribute to them. But all good Saints preserve us, Earl of Westport, if you feel proud to own this poor estate of Brede, think how little it weighed with my father, who all his life did not take the trouble to come over and look at it. Need I say more about Kinsale when you hear that? And as for myself, did I attempt to lay hands on this trivial bit of earth because I held the papers? You know I tossed them into your daughter's lap because she was the finest-looking girl I have seen since I landed on these shores."

"Well, well, well, well," growled the Earl, "I admit I have acted rashly and harshly in this matter, and it is likely I have done wrong to an honourable gentleman, therefore I apologize for it. Now, what have you to propose?"

"I have to propose myself as the husband of your daughter, Lady Mary, and as for our dowry, there it is on the floor for the picking up, and I'm content with that much if I get the lady herself."

His lordship slowly turned his head around and gazed at his daughter, who now was looking full at me with a frown on her brow. Although I knew I had depressed the old people, I had an uneasy feeling that I had displeased Lady Mary herself by my impulsive action and my bragging words. A curious mildness came into the harsh voice of the old Earl, and he said, still looking at his daughter:

"What does Mary say to this?"

The old woman could not keep her eyes from the gold, which somehow held her tongue still, yet I knew she was hearing every word that was said, although she made no comment. Lady Mary shook herself, as if to arouse herself from a trance, then she said in a low voice:

"I can never marry a man I do not love."

"What's that? what's that?" shrieked her mother, turning fiercely round upon her, whereat Lady Mary took a step back. "Love, love? What nonsense is this I hear? You say you will not marry this man to save the estate of Brede?"

"I shall marry no man whom I do not love," repeated Lady Mary firmly.

As for me, I stood there, hat in hand, with my jaw dropped, as if Sullivan had given me a stunning blow in the ear; then the old Earl said sternly:

"I cannot force my daughter: this conference is at an end. The law must decide between us."

"The law, you old dotard," cried the Countess, rounding then on him with a suddenness that made him seem to shrink into his shell. "The law! Is a silly wench to run us into danger of losing what is ours? He shall marry her. If you will not force her, then I'll coerce her;" and with that she turned upon her daughter, grasped her by her two shoulders and shook her as a terrier shakes a rat. At this Lady Mary began to weep, and indeed she had good cause to do so.

"Hold, madam," shouted I, springing toward her. "Leave the girl alone. I agree with his lordship, no woman shall be coerced on account of me."

My intervention turned the Countess from her victim upon me.

"You agree with his lordship, you Irish baboon? Don't think she'll marry you because of any liking for you, you chattering ape, who resemble a monkey in a show with those trappings upon you. She'll marry you because I say she'll marry you, and you'll give up those papers to me, who have sense enough to take care of them. If I have a doddering husband, who at the same time lost his breeches and his papers, I shall make amends for his folly."

"Madam," said I, "you shall have the papers; and as for the breeches, by the terror you spread around you, I learn they are already in your possession."

I thought she would have torn my eyes out, but I stepped back and saved myself.

"To your room, you huzzy," she cried to her daughter, and Mary fled toward the door. I leaped forward and opened it for her. She paused on the threshold, pretending again to cry, but instead whispered:

"My mother is the danger. Leave things alone," she said quickly. "We can easily get poor father's consent."

With that she was gone. I closed the door and returned to the centre of the room.

"Madam," said I, "I will not have your daughter browbeaten. It is quite evident she refuses to marry me."

"Hold your tongue, and keep to your word, you idiot," she rejoined, hitting me a bewildering slap on the side of the face, after which she flounced out by the way her daughter had departed.

The old Earl said nothing, but gazed gloomily into space from out the depths of his chair. Father Donovan seemed inexpressibly shocked, but my Lord Strepp, accustomed to his mother's tantrums, laughed outright as soon as the door was closed. All through he had not been in the least deceived by his sister's pretended reluctance, and recognized that the only way to get the mother's consent was through opposition. He sprang up and grasped me by the hand and said:

"Well, O'Ruddy, I think your troubles are at an end, or," he cried, laughing again, "just beginning, but you'll be able to say more on that subject this time next year. Never mind my mother; Mary is, and always will be, the best girl in the world."

"I believe you," said I, returning his handshake as cordially as he had bestowed it.

"Hush!" he cried, jumping back into his seat again. "Let us all look dejected. Hang your head, O'Ruddy!" and again the door opened, this time the Countess leading Lady Mary, her long fingers grasping that slim wrist.

"She gives her consent," snapped the Countess, as if she were pronouncing sentence. I strode forward toward her, but Mary wrenched her wrist free, slipped past me, and dropped at the feet of Father Donovan, who had risen as she came in.

"Your blessing on me, dear Father," she cried, bowing her head, "and pray on my behalf that there may be no more turbulence in my life."

The old father crossed his hands on her shapely head, and for a moment or two it seemed as if he could not command his voice, and I saw the tears fill his eyes. At last he said simply and solemnly:—

"May God bless you and yours, my dear daughter."

We were married by Father Donovan with pomp and ceremony in the chapel of the old house, and in the same house I now pen the last words of these memoirs, which I began at the request of Lady Mary herself, and continued for the pleasure she expressed as they went on. If this recital is disjointed in parts, it must be remembered I was always more used to the sword than to the pen, and that it is difficult to write with Patrick and little Mary and Terence and Kathleen and Michael and Bridget and Donovan playing about me and asking questions, but I would not have the darlings sent from the room for all the writings there is in the world.

About Author

In 1896, Crane endured a highly publicized scandal after appearing as a witness in the trial of a suspected prostitute, an acquaintance named Dora Clark. Late that year he accepted an offer to travel to Cuba as a war correspondent. As he waited in Jacksonville, Florida for passage, he met Cora Taylor, with whom he began a lasting relationship. En route to Cuba, Crane's vessel the SS Commodore sank off the coast of Florida, leaving him and others adrift for 30 hours in a dinghy. Crane described the ordeal in "The Open Boat". During the final years of his life, he covered conflicts in Greece (accompanied by Cora, recognized as the first woman war correspondent) and later lived in England with her. He was befriended by writers such as Joseph Conrad and H. G. Wells. Plagued by financial difficulties and ill health, Crane died of tuberculosis in a Black Forest sanatorium in Germany at the age of 28.

At the time of his death, Crane was considered an important figure in American literature. After he was nearly forgotten for two decades, critics revived interest in his life and work. Crane's writing is characterized by vivid intensity, distinctive dialects, and irony. Common themes involve fear, spiritual crises and social isolation. Although recognized primarily for The Red Badge of Courage, which has become an American classic, Crane is also known for his poetry, journalism, and short stories such as "The Open Boat", "The Blue Hotel", "The Bride Comes to Yellow Sky", and The Monster. His writing made a deep impression on 20th-century writers, most prominent among them Ernest Hemingway, and is thought to have inspired the Modernists and the Imagists.

Early years

Stephen Crane was born on November 1, 1871, in Newark, New Jersey, to Jonathan Townley Crane, a minister in the Methodist Episcopal church, and Mary Helen Peck Crane, daughter of a clergyman, George Peck. He was the fourteenth and last child born to the couple. At 45, Helen Crane had suffered the early deaths of her previous four children, each of whom died within one year of birth. Nicknamed "Stevie" by the family, he joined eight surviving brothers and sisters—Mary Helen, George Peck, Jonathan Townley, William Howe, Agnes Elizabeth, Edmund Byran, Wilbur Fiske, and Luther.

The Cranes were descended from Jaspar Crane, a founder of New Haven Colony, who had migrated there from England in 1639. Stephen was named for a putative founder of Elizabethtown, New Jersey, who had, according to family tradition, come from England or Wales in 1665, as well as his great-great-grandfather Stephen Crane (1709–1780), a Revolutionary War patriot who served as New Jersey delegate to the First Continental Congress in Philadelphia. Crane later wrote that his father, Dr. Crane, "was a great, fine, simple mind," who had written numerous tracts on theology. Although his mother was a popular spokeswoman for the Woman's Christian Temperance Union and a highly religious woman, Crane wrote that he did not believe "she was as narrow as most of her friends or family." The young Stephen was raised primarily by his sister Agnes, who was 15 years his senior. The family moved to Port Jervis, New York, in 1876, where Dr. Crane became the pastor of Drew Methodist Church, a position that he retained until his death.

As a child, Stephen was often sickly and afflicted by constant colds. When the boy was almost two, his father wrote in his diary that his youngest son became "so sick that we are anxious about him." Despite his fragile nature, Crane was an intelligent child who taught himself to read before the age of four. His first known inquiry, recorded by his father, dealt with writing; at the age of three, while imitating his brother Townley's writing, he asked his mother, "how do you spell O?" In December 1879, Crane wrote a poem about wanting a dog for Christmas. Entitled "I'd Rather Have –", it is his first surviving poem. Stephen was not regularly enrolled in school until January 1880, but he had no difficulty in completing two grades in six weeks. Recalling this feat, he wrote that it "sounds like the lie of a fond mother at a teaparty, but I do remember that I got ahead very fast and that father was very pleased with me."

Dr. Crane died on February 16, 1880, at the age of 60; Stephen was eight years old. Some 1,400 people mourned Dr. Crane at his funeral, more than double the size of his congregation. After her husband's death, Mrs. Crane moved to Roseville, near Newark, leaving Stephen in the care of his older brother Edmund, with whom the young boy lived with cousins in Sussex County. He next lived with his brother William, a lawyer, in Port Jervis for several years.

His older sister Helen took him to Asbury Park to be with their brother Townley and his wife, Fannie. Townley was a professional journalist; he headed the Long Branch department of both the New-York Tribune and the Associated Press, and also served as editor of the Asbury Park Shore Press. Agnes, another Crane sister, joined the siblings in New Jersey. She took a position at Asbury Park's intermediate school and moved in with Helen to care for the young Stephen.

Within a couple of years, the Crane family suffered more losses. First, Townley and his wife lost their two young children. His wife Fannie died of Bright's disease in November 1883. Agnes Crane became ill and died on June 10, 1884, of meningitis at the age of 28.

Schooling

Crane wrote his first known story, "Uncle Jake and the Bell Handle", when he was 14. In late 1885, he enrolled at Pennington Seminary, a ministry-focused coeducational boarding school 7 miles (11 km) north of Trenton. His father had been principal there from 1849 to 1858. Soon after her youngest son left for school, Mrs. Crane began suffering what the Asbury Park Shore Press reported as "a temporary aberration of the mind." She had apparently recovered by early 1886, but later that year, her son, 23-year-old Luther Crane, died after falling in front of an oncoming train while working as a flagman for the Erie Railroad. It was the fourth death in six years among Stephen's immediate family.

After two years, Crane left Pennington for Claverack College, a quasi-military school. He later looked back on his time at Claverack as "the happiest period of my life although I was not aware of it." A classmate remembered him as a highly literate but erratic student, lucky to pass examinations in math and science, and yet "far in advance of his fellow students in his knowledge of History and Literature", his favorite subjects. While he held an impressive record on the drill field and baseball diamond, Crane generally did not excel in the classroom. Not having a middle name, as was customary among other students, he took to signing his name "Stephen T. Crane" in order "to win recognition as a regular fellow". Crane was seen as friendly, but also moody and rebellious. He sometimes skipped class in order to play baseball, a game in which he starred as catcher. He was also greatly interested in the school's military training program. He rose rapidly in the ranks of the student battalion. One classmate described him as "indeed physically attractive without being handsome", but he was aloof, reserved and not generally popular at Claverack. Although academically weak, Crane gained experience at Claverack that provided background (and likely some anecdotes from the Civil War veterans on the staff) that proved useful when he came to write The Red Badge of Courage.

In mid-1888, Crane became his brother Townley's assistant at a New Jersey shore news bureau, working there every summer until 1892. Crane's first publication under his byline was an article on the explorer Henry M. Stanley's famous quest to find the Scottish missionary David Livingstone in Africa. It appeared in the February 1890 Claverack College Vidette. Within a few months, Crane was persuaded by his family to forgo a military career and transfer to Lafayette College in Easton, Pennsylvania, in order to pursue a mining engineering degree. He registered at Lafayette on September 12, and promptly became involved in extracurricular activities; he took up baseball again and joined the largest fraternity, Delta Upsilon. He also joined both rival literary societies, named for (George) Washington and (Benjamin) Franklin. Crane infrequently attended classes and ended the semester with grades for four of the seven courses he had taken.

After one semester, Crane transferred to Syracuse University, where he enrolled as a non-degree candidate in the College of Liberal Arts. He roomed in the Delta Upsilon fraternity house and joined the baseball team. Attending just one class (English Literature) during the middle trimester, he remained in residence while taking no courses in the third semester.

Concentrating on his writing, Crane began to experiment with tone and style while trying out different subjects. He published his fictional story, "Great Bugs of Onondaga," simultaneously in the Syracuse Daily Standard and the New York Tribune. Declaring college "a waste of time", Crane decided to become a full-time writer and reporter. He attended a Delta Upsilon chapter meeting on June 12, 1891, but shortly afterward left college for good.

Full-time writer

In the summer of 1891, Crane often camped with friends in the nearby area of Sullivan County, New York, where his brother Edmund occupied a house obtained as part of their brother William's Hartwood Club (Association) land dealings. He used this area as the geographic setting for several short stories, which were posthumously published in a collection under the title Stephen Crane: Sullivan County Tales and Sketches. Crane showed two of these works to Tribune editor Willis Fletcher Johnson, a friend of the family, who accepted them for the publication. "Hunting Wild Dogs" and "The Last of the Mohicans" were the first of fourteen unsigned Sullivan County sketches and tales that were published in the Tribune between February and July 1892. Crane also showed Johnson an early draft of his first novel, Maggie: A Girl of the Streets.

Later that summer, Crane met and befriended author Hamlin Garland, who had been lecturing locally on American literature and the expressive arts; on August 17 he gave a talk on novelist William Dean Howells, which Crane wrote up for the Tribune. Garland became a mentor for and champion of the young writer, whose intellectual honesty impressed him. Their relationship suffered in later years, however, because Garland disapproved of Crane's alleged immorality, related to his living with a woman married to another man.

Stephen moved into his brother Edmund's house in Lakeview, a suburb of Paterson, New Jersey, in the fall of 1891. From here he made frequent trips into New York City, writing and reporting particularly on its impoverished tenement districts. Crane focused particularly on The Bowery, a small and once prosperous neighborhood in the southern part of Manhattan. After the Civil War, Bowery shops and mansions had given way to saloons, dance halls, brothels and flophouses, all of which Crane frequented. He later said he did so for research. He was attracted to the human nature found in the slums, considering it "open and plain, with nothing hidden". Believing nothing honest and unsentimental had been written about the Bowery, Crane became determined to do so himself; this was the setting of his first novel. On December 7, 1891, Crane's mother died at the age of 64, and the 20-year-old appointed Edmund as his guardian.

Despite being frail, undernourished and suffering from a hacking cough, which did not prevent him from smoking cigarettes, in the spring of 1892 Crane began a romance with Lily Brandon Munroe, a married woman who was estranged from her husband. Although Munroe later said Crane "was not a handsome man", she admired his "remarkable almond-shaped gray eyes." He begged her to elope with him, but her family opposed the match because Crane lacked money and prospects, and she declined. Their last meeting likely occurred in April 1898, when he again asked her to run away with him and she again refused.

Such an assemblage of the spraddle-legged men of the middle class, whose hands were bent and shoulders stooped from delving and constructing, had never appeared to an Asbury Park summer crowd, and the latter was vaguely amused.

— Stephen Crane, account of the JOUAM parade as it appeared in the Tribune

Between July 2 and September 11, 1892, Crane published at least ten news reports on Asbury Park affairs. Although a Tribune colleague stated that Crane "was not highly distinguished above any other boy of twenty who had gained a reputation for saying and writing bright things," that summer his reporting took on a more skeptical, hypocrisy-deflating tone. A storm of controversy erupted over a report he wrote on the Junior Order of United American Mechanics' American Day Parade, entitled "Parades and Entertainments". Published on August 21, the report juxtaposes the "bronzed, slope-shouldered, uncouth" marching men "begrimed with dust" and the spectators dressed in "summer gowns, lace parasols, tennis trousers, straw hats and indifferent smiles". Believing they were being ridiculed, some JOUAM marchers were outraged and wrote to the editor. The owner of the Tribune, Whitelaw Reid, was that year's Republican vice-presidential candidate, and this likely increased the sensitivity of the paper's management to the issue. Although Townley wrote a piece for the Asbury Park Daily Press in his brother's defense, the Tribune quickly apologized to its readers, calling Stephen Crane's piece "a bit of random correspondence, passed inadvertently by the copy editor". Hamlin Garland and biographer John Barry attested that Crane told them he had been dismissed by the Tribune, although Willis Fletcher Johnson later denied this. The paper did not publish any of Crane's work after 1892.

Life in New York

Crane struggled to make a living as a free-lance writer, contributing sketches and feature articles to various New York newspapers. In October 1892, he moved into a rooming house in Manhattan whose boarders were a group of medical students. During this time, he expanded or entirely reworked Maggie: A Girl of the Streets, which is about a girl who "blossoms in a mud-puddle" and becomes a pitiful victim of circumstance. In the winter of 1893, Crane took the manuscript of Maggie to Richard Watson Gilder, who rejected it for publication in The Century Magazine.

Crane decided to publish it privately, with money he had inherited from his mother. The novel was published in late February or early March 1893 by a small printing shop that usually printed medical books and religious tracts. The typewritten title page for the Library of Congress copyright application read simply: "A Girl of the Streets, / A Story of New York. / —By—/Stephen Crane." The name "Maggie" was added to the title later. Crane used the pseudonym "Johnston Smith" for the novel's initial publication, later telling friend and artist Corwin Knapp Linson that the nom de plume was the "commonest name I could think of. I had an editor friend named Johnson, and put in the "t", and no one could find me in the mob of Smiths." Hamlin Garland reviewed the work in the June 1893 issue of The Arena, calling it "the most truthful and unhackneyed study of the slums I have yet read, fragment though it is." Despite this early praise, Crane became depressed and destitute from having spent $869 for 1,100 copies of a novel that did not sell; he ended up giving a hundred copies away. He would later remember "how I looked forward to publication and pictured the sensation I thought it would make. It fell flat. Nobody seemed to notice it or care for it... Poor Maggie! She was one of my first loves."

In March 1893, Crane spent hours lounging in Linson's studio while having his portrait painted. He became fascinated with issues of the Century that were largely devoted to famous battles and military leaders from the Civil War. Frustrated with the dryly written stories, Crane stated, "I wonder that some of those fellows don't tell how they felt in those scraps. They spout enough of what they did, but they're as emotionless as rocks." Crane returned to these magazines during subsequent visits to Linson's studio, and eventually the idea of writing a war novel overtook him. He would later state that he "had been unconsciously working the detail of the story out through most of his boyhood" and had imagined "war stories ever since he was out of knickerbockers." This novel would ultimately become The Red Badge of Courage.

A river, amber-tinted in the shadow of its banks, purled at the army's feet; and at night, when the stream had become of a sorrowful blackness, one could see across it the red, eyelike gleam of hostile camp-fires set in the low brows of distant hills.

— Stephen Crane, The Red Badge of Courage

From the beginning, Crane wished to show how it felt to be in a war by writing "a psychological portrayal of fear." Conceiving his story from the point of view of a young private who is at first filled with boyish dreams of the glory of war and then quickly becomes disillusioned by war's reality, Crane borrowed the private's surname, "Fleming", from his sister-in-law's maiden name. He later said that the first paragraphs came to him with "every word in place, every comma, every period fixed." Working mostly nights, he wrote from around midnight until four or five in the morning. Because he could not afford a typewriter, he wrote carefully in ink on legal-sized paper, seldom crossing through or interlining a word. If he did change something, he would rewrite the whole page.

While working on his second novel, Crane remained prolific, concentrating on publishing stories to stave off poverty; "An Experiment in Misery", based on Crane's experiences in the Bowery, was printed by the New York Press. He also wrote five or six poems a day. In early 1894, he showed some of his poems or "lines" as he called them, to Hamlin Garland, who said he read "some thirty in all" with "growing wonder." Although Garland and William Dean Howells encouraged him to submit his poetry for publication, Crane's free verse was too unconventional for most. After brief wrangling between poet and publisher, Copeland & Day accepted Crane's first book of poems, The Black Riders and Other Lines, although it would not be published until after The Red Badge of Courage. He received a 10 percent royalty and the publisher assured him that the book would be in a form "more severely classic than any book ever yet issued in America."

In the spring of 1894, Crane offered the finished manuscript of The Red Badge of Courage to McClure's Magazine, which had become the foremost magazine for Civil War literature. While McClure's delayed giving him an answer on his novel, they offered him an assignment writing about the Pennsylvania coal mines. "In the Depths of a Coal Mine", a story with pictures by Linson, was syndicated by McClure's in a number of newspapers, heavily edited. Crane was reportedly disgusted by the cuts, asking Linson: "Why the hell did they send me up there then? Do they want the public to think the coal mines gilded ball-rooms with the miners eating ice-cream in boiled shirt-fronts?"

Sources report that following an encounter with a male prostitute that spring, Crane began a novel on the subject entitled Flowers of Asphalt, which he later abandoned. The manuscript has never been recovered.

After discovering that McClure's could not afford to pay him, Crane took his war novel to Irving Bacheller of the Bacheller-Johnson Newspaper Syndicate, which agreed to publish The Red Badge of Courage in serial form. Between the third and the ninth of December 1894, The Red Badge of Courage was published in some half-dozen newspapers in the United States.

Although it was greatly cut for syndication, Bacheller attested to its causing a stir, saying "its quality [was] immediately felt and recognized." The lead editorial in the Philadelphia Press of December 7 said that Crane "is a new name now and unknown, but everybody will be talking about him if he goes on as he has begun".

Travels and fame

At the end of January 1895, Crane left on what he called "a very long and circuitous newspaper trip" to the west. While writing feature articles for the Bacheller syndicate, he traveled to Saint Louis, Missouri, Nebraska, New Orleans, Galveston, Texas and then Mexico City. Irving Bacheller would later state that he "sent Crane to Mexico for new color", which the author found in the form of Mexican slum life. Whereas he found the lower class in New York pitiful, he was impressed by the "superiority" of the Mexican peasants' contentment and "even refuse[d] to pity them."

Returning to New York five months later, Crane joined the Lantern (alternately spelled "Lanthom" or "Lanthorne") Club organized by a group of young writers and journalists. The Club, located on the roof of an old house on William Street near the Brooklyn Bridge, served as a drinking establishment of sorts and was decorated to look like a ship's cabin. There Crane ate one good meal a day, although friends were troubled by his "constant smoking, too much coffee, lack of food and poor teeth", as Nelson Greene put it. Living in near-poverty and greatly anticipating the publication of his books, Crane began work on two more novels: The Third Violet and George's Mother.

The Black Riders was published by Copeland & Day shortly before his return to New York in May, but it received mostly criticism, if not abuse, for the poems' unconventional style and use of free verse. A piece in the Bookman called Crane "the Aubrey Beardsley of poetry," and a commentator from the Chicago Daily Inter-Ocean stated that "there is not a line of poetry from the opening to the closing page. Whitman's Leaves of Grass were luminous in comparison. Poetic lunacy would be a better name for the book." In June, the New York Tribune dismissed the book as "so much trash." Crane was pleased that the book was "making some stir".

In contrast to the reception for Crane's poetry, The Red Badge of Courage was welcomed with acclaim after its publication by Appleton in September 1895. For the next four months, the book was in the top six on various bestseller lists around the country. It arrived on the literary scene "like a flash of lightning out of a clear winter sky", according to H. L. Mencken, who was about 15 at the time. The novel also became popular in Britain; Joseph Conrad, a future friend of Crane, wrote that the novel "detonated... with the impact and force of a twelve-inch shell charged with a very high explosive." Appleton published two, possibly three, printings in 1895 and as many as eleven more in 1896. Although some critics considered the work overly graphic and profane, it was widely heralded for its realistic portrayal of war and unique writing style. The Detroit Free Press declared that The Red Badge would give readers "so vivid a picture of the emotions and the horrors of the battlefield that you will pray your eyes may never look upon the reality."

Wanting to capitalize on the success of The Red Badge, McClure Syndicate offered Crane a contract to write a series on Civil War battlefields. Because it was a wish of his to "visit the battlefield—which I was to describe—at the time of year when it was fought", Crane agreed to take the assignment. Visiting battlefields in Northern Virginia, including Fredericksburg, he would later produce five more Civil War tales: "Three Miraculous Soldiers", "The Veteran", "An Indiana Campaign", "An Episode of War" and The Little Regiment.

Scandal

At the age of 24, Crane, who was reveling in his success, became involved in a highly publicized case involving a suspected prostitute named Dora Clark. At 2 a.m. on September 16, 1896, he escorted two chorus girls and Clark from New York City's Broadway Garden, a popular "resort" where he had interviewed the women for a series he was writing. As Crane saw one woman safely to a streetcar, a plainclothes policeman named Charles Becker arrested the other two for solicitation; Crane was threatened with arrest when he tried to interfere. One of the women was released after Crane confirmed her erroneous claim that she was his wife, but Clark was charged and taken to the precinct. Against the advice of the arresting sergeant, Crane made a statement confirming Dora Clark's innocence, stating that "I only know that while with me she acted respectably, and that the policeman's charge was false." On the basis of Crane's testimony, Clark was discharged. The media seized upon the story; news spread to Philadelphia, Boston and beyond, with papers focusing on Crane's courage. The Stephen Crane story, as it became known, soon became a source for ridicule; the Chicago Dispatch in particular quipped that "Stephen Crane is respectfully informed that association with women in scarlet is not necessarily a 'Red Badge of Courage' ".

A couple of weeks after her trial, Clark pressed charges of false arrest against the officer who had arrested her. The next day, the officer physically attacked Clark in the presence of witnesses for having brought charges against him. Crane, who initially went briefly to Philadelphia to escape the pressure of publicity, returned to New York to give testimony at Becker's trial despite advice given to him from Theodore Roosevelt, who was Police Commissioner at the time and a new acquaintance of Crane. The defense targeted Crane: police raided his apartment and interviewed people who knew him, trying to find incriminating evidence in order to lessen the effect of his testimony. A vigorous cross-examination took place that sought to portray Crane as a man of dubious morals; while the prosecution proved that he frequented brothels, Crane claimed this was merely for research purposes. After the trial ended on October 16, the arresting officer was exonerated, and Crane's reputation was ruined.

Cora Taylor and the Commodore shipwreck

None of them knew the color of the sky. Their eyes glanced level and were fastened upon the waves that swept toward them. These waves were of the hue of slate, save for the tops, which were of foaming white, and all of the men knew the colors of the sea.

— Stephen Crane, "The Open Boat"

Given $700 in Spanish gold by the Bacheller-Johnson syndicate to work as a war correspondent in Cuba as the Spanish–American War was pending, the 25-year-old Crane left New York on November 27, 1896, on a train bound for Jacksonville, Florida. Upon arrival in Jacksonville, he registered at the St. James Hotel under the alias of Samuel Carleton to maintain anonymity while seeking passage to Cuba. While waiting for a boat, he toured the city and visited the local brothels. Within days he met 31-year-old Cora Taylor, proprietor of the downtown bawdy house Hotel de Dream. Born into a respectable Boston family, Taylor (whose legal name was Cora Ethel Stewart) had already had two brief marriages; her first husband, Vinton Murphy, divorced her on grounds of adultery. In 1889, she had married British Captain Donald William Stewart. She left him in 1892 for another man, but was still legally married. By the time Crane arrived, Taylor had been in Jacksonville for two years. She lived a bohemian lifestyle, owned a hotel of assignation, and was a well-known and respected local figure. The two spent much time together while Crane awaited his departure. He was finally cleared to leave for the Cuban port of Cienfuegos on New Year's Eve aboard the SS Commodore.

The ship sailed from Jacksonville with 27 or 28 men and a cargo of supplies and ammunition for the Cuban rebels. On the St. Johns River and less than 2 miles (3.2 km) from Jacksonville, Commodore struck a sandbar in a dense fog and damaged its hull. Although towed off the sandbar the following day, it was beached again in Mayport and again damaged. A leak began in the boiler room that evening and, as a result of malfunctioning water pumps, the ship came to a standstill about 16 miles (26 km) from Mosquito Inlet. As the ship took on more water, Crane described the engine room as resembling "a scene at this time taken from the middle kitchen of hades." Commodore's lifeboats were lowered in the early hours of the morning on January 2, 1897 and the ship ultimately sank at 7 a.m. Crane was one of the last to leave the ship in a 10-foot (3.0 m) dinghy. In an ordeal that he recounted in the short story "The Open Boat", Crane and three other men (including the ship's Captain) floundered off the coast of Florida for a day and a half before trying to land the dinghy at Daytona Beach. The small boat overturned in the surf, forcing the exhausted men to swim to shore; one of them died. Having lost the gold given to him for his journey, Crane wired Cora Taylor for help. She traveled to Daytona and returned to Jacksonville with Crane the next day, only four days after he had left on the Commodore.

The disaster was reported on the front pages of newspapers across the country. Rumors that the ship had been sabotaged were widely circulated but never substantiated. Portrayed favorably and heroically by the press, Crane emerged from the ordeal with his reputation enhanced, if not restored, after the battering he had received in the Dora Clark affair. Meanwhile, Crane's affair with Taylor blossomed.

Three seasons of archaeological investigation were conducted in 2002-04 to examine and document the exposed remains of a wreck near Ponce Inlet, FL conjectured to be that of the SS Commodore. The collected data, and other accumulated evidence, finally substantiated the identification of the Commodore beyond a reasonable doubt.

Greco-Turkish War

Despite contentment in Jacksonville and the need for rest after his ordeal, Crane became restless. He left Jacksonville on January 11 for New York City, where he applied for a passport to Cuba, Mexico and the West Indies. Spending three weeks in New York, he completed "The Open Boat" and periodically visited Port Jervis to see family. By this time, however, blockades had formed along the Florida coast as tensions rose with Spain, and Crane concluded that he would never be able to travel to Cuba. He sold "The Open Boat" to Scribner's for $300 in early March. Determined to work as a war correspondent, Crane signed on with William Randolph Hearst's New York Journal to cover the impending Greco-Turkish conflict. He brought along Taylor, who had sold the Hotel de Dream in order to follow him.

On March 20, they sailed first to England, where Crane was warmly received. They arrived in Athens in early April; between April 17 (when Turkey declared war on Greece) and April 22, Crane wrote his first published report of the war, "An Impression of the 'Concert' ". When he left for Epirus in the northwest, Taylor remained in Athens, where she became the Greek war's first woman war correspondent. She wrote under the pseudonym "Imogene Carter" for the New York Journal, a job that Crane had secured for her. They wrote frequently, traveling throughout the country separately and together. The first large battle that Crane witnessed was the Turks' assault on General

Constantine Smolenski's Greek forces at Velestino. Crane wrote, "It is a great thing to survey the army of the enemy. Just where and how it takes hold upon the heart is difficult of description." During this battle, Crane encountered "a fat waddling puppy" that he immediately claimed, dubbing it "Velestino, the Journal dog". Greece and Turkey signed an armistice on May 20, ending the 30-day war; Crane and Taylor left Greece for England, taking two Greek brothers as servants and Velestino the dog with them.

Spanish–American War

After staying in Limpsfield, Surrey, for a few days, Crane and Taylor settled in Ravensbrook, a plain brick villa in Oxted. Referring to themselves as Mr. and Mrs. Crane, the couple lived openly in England, but Crane concealed the relationship from his friends and family in the United States. Admired in England, Crane thought himself attacked back home: "There seem so many of them in America who want to kill, bury and forget me purely out of unkindness and envy and—my unworthiness, if you choose", he wrote. Velestino the dog sickened and died soon after their arrival in England, on August 1. Crane, who had a great love for dogs, wrote an emotional letter to a friend an hour after the dog's death, stating that "for eleven days we fought death for him, thinking nothing of anything but his life." The Limpsfield-Oxted area was home to members of the socialist Fabian Society and a magnet for writers such as Edmund Gosse, Ford Madox Ford and Edward Garnett. Crane also met the Polish-born novelist Joseph Conrad in October 1897, with whom he would have what Crane called a "warm and endless friendship".

Although Crane was confident among peers, strong negative reviews of the recently published The Third Violet were causing his literary reputation to dwindle. Reviewers were also highly critical of Crane's war letters, deeming them self-centered. Although The Red Badge of Courage had by this time gone through fourteen printings in the United States and six in England, Crane was running out of money. To survive financially, he worked at a feverish pitch, writing prolifically for both the English and the American markets. He wrote in quick succession stories such as The Monster, "The Bride Comes to Yellow Sky", "Death and the Child" and "The Blue Hotel".

Crane began to attach price tags to his new works of fiction, hoping that "The Bride", for example, would fetch $175.

As 1897 ended, Crane's money crisis worsened. Amy Leslie, a reporter from Chicago and a former lover, sued him for $550. The New York Times reported that Leslie gave him $800 in November 1896 but that he'd repaid only a quarter of the sum. In February he was summoned to answer Leslie's claim. The claim was apparently settled out of court, because no record of adjudication exists. Meanwhile, Crane felt "heavy with troubles" and "chased to the wall" by expenses. He confided to his agent that he was $2,000 in debt but that he would "beat it" with more literary output.

Soon after the USS Maine exploded in Havana Harbor on February 15, 1898, under suspicious circumstances, Crane was offered a £60 advance by Blackwood's Magazine for articles "from the seat of war in the event of a war breaking out" between the United States and Spain. His health was failing, and it is believed that signs of his pulmonary tuberculosis, which he may have contracted in childhood, became apparent. With almost no money coming in from his finished stories, Crane accepted the assignment and left Oxted for New York. Taylor and the rest of the household stayed behind to fend off local creditors. Crane applied for a passport and left New York for Key West two days before Congress declared war. While the war idled, he interviewed people and produced occasional copy.

In early June, he observed the establishment of an American base in Cuba when Marines seized Guantánamo Bay. He went ashore with the Marines, planning "to gather impressions and write them as the spirit moved." Although he wrote honestly about his fear in battle, others observed his calmness and composure. He would later recall "this prolonged tragedy of the night" in the war tale "Marines Signaling Under Fire at Guantanamo". After showing a willingness to serve during fighting at Cuzco, Cuba, by carrying messages to company commanders, Crane was officially cited for his "material aid during the action".

He continued to report upon various battles and the worsening military conditions and praised Theodore Roosevelt's Rough Riders, despite past tensions with the Commissioner. In early July, Crane was sent to the United States for medical treatment for a high fever. He was diagnosed with yellow fever, then malaria. Upon arrival in Old Point Comfort, Virginia, he spent a few weeks resting in a hotel. Although Crane had filed more than twenty dispatches in the three months he had covered the war, the World's business manager believed that the paper had not received its money's worth and fired him. In retaliation, Crane signed with Hearst's New York Journal with the wish to return to Cuba. He traveled first to Puerto Rico and then to Havana. In September, rumors began to spread that Crane, who was working anonymously, had either been killed or disappeared. He sporadically sent out dispatches and stories; he wrote about the mood in Havana, the crowded city sidewalks, and other topics, but he was soon desperate for money again. Taylor, left alone in England, was also penniless. She became frantic with worry over her lover's whereabouts; they were not in direct communication until the end of the year. Crane left Havana and arrived in England on January 11, 1899.

Death

Rent on Ravensbrook had not been paid for a year. Upon returning to England, Crane secured a solicitor to act as guarantor for their debts, after which Crane and Taylor relocated to Brede Place. This manor in Sussex, which dated to the 14th century and had neither electricity nor indoor plumbing, was offered to them by friends at a modest rent. The relocation appeared to give hope to Crane, but his money problems continued. Deciding that he could no longer afford to write for American publications, he concentrated on publishing in English magazines.

Crane pushed himself to write feverishly during the first months at Brede; he told his publisher that he was "doing more work now than I have at any other period in my life". His health worsened, and by late 1899 he was asking friends about health resorts. The Monster and Other Stories was in production and War Is Kind, his second collection of poems, was published in the United States in May. None of his books after The Red Badge of Courage had sold well, and he bought a typewriter to spur output. Active Service, a novella based on Crane's correspondence experience, was published in October. The New York Times reviewer questioned "whether the author of 'Active Service' himself really sees anything remarkable in his newspapery hero."

In December, the couple held an elaborate Christmas party at Brede, attended by Conrad, Henry James, H. G. Wells and other friends; it lasted several days. On December 29 Crane suffered a severe pulmonary hemorrhage. In January 1900 he'd recovered sufficiently to work on a new novel, The O'Ruddy, completing 25 of the 33 chapters. Plans were made for him to travel as a correspondent to Gibraltar to write sketches from Saint Helena, the site of a Boer prison, but at the end of March and in early April he suffered two more hemorrhages. Taylor took over most of Crane's correspondence while he was ill, writing to friends for monetary aid. The couple planned to travel on the continent, but Conrad, upon visiting Crane for the last time, remarked that his friend's "wasted face was enough to tell me that it was the most forlorn of all hopes."

On May 28, the couple arrived at Badenweiler, Germany, a health spa on the edge of the Black Forest. Despite his weakened condition, Crane continued to dictate fragmentary episodes for the completion of The O'Ruddy. He died on June 5, 1900, at the age of 28. In his will he left everything to Taylor, who took his body to New Jersey for burial. Crane was interred in Evergreen Cemetery in what is now Hillside, New Jersey.

Style and technique

Stephen Crane's fiction is typically categorized as representative of Naturalism, American realism, Impressionism or a mixture of the three. Critic Sergio Perosa, for example, wrote in his essay, "Stephen Crane fra naturalismo e impressionismo," that the work presents a "symbiosis" of Naturalistic ideals and Impressionistic methods. When asked whether or not he would write an autobiography in 1896, Crane responded that he "dare not say that I am honest. I merely say that I am as nearly honest as a weak mental machinery will allow." Similarities between the stylistic techniques in Crane's writing and Impressionist painting—including the use of color and chiaroscuro—are often cited to support the theory that Crane was not only an Impressionist but also influenced by the movement. H. G. Wells remarked upon "the great influence of the studio" on Crane's work, quoting a passage from The Red Badge of Courage as an example: "At nightfall the column broke into regimental pieces, and the fragments went into the fields to camp. Tents sprang up like strange plants. Camp fires, like red, peculiar blossoms, dotted the night.... From this little distance the many fires, with the black forms of men passing to and fro before the crimson rays, made weird and satanic effects." Although no direct evidence exists that Crane formulated a precise theory of his craft, he vehemently rejected sentimentality, asserting that "a story should be logical in its action and faithful to character. Truth to life itself was the only test, the greatest artists were the simplest, and simple because they were true."

Poet and biographer John Berryman suggested that there were three basic variations, or "norms", of Crane's narrative style. The first, being "flexible, swift, abrupt and nervous", is best exemplified in The Red Badge of Courage, while the second ("supple majesty") is believed to relate to "The Open Boat", and the third ("much more closed, circumstantial and 'normal' in feeling and syntax") to later works such as The Monster. Crane's work, however, cannot be determined by style solely on chronology. Not only does his fiction not take place in any particular region with similar characters, but it varies from serious in tone to reportorial writing and light fiction. Crane's writing, both fiction and nonfiction, is consistently driven by immediacy and is at once concentrated, vivid and intense. The novels and short stories contain poetic characteristics such as shorthand prose, suggestibility, shifts in perspective and ellipses between and within sentences. Similarly, omission plays a large part in Crane's work; the names of his protagonists are not commonly used and sometimes they are not named at all.

Crane was often criticized by early reviewers for his frequent incorporation of everyday speech into dialogue, mimicking the regional accents of his characters with colloquial stylization. This is apparent in his first novel, in which Crane ignored the romantic, sentimental approach of slum fiction; he instead concentrated on the cruelty and sordid aspects of poverty, expressed by the brashness of the Bowery's crude dialect and profanity, which he used lavishly. The distinct dialect of his Bowery characters is apparent at the beginning of the text; the title character admonishes her brother saying: "Yeh knows it puts mudder out when yes comes home half dead, an' it's like we'll all get a poundin'."

Major themes

Crane's work is often thematically driven by Naturalistic and Realistic concerns, including ideals versus realities, spiritual crises and fear. These themes are particularly evident in Crane's first three novels, Maggie: A Girl of the Streets, The Red Badge of Courage and George's Mother. The three main characters search for a way to make their dreams come true, but ultimately suffer from crises of identity. Crane was fascinated by war and death, as well as fire, disfigurement, fear and courage, all of which inspired him to write many works based on these concepts. In The Red Badge of Courage, the main character both longs for the heroics of battle but ultimately fears it, demonstrating the dichotomy of courage and cowardice. He experiences the threat of death, misery and a loss of self.

Extreme isolation from society and community is also apparent in Crane's work. During the most intense battle scenes in The Red Badge of Courage, for example, the story's focus is mainly "on the inner responses of a self unaware of others". In "The Open Boat", "An Experiment in Misery" and other stories, Crane uses light, motion and color to express degrees of epistemological uncertainty. Similar to other Naturalistic writers, Crane scrutinizes the position of man, who has been isolated not only from society, but also from God and nature. "The Open Boat", for example, distances itself from Romantic optimism and affirmation of man's place in the world by concentrating on the characters' isolation.

While he lived, Stephen Crane was denominated by critical readers a realist, a naturalist, an impressionist, symbolist, Symboliste, expressionist and ironist; his posthumous life was enriched by critics who read him as nihilistic, existentialist, a neo-Romantic, a sentimentalist, protomodernist, pointilliste, visionist, imagist and, by his most recent biographer, a "bleak naturalist." At midcentury he was a "predisciple of the New Criticism"; by its end he was "a proto-deconstructionist anti-artist hero" who had "leapfrogged modernism, landing on postmodernist ground." Or, as Sergio Perosa wrote in 1964, "The critic wanders in a labyrinth of possibilities, which every new turn taken by Crane's fiction seems to explode or deny."

One undeniable fact about Crane's work, as Anthony Splendora noted in 2015, is that Death haunts it; like a threatening eclipse it overshadows his best efforts, each of which features the signal demise of a main character. Allegorically, "The Blue Hotel," at the pinnacle of the short story form, may even be an autothanatography, the author's intentional exteriorization or objectification, in this case for the purpose of purgation, of his own impending death. Crane's "Swede" in that story can be taken, following current psychoanalytical theory, as a surrogative, sacrificial victim, ritually to be purged.

Transcending this "dark circumstance of composition," Crane had a particular telos and impetus for his creation: beyond the tautologies that all art is alterity and to some formal extent mimesis, Crane sought and obviously found "a form of catharsis" in writing. This view accounts for his uniqueness, especially as operative through his notorious "disgust" with his family's religion, their "vacuous, futile psalm-singing". His favorite book, for example, was Mark Twain's Life on the Mississippi, in which God is mentioned only twice—once as irony and once as "a swindle." Not only did Crane call out God specifically with the lines "Well then I hate thee / righteous image" in "The Black Riders" (1895), but even his most hopeful tropes, such as the "comradeship" of his "Open Boat" survivors, make no mention of deity, specifying only "indifferent nature." His antitheism is most evident in his characterization of the human race as "lice clinging to a space-lost bulb," a climax-nearing speech in "The Blue Hotel," Ch. VI. It is possible that Crane utilized religion's formal psychic space, now suddenly available resulting from the recent "Death of God", as a milieu for his compensatory art.

Novels

Beginning with the publication of Maggie: A Girl of the Streets in 1893, Crane was recognized by critics mainly as a novelist. Maggie was initially rejected by numerous publishers because of its atypical and true-to-life depictions of class warfare, which clashed with the sentimental tales of that time. Rather than focusing on the very rich or middle class, the novel's characters are lower-class denizens of New York's Bowery. The main character, Maggie, descends into prostitution after being led astray by her lover. Although the novel's plot is simple, its dramatic mood, quick pace and portrayal of Bowery life have made it memorable. Maggie is not merely an account of slum life, but also represents eternal symbols. In his first draft, Crane did not give his characters proper names. Instead, they were identified by epithets: Maggie, for example, was the girl who "blossomed in a mud-puddle" and Pete, her seducer, was a "knight". The novel is dominated by bitter irony and anger, as well as destructive morality and treacherous sentiment. Critics would later call the novel "the first dark flower of American Naturalism" for its distinctive elements of naturalistic fiction.

Written thirty years after the end of the Civil War and before Crane had any experience of battle, The Red Badge of Courage was innovative stylistically as well as psychologically. Often described as a war novel, it focuses less on battle and more on the main character's psyche and his reactions and responses in war. It is believed that Crane based the fictional battle in the novel on that of Chancellorsville; he may also have interviewed veterans of the 124th New York Volunteer Infantry Regiment, commonly known as the Orange Blossoms, in Port Jervis, New York. Told in a third-person limited point of view, it reflects the private experience of Henry Fleming, a young soldier who flees from combat. The Red Badge of Courage is notable in its vivid descriptions and well-cadenced prose, both of which help create suspense within the story. Similarly, by substituting epithets for characters' names ("the youth", "the tattered soldier"), Crane injects an allegorical quality into his work, making his characters point to a specific characteristic of man. Like Crane's first novel, The Red Badge of Courage has a deeply ironic tone which increases in severity as the novel progresses. The title of the work is ironic; Henry wishes "that he, too, had a wound, a red badge of courage", echoing a wish to have been wounded in battle. The wound he does receive (from the rifle butt of a fleeing Union soldier) is not a badge of courage but a badge of shame.

The novel expresses a strong connection between humankind and nature, a frequent and prominent concern in Crane's fiction and poetry throughout his career. Whereas contemporary writers (Ralph Waldo Emerson, Nathaniel Hawthorne, Henry David Thoreau) focused on a sympathetic bond on the two elements, Crane wrote from the perspective that human consciousness distanced humans from nature. In The Red Badge of Courage, this distance is paired with a great number of references to animals, and men with animalistic characteristics: people "howl", "squawk", "growl", or "snarl".

Since the resurgence of Crane's popularity in the 1920s, The Red Badge of Courage has been deemed a major American text. The novel has been anthologized numerous times, including in the 1942 collection Men at War: The Best War Stories of All Time, edited by Ernest Hemingway. In the introduction, Hemingway wrote that the novel "is one of the finest books of our literature, and I include it entire because it is all as much of a piece as a great poem is."

Crane's later novels have not received as much critical praise. After the success of The Red Badge of Courage, Crane wrote another tale set in the Bowery. George's Mother is less allegorical and more personal than his two previous novels, and it focuses on the conflict between a church-going, temperance-adhering woman (thought to be based on Crane's mother) and her single remaining offspring, who is a naive dreamer. Critical response to the novel was mixed. The Third Violet, a romance that he wrote quickly after publishing The Red Badge of Courage, is typically considered as Crane's attempt to appeal to popular audiences. Crane considered it a "quiet little story." Although it contained autobiographical details, the characters have been deemed inauthentic and stereotypical. Crane's second to last novel, Active Service, revolves around the Greco-Turkish War of 1897, with which the author was familiar. Although noted for its satirical take on the melodramatic and highly passionate works that were popular of the nineteenth century, the novel was not successful. It is generally accepted by critics that Crane's work suffered at this point due to the speed which he wrote in order to meet his high expenses. His last novel, a suspenseful and picaresque work entitled The O'Ruddy, was finished posthumously by Robert Barr and published in 1903.

Short fiction

Crane wrote many different types of fictional pieces while indiscriminately applying to them terms such as "story", "tale" and "sketch". For this reason, critics have found clear-cut classification of Crane's work problematic. While "The Open Boat" and "The Bride Comes to Yellow Sky" are often considered short stories, others are variously identified.

In an 1896 interview with Herbert P. Williams, a reporter for the Boston Herald, Crane said that he did "not find that short stories are utterly different in character from other fiction. It seems to me that short stories are the easiest things we write." During his brief literary career, he wrote more than a hundred short stories and fictional sketches. Crane's early fiction was based in camping expeditions in his teen years; these stories eventually became known as The Sullivan County Tales and Sketches. He considered these "sketches", which are mostly humorous and not of the same caliber of work as his later fiction, to be "articles of many kinds," in that they are part fiction and part journalism.

The subject matter for his stories varied extensively. His early New York City sketches and Bowery tales accurately described the results of industrialization, immigration and the growth of cities and their slums. His collection of six short stories, The Little Regiment, covered familiar ground with the American Civil War, a subject for which he became famous with The Red Badge of Courage. Although similar to Crane's noted novel, The Little Regiment was believed to lack vigor and originality. Realizing the limitations of these tales, Crane wrote: "I have invented the sum of my invention with regard to war and this story keeps me in internal despair."

The Open Boat and Other Tales of Adventure (1898) contains thirteen short stories that deal with three periods in Crane's life: his Asbury Park boyhood, his trip to the West and Mexico in 1895, and his Cuban adventure in 1897. This collection was well received and included several of his most critically successful works. His 1899 collection, The Monster and Other Stories, was similarly well received.

Two posthumously published collections were not as successful. In

August 1900 The Whilomville Stories were published, a collection of thirteen stories that Crane wrote during the last year of his life. The work deals almost exclusively with boyhood, and the stories are drawn from events occurring in Port Jervis, where Crane lived from the age of six to eleven. Focusing on small-town America, the stories tend toward sentimentality, but remain perceptive of the lives of children. Wounds in the Rain, published in September 1900, contains fictional tales based on Crane's reports for the World and the Journal during the Spanish–American War. These stories, which Crane wrote while desperately ill, include "The Price of the Harness" and "The Lone Charge of William B. Perkins" and are dramatic, ironic and sometimes humorous.

Despite Crane's prolific output, only four stories--"The Open Boat", "The Blue Hotel", "The Bride Comes to Yellow Sky", and The Monster— have received extensive attention from scholars. H. G. Wells considered "The Open Boat" to be "beyond all question, the crown of all his work", and it is one of the most frequently discussed of Crane's works.

Poetry

Many red devils ran from my heart

And out upon the page.

They were so tiny

The pen could mash them.

And many struggled in the ink.

It was strange

To write in this red muck

Of things from my heart.

— Stephen Crane

Crane's poems, which he preferred to call "lines", are typically not given as much scholarly attention as his fiction; no anthology contained Crane's verse until 1926. Although it is not certain when Crane began to write poetry seriously, he once said that his overall poetic aim was "to give my ideas of life as a whole, so far as I know it". The poetic style used in both of his books of poetry, The Black Riders and Other Lines and War is Kind, was unconventional for the time in that it was written in free verse without rhyme, meter, or even titles for individual works. They are typically short in length; although several poems, such as "Do not weep, maiden, for war is kind", use stanzas and refrains, most do not. Crane also differed from his peers and poets of later generations in that his work contains allegory, dialectic and narrative situations.

Critic Ruth Miller claimed that Crane wrote "an intellectual poetry rather than a poetry that evokes feeling, a poetry that stimulates the mind rather than arouses the heart". In the most complexly organized poems, the significance of the states of mind or feelings is ambiguous, but Crane's poems tend to affirm certain elemental attitudes, beliefs, opinions and stances toward God, man and the universe. The Black Riders in particular is essentially a dramatic concept and the poems provide continuity within the dramatic structure. There is also a dramatic interplay in which there is frequently a major voice reporting an incident seen ("In the desert / I saw a creature, naked, bestial") or experienced ("A learned man came to me once"). The second voice or additional voices represent a point of view which is revealed to be inferior; when these clash, a dominant attitude emerges.

Legacy

In four years, Crane published five novels, two volumes of poetry, three short story collections, two books of war stories, and numerous works of short fiction and reporting. Today he is mainly remembered for The Red Badge of Courage, which is regarded as an American classic. The novel has been adapted several times for the screen, including John Huston's 1951 version. By the time of his death, Crane had become one of the best known writers of his generation. His eccentric lifestyle, frequent newspaper reporting, association with other famous authors, and expatriate status made him somewhat of an international celebrity. Although most stories about his life tended toward the romantic, rumors about his alleged drug use and alcoholism persisted long after his death.

By the early 1920s, Crane and his work were nearly forgotten. It was not until Thomas Beer published his biography in 1923, which was followed by editor Wilson Follett's The Work of Stephen Crane (1925–1927), that Crane's writing came to the attention of a scholarly audience. Crane's reputation was then enhanced by faithful support from writer friends such as Joseph Conrad, H. G. Wells and Ford Madox Ford, all of whom either published recollections or commented upon their time with Crane. John Berryman's 1950 biography of Crane further established him as an important American author. Since 1951 there has been a steady outpouring of articles, monographs and reprints in Crane scholarship.

Today, Crane is considered one of the most innovative writers of the 1890s. His peers, including Conrad and James, as well as later writers such as Robert Frost, Ezra Pound and Willa Cather, hailed Crane as one of the finest creative spirits of his time. His work was described by Wells as "the first expression of the opening mind of a new period, or, at least, the early emphatic phase of a new initiative." Wells said that "beyond dispute", Crane was "the best writer of our generation, and his untimely death was an irreparable loss to our literature." Conrad wrote that Crane was an "artist" and "a seer with a gift for rendering the significant on the surface of things and with an incomparable insight into primitive emotions". Crane's work has proved inspirational for future writers; not only have scholars drawn similarities between Hemingway's A Farewell to Arms and The Red Badge of Courage, but Crane's fiction is thought to have been an important inspiration for Hemingway and his fellow Modernists. In 1936, Hemingway wrote in The Green Hills of Africa that "The good writers are Henry James, Stephen Crane, and Mark Twain. That's not the order they're good in. There is no order for good writers." Crane's poetry is thought to have been a precursor to the Imagist movement, and his short fiction has also influenced American literature. "The Open Boat", "The Blue Hotel", The Monster and "The Bride Comes to Yellow Sky" are generally considered by critics to be examples of Crane's best work.

Several institutions and places have endeavored to keep Crane's legacy alive. Badenweiler and the house where he died became something of a tourist attraction for its fleeting association with the American author; Alexander Woollcott attested to the fact that, long after Crane's death, tourists would be directed to the room where he died. Columbia University Rare Book and Manuscript Library has a collection of Crane and Taylor's personal correspondence dating from 1895 to 1908. Near his brother Edmund's Sullivan County home in New York, where Crane stayed for a short time, a pond is named after him. The Stephen Crane House in Asbury Park, New Jersey, where the author lived with his siblings for nine years, is operated as a museum dedicated to his life and work. Syracuse University has an annual Stephen Crane Lecture Series which is sponsored by the Dikaia Foundation.

Columbia University purchased much of the Stephen Crane materials held by Cora Crane at her death. The Crane Collection is one of the largest in the nation of his materials. Columbia University had an exhibit: 'The Tall Swift Shadow of a Ship at Night': Stephen and Cora Crane, November 2, 1995 through February 16, 1996, about the lives of the couple, featuring letters and other documents and memorabilia. (Source: Wikipedia)

CPSIA information can be obtained
at www.ICGtesting.com
Printed in the USA
LVHW050116140720
660559LV00004B/319

9 789390 194100